FIELD INSPECTION HANDBOOK

Other McGraw-Hill Handbooks of Interest

Alpern • Handbook of Specialty Elements in Architecture
Baumeister • Marks' Standard Handbook for Mechanical Engineers
Brady and Clauser • Materials Handbook
Brater • Handbook of Hydraulics
Callender • Time-Saver Standards for Architectural Design Data
Church • Excavation Handbook
Conover • Grounds Maintenance Handbook
Crocker and King • Piping Handbook
Croft, Carr, Watt, and Summers • American Electricians' Handbook
Davis and Sorensen • Handbook of Applied Hydraulics
DeChiara and Callender • Time-Saver Standards for Building Types
Fink and Beaty • Standard Handbook for Electrical Engineers
Gaylord and Gaylord • Structural Engineering Handbook
Gieck • Engineering Formulas
Harris • Handbook of Noise Control
Harris and Crede • Shock and Vibration Handbook
Havers and Stubbs • Handbook of Heavy Construction
Hicks • Standard Handbook of Engineering Calculations
Higgins • Handbook of Construction Equipment Maintenance
Higgins and Morrow • Maintenance Engineering Handbook
King and Brater • Handbook of Hydraulics
Kong, Evans, Cohen, and Roll • Handbook of Structural Concrete
Manas • National Plumbing Code Handbook
McPartland • McGraw-Hill's National Electrical Code® Handbook
McPartland • Handbook of Practical Electrical Design
Merritt • Standard Handbook for Civil Engineers
Merritt • Building Design and Construction Handbook
Merritt • Structural Steel Designers' Handbook
O'Brien • Contractor's Management Handbook
Parmley • Field Engineer's Manual
Rosaler and Rice • Standard Handbook of Plant Engineering
Rossnagel • Handbook of Rigging
Tuma • Engineering Mathematics Handbook
Tuma • Handbook of Physical Calculations
Tuma • Technology Mathematics Handbook
Turner and Malloy • Thermal Insulation Handbook
Waddell • Concrete Construction Handbook
Woods • Highway Engineering Handbook

FIELD INSPECTION HANDBOOK

An On-the-Job Guide for Construction Inspectors, Contractors, Architects, and Engineers

Dan S. Brock, Editor
Lystre L. Sutcliffe, Jr., Associate Editor

McGraw-Hill Book Company

*New York   St. Louis   San Francisco   Auckland
Bogotá   Hamburg   London   Madrid
Mexico   Montreal   New Delhi   Panama   Paris
São Paulo   Singapore   Sydney   Tokyo   Toronto*

Library of Congress Cataloging-in-Publication Data
Main entry under title:

Field inspection handbook.

Includes index.
1. Engineering—Management—Handbooks, Manuals, etc.
2. Building inspection—Handbooks, manuals, etc.
3. Building sites—Handbooks, manuals, etc.   I. Brock,
Dan S.   II. Sutcliffe, Lystre L.
TH439.F54   1986   690'.28'7   85-24127

    67890   DOC/DOC   93

ISBN 0-07-007932-3

The editors for this book were Harold B. Crawford and Beatrice E.
Eckes, the designer was Mark E. Safran, and the production super-
visor was Sally Fliess. It was set in ITC Baskerville by The Saybrook
Press, Inc.

Printed and bound by R. R. Donnelley & Sons Company.

This book is printed on acid-free paper.

Contents

Contributors

Michael J. Abrahams, P.E., Vice President and Manager of Structures Department, Parsons Brinckerhoff Quade & Douglas, Inc., New York, New York, B.S., M.S., Columbia School of Engineering, ACI, ASCE, Structural Stability Research Council (*Chapter 2.7*)

C. Gary Altoonian, Jr., P.E., Assistant Vice President and Manager of Construction Engineering Services, Parsons Brinckerhoff Construction Services, Inc., McLean, Virginia, B.S.C.E., Drexel University, ASCE, CMAA (Construction Management Association of America) (*Chapter 2.4*)

Louis F. Booth, P.E., Consultant, St. Petersburg Beach, Florida, B.S.C.E., C.E., Purdue University, ASCE, NSPE. Formerly General Contractor, Manager of Construction, The Port of New York Authority (*Chapters 1.1, 1.2*)

Edward A. Donoghue, Manager—Codes and Safety, National Elevator Industry, Inc., New York, New York, ASME, ANS, ASTM (*Chapter 2.9*)

Frank M. Fuller, P.E., Consultant, Osterville, Massachusetts, B.C.E., Rensselaer Polytechnic Institute, life fellow, ASCE, ACI, ASTM, PCI, TRB. Formerly Assistant Vice President, Raymond International Builders, Inc. (*Chapter 2.3*)

Bill S. Hanshew, Jr., P.E., Specification Engineer, West Virginia Department of Highways, Charlestown, West Virginia, B.S.C.E., West Virginia University (*Chapter 2.6*)

Gerald J. Hill, Consultant, Williamston, Michigan, B.S.C.E., Michigan Technological University, graduate studies, University of Michigan, AWS (American Welding Society), ASNT (American Society of Nondestructive Testing). Formerly Neyer, Tiseo & Hindo, Ltd., Consulting Engineers, Jutton, Kelly Co., Bridge Construction Contractor, Michigan Department of Transportation (*Chapter 2.5*)

F. A. Jarrett, L.S., Chief of Surveys, Parsons Brinckerhoff Quade & Douglas, Inc., New York, New York, U.S. Navy Survey School (*Chapter 1.3*)

Monroe M. Johnston, P.E., Consultant, Ormond Beach, Florida, Civil Engineering Professor, Daytona Beach Community College, B.S.C.E., Georgia Institute of Technology, postgraduate study at Georgia Institute of Technology, University of California, and Harvard University. Formerly Chief of Geotechnical Branch, Engineering Division, Office of the Chief, U.S. Army Engineers, ASCE, NSPE (*Chapter 2.1*)

Lt. Gen. John W. Morris, U.S. Army (Ret.) J. W. Morris, Ltd., Construction Consultants, Arlington, Virginia, Graduate of United States Military Academy, Master's degree in engineering, University of Iowa, ENR, Construction Man of the Year Award, National Academy of Engineering, Construction Management Professor, University of Maryland. Formerly Chief of Engineers, U.S. Army Corps of Engineers (*Chapter 1.4*)

Donald R. O'Hearn, Manager, Program Control, Parsons Brinckerhoff Quade & Douglas, Inc., New York, New York, B.S.C.E., University of Florida, ASCE, PMI (Project Management Institute) (*Chapter 1.5*)

Kenneth D. Pendergrass, Senior Quality Assurance Consultant, F&M Technical Services, Inc., Dallas, Texas, B.S., University of Texas, Certified quality engineer (*Chapter 2.8*)

Earl R. Scyoc, P.E., Chief Engineer of Construction, West Virginia Department of Highways, Charleston, West Virginia, B.S.C.E., Ohio University, AASHTO, TRB (*Chapter 2.6*)

Robert L. Seymour, Vertical Transportation Consultant, Lerch, Bates & Associates, Inc., Elevator Consulting Engineers, Crofton, Maryland, Electrical Engineering, Johns Hopkins University, ASME, Chairman, Main Committee, ANSI/ASME, A 17, Safety Code for Elevators and Escalators (*Chapter 2.9*)

J. Thomas Sheakley, Senior Engineer, Transportation Division, Westinghouse Electric Corporation, West Mifflin, Pennsylvania, B.M.E., Gannon University, M.E.A., George Washington University, M.S.C.E., State University of New York at Buffalo, ASME, ASCE (*Chapter 2.10*)

Lystre L. Sutcliffe, Jr., P.E., Vice President and Manager of Construction Engineering Services Department, Parsons Brinckerhoff Construction Services, Inc., Trenton, New Jersey, B.S.C.E., University of Florida (*Chapters 1.3, 2.4*)

Robert E. White, P.E., Consultant, Larchmont, New York, C.E., Harvard Engineering School. Formerly President, Spencer, White & Prentis, Inc., Manager, Underpinning and Shoring of the White House (*Chapter 2.2*)

Preface

The basic purpose of this *Handbook* is to provide a tool to assist in converting the design of a structure into a completed facility by providing the inspector with the engineering, technological, and practical guidelines to assure that the contractor's performance conforms fully and in detail with the intent of the designer. The best design loses its value if poorly constructed, that is, if the quality of inspection during construction fails to assure full adherence to the intent of the plans and specifications.

In the early years of the modern construction industry, many aspects of inspection lacked the engineering and technical competence we take for granted as basic today, with the result that perhaps too often some inspection decisions were made by the "seat of the pants" approach. Today, this process has been upgraded to provide a practical blend of engineering, design, and technology with clearly defined tests and construction procedures to produce the best end product, whether it is an earth-fill dam, a bridge, or a specialized facility such as a people mover.

This book is designed as a reference book for the resident engineer, inspector, or technician who is a civil engineer or one with less formal education, who is beginning a career of field engineering or inspection with limited field experience. It will be equally useful for those with prior experience who may have been involved in other construction activities during an interim period. To those in both of these categories, this book will serve as a comprehensive how-to guide and will provide a refresher course in all aspects of the subjects covered.

The best structure results from a basic design that is practical, functional, and not unnecessarily complicated and that is built by sound construction methods confirmed by competent inspection. The contributing authors, who are all eminent specialists in their respective fields, were selected to bring their expertise, which has been seasoned with many years' experience, to provide a sound blend of professional knowledge and practical experience in the application of responsible inspection procedures.

The inspection process must recognize the need not only for quality construction consistent with the intent of the project plans and specifications but also for on-time contract performance. The best inspector will make a valuable contribution to the project by assisting the contractor with suggestions for timely scheduling of individual operations to assure earliest project completion and also in the recognition of questionable methods and potential quality problems before rather than after work has been performed. The inspector will also recommend design changes to the engineer, when appropriate, to fit site conditions better or to facilitate the construction process. It is also important that the inspector-contractor relationship be equitable, by timely recognition of contract changes involving additional cost, thus avoiding subsequent costly litigation.

The 15 chapters have been selected for their general application to all construction projects and to certain types of construction operations involved in most projects. Some specialized types of construction and other aspects important to the construction and maintenance process not widely covered in other publications are also included. It is our hope that this *Handbook* will provide invaluable assistance to those responsible for achieving the best-quality construction.

DAN S. BROCK
LYSTRE L. SUTCLIFFE, JR.

SECTION 1

General Construction

General Duties and Responsibilities of the Inspector

Louis F. Booth, P.E.
Consultant
St. Petersburg Beach, Florida

<u>Formerly</u>

General Contractor
Manager of Construction
The Port of New York Authority

ADMINISTRATION

The administrative functions and responsibilities of the construction inspector's role vary widely with the character and size of the project being inspected and also with the nature of the contractual relationships of owner, engineer-architect, and contractor under which the work is being done. Construction projects range from single-family dwellings through multistory apartment buildings and office structures, from small one-story factories or warehouses through vast complex industrial and process plants, and from 2-lane county roads through 16-lane superhighways with four-level interchanges. Inspection coverage varies from, on a small job, 1- or 2-hour weekly visits by a representative of the owner or engineer or architect to continuous 24-hour inspection by a staff of technicians including specialists in every trade or field on large projects.

The portion of the control and supervision of construction activity included in the broad term *inspection*, which at one time required largely common sense and experience, now also needs a high degree of both technical competence and administrative ability. Individual sections of this *Handbook* treat the methods and techniques of inspection used in the various trades and fields to ensure high quality of materials and workmanship. It is to the administrative problems that this chapter is directed.

In the same way that the actual processes of physical inspection vary with the size and complexity of the job, so do the administrative requirements of the inspector's function. Let us start at the small end of the range: a single residence, a small store, or a similar simple structure. Here inspection is usually performed on an intermittent basis by an architect's agent on visits to the site or by a so-called clerk of the works, who may cover a number of small jobs for an owner or a public agency.

Here the physical inspection usually consists simply of visual examination of the quality of the materials at the site, verification of the proper completion of the work in place, and observance of the methods and competence of the persons engaged in the work. Few, if any, actual materials tests will be required; and the only formal tests might be on the operaton of heating, plumbing, ventilation, air-conditioning, and electrical systems.

Administrative responsibilities on small jobs usually consist of acting as liaison between owner or architect and contractor in the transmittal of plans and information, checking the progess of the work to see that it is abreast of the completion schedule, checking the quantities of materials delivered or installed in order to approve contract payments, reviewing and ruling on questions which may arise in the contractor's interpretation of the plans, and evaluating the cost of changes from the contract plans and specifications which the owner or architect wants to make or which unexpected field conditions dictate. On small work, where the inspector is a member of the owner's or architect's staff, all these responsibilities are obvious and direct and can be discharged in a routine manner.

Except in cases of very small projects, however, these aspects of the inspector's work will become more complex and demanding as the size of the operation increases. They are treated in detail under the following headings.

CONTRACTUAL RELATIONSHIPS

Construction contracts in a broad sense fall into one or the other of two very general categories: *fixed-price* or *cost-plus*. In many instances they are variations which include some aspects of each.

Fixed-Price Contracts. Lump-sum contracts, one form of fixed-price contracts, are those in which the contractor has estimated the cost of the work, submitted a proposal, and entered into an agreement with the owner to furnish all materials, labor, equipment, and supervision needed to complete the construction of the project in accordance with detailed plans and specifications for the fixed sum of money stated in the bid and agreed to by the owner in the contract document.

Prime requirements for the successful use of the lump-sum form of contract are the availability of complete and detailed drawings and specifications and a thorough knowledge on the part of both owner and contractor of the conditions at the site which will affect the cost of accomplishing the work. It is also important that the general conditions be well defined. Economic factors and governmental regulations which might influence labor rates, materials availability, or environmental requirements could have important effects upon the cost of doing the work. When these factors are uncertain and could have a serious effect, lump-sum contracts, except for projects of extremely short duration, are usually not advisable.

Unit-Price Contracts.   Frequently used on public works projects, a unit-price contract is an agreement in which the payment amount is arrived at by adding the costs of a number of work items each of which is the result of the multiplication of an agreed-upon unit price by the actual number of units of work performed in that item. On this type of contract, an important duty of the inspection staff is the measurement of, and agreement upon, the quantity of work performed in the various items or trades.

Cost-Plus Contracts.   In a cost-plus contract the contractor's compensation is based upon the actual cost of doing the work, plus agreed-upon allowances to cover overhead expenses and profit. This type of contract usually is used when plans and specifications are not complete or final or when the physical site conditions or general construction environment factors are uncertain so that a cost estimate cannot be accurately made.

Upset-Limit-Fee Contracts.   Also called *cost-plus-fee-with-guaranteed-maximum contracts,* these are another quite common form of cost-plus contracts. With this type the contractor is paid on a cost-plus basis for work performed but has guaranteed that the total cost to the owner will not exceed a stated limit. This form is frequently used when plans and specifications are complete and adequate for dependable estimates but the project is so large and its duration so long that general outside conditions which would affect cost cannot be accurately predicted. Provisions would be included in the contract terms for adjustment of the upset limit when conditions beyond the contractor's control change. Also under this type of contract, the contractor is often given a share of any savings made under the budget figure and, conversely, is penalized by a deduction from the fee of some portion of any amount by which the actual cost exceeds the upset limit.

Inspector's Responsibilities.   There are other construction contract forms and terms which include some aspects of each of the foregoing categories.

However, the position within the two broad classifications determines the basic relationship between the inspection staff and the contractor and governs the inspector's attitude in the performance of all duties.

On fixed-price work, the inspector's prime responsibility is to see that the work is well done to the degree that the owner receives from the contractor all that the drawings and specifications prescribe. On cost-plus contracts, the inspector has the added responsibility of monitoring the contractor's methods and operations to ensure that funds are economically and efficiently spent and that the owner is receiving full value for any expenditure. On either type of contract, other important functions of the inspection staff include monitoring the status of the work in relation to progress schedules and payment requisitions, reviewing changes and change orders, and filing the necessary reports to keep the owner and architect advised. These and other duties are covered in detail under the following headings.

CONTRACTS AND SPECIFICATIONS

The contract is the basic document which delineates the work to be done by the contractor, the time of performance, and the amount and method of payment by the owner. The plans and specifications are the detailed descriptions and illustrations of the materials and methods that are to be used and the result that is to be accomplished. Usually by the wording of the contract, the plans and specifications are made a legal part of it.

A number of standard contract forms are promulgated by various governmental agencies, by the American Institute of Architects (AIA), by the Associated General Contractors of America (AGCA), and by the many public or quasi-public authorities. Many corporations have their own contract forms, prepared by their legal staffs and adapted to the differing needs of their individual projects. In some instances, the contract form is also the proposal form, in which bidders are required simply to fill in the money amounts of their bids; this proposal becomes a contract by the act of acceptance and signature on the part of the owner.

General Conditions.   An important part of most contract forms is a section of the specifications frequently termed the *general conditions.* This part is important because it prescribes in precise terms the understandings between the owner and the contractor in all aspects of their relationship and embodies a wide range of topics including:

Areas available for contractor's use

Maintenance of site, cleanup and debris removal, and general housekeeping

Provisions for cooperation with other contractors

Progress schedules

Bid analysis and unit prices

Furnishing of shop drawings, working drawings, catalog cuts, and samples

Materials inspection, testing, and acceptance or rejection

Manufacturer's certifications

Responsibility for and method of handling of errors and discrepancies

Accident and first-aid provisions

Project safety and sanitary provisions

Public safety provisions

Minimum equipment requirements

Progress reports, equipment reports, and labor reports

Laws and ordinances

Field office provisions

Signs and advertising

Temporary structures, barricades, and scaffolding

Utilities services

Final inspection and acceptance

As-built drawings, bonds, and guarantees

In some contracts, the time and method of requisitioning, payment, and the method of handling and approving changes are included in the general conditions of the specifications. More often, however, these are separate sections in the contract document.

Special Conditions.   Some specifications, in addition to the ordinary general conditions clauses, contain a section called *special conditions* which includes clauses covering various unusual provisions or requirements applicable to this specific contract. Requirements peculiar to a certain owner or agency—for example, minority hiring quotas stipulated by some public works agencies and, indeed, by corporate owners when public funds are involved—are sometimes covered here. In the labor field, special conditions clauses sometimes require the use of only union workers and sometimes prescribe minimum-wage schedules. In the area of management, clauses that require a certain minimum proportion of the work to be done by the forces of the contractor rather than by subcontractors may be included. Similarly, a clause may require that certain portions of the work be sublet to small business firms or to minority subcontractors. Preferential purchase of American-made materials, environmental-protection provisions, and other similar items which are somewhat indirect in the owner-contractor relationship are frequently included in the special conditions section of the specifications.

Inspector's Responsibility. On small projects, the single individual who handles all inspections as well as the other aspects of the relationship between owner, architect, engineer, and contractor must be completely familiar with all the terms of the contract documents and must have available for continuous reference both the plans and specifications and the contract. (In some cases, owners may be reluctant to have documents with money information in them openly available in field office files; in such cases, copies should be furnished with any confidential figures deleted.) An inspector who covers a number of small jobs and spends a limited time at each could possibly work satisfactorily from the contractor's field drawings, but when it is at all possible, the inspector should maintain separate files of plans and specifications and also of the shop drawings prepared by the subcontractors or vendors.

On larger work where a supervisory staff is at the site, the entire inspection group should be familiar with the general-contract terms and requirements as well as with the plans and specifications covering the work to which individual members are assigned. This is not to say that on large projects every individual field inspector covering a single trade need be concerned with the legalities of the general-contract agreement, but each inspector should be acquainted with the terms of the subcontract covering the assigned work and with any sections of the general contract which could have even an indirect bearing upon that work. The supervising inspection personnel should of course be acquainted with *all* the contract documents.

More important to the actual field inspectors are the drawings and specifications. These are usually lengthy and detailed and cover materials, workmanship, the various tests required, and, in some cases, methods of construction.

Some specifications, known generally as the *performance* type, avoid any prescription of construction *methods,* leaving that aspect up to the contractor's discretion, but they specify in detail the desired result. This type of specification is more often used on *package* contracts, the type in which an owner buys both design and construction from one firm, since design options would considerably affect construction-methods alternatives.

On most construction projects, however, the specifications *do* include detailed prescription of construction methods, and in many instances the inspector's monitoring of these procedures is as important as actual examination of the work in place in the task of getting the quality of work the owner has specified and is paying for.

The degree of detail in specifications varies widely between different architects, engineers, designers, and agencies. In general, it can be said that the more detailed and complete the specifications are, the less is the likelihood of questions or legal claims arising from their use.

PROGRESS CHECKING AND SCHEDULES

The primary function of the inspector's role is the examination of materials and workmanship to ensure finished construction of the standard required by the plans and specifications and contracted for between the owner and the contractor. The methods and techniques required for this work in different trades or varying types of construction are detailed in Sec. 2 of the *Handbook*.

Among the numerous secondary functions of the inspector or the inspection staff, one of the more important is the monitoring of the progess of the work to assure, during its course, that completion dates will be met or to gauge the amount and direction by which they will be missed. While on small work this is a matter of simple observation, on large projects with a great many interdependent activities this monitoring is accomplished by the use of *progress schedules*. These vary in scope and complexity from a simple list of the starting and completion dates of the more important work items to the comprehensive and intricate network of materials-procurement times and site-work durations known as critical-path-method (CPM) scheduling.

Bar Charts. Probably the most widely used and certainly the oldest type of schedule is the *bar chart* (see Fig. 1.1-1). Here the principal construction operations or trades are listed in the order of their starting dates, usually on the left side of a sheet wide enough to accommodate calendar weeks or months plotted as successive columns extending from the starting date and working to the right far enough to include a safety margin beyond the expected completion date.

On the line of each listed operation or trade a bar is plotted, its left end at the expected starting date and its right end at the expected completion date of that particular work time. Selection of the various starting dates is a reflection of the true interdependence of each work item or trade with those preceding it. The completion date for each item is determined by applying to the known quantity of work an assumed production rate for the available crew and equipment, usually with a time allowance for normal contingencies or interruptions.

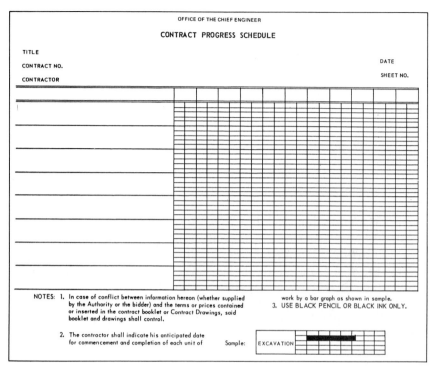

FIG. 1.1-1 Contract progress schedule: bar chart.

A good graphic representation of work versus time is provided by the bar chart, and for both the contractor's planning and the inspection staff's monitoring it is a basic tool. It is usually prepared by the contractor, who has the necessary knowledge of what the crew and equipment can do, and it is reviewed by the architect or engineer and owner before ever coming into the purview of the inspector. However, in the event of changes in the work, delays, or other factors that require revision of the schedule, the inspector or inspection staff should be prepared to judge the validity of the revisions.

Many variations or expansions of the basic bar chart are possible. The chart can be enlarged to include such diverse aspects as, at the start, land procurement, design time, materials fabrication, or procurement time and, at the end, inspections and tests, tenant charges, and occupancy-permit issuance times. Also, in many chart forms there is provision for plotting the actual progress in each item against the bar representing the planned progress. This practice results in an easily read chart which gives the inspector, the contractor, and the owner a quick view of the progress status of the work and is a dependable basis for forecasting actual completion times and dates.

CPM Schedules.   A logical development from the simple bar chart has been the use of what is termed the *critical-path-method* (CPM) schedule. This system utilizes an aggregation of anticipated times for the various operations, plotted in such a way that the shortest possible combination of sequences can be determined. In CPM scheduling, too, there is wide variation in complexity, from very simple CPM schedules (see Fig. 1.1-2) which plot only a few key operations to extremely complicated ones which include both time and some financial aspects and are adapted to periodic computer follow-up.

Program evaluation and review technique (PERT), a variation of CPM, frequently is used on military construction projects. However, it is sufficiently similar to CPM that the following explanations will suffice for either.

Both systems require that the project work be broken down into *activities* that can be diagramed to show the sequential relationship between them. This diagram, called a *network,* consists basically of *arrows,* representing the time required to complete an activity, which are connected to *nodes,* which represent *events,* or points in time at which an activity can be started or has been completed. Descriptive labels identify the arrows, and the nodes are numbered in the order of their dates.

Sometimes a network is drawn to a time scale, in which case the length of the arrow represents the time required for that activity and the nodes are at calendar dates. More often, however, this is impractical, and the length of the arrow has no meaning. But the arrangement of the arrows does indicate the logical sequence in which the work is to be performed, and it shows which activities must precede others, which may be done concurrently, and which must await completion of earlier ones. The events, or nodes, are junction points of arrows and appear as circles on the network. Each represents a specific point in time when all the activities leading to that node are completed and when succeeding activities represented by arrows leading away from it can be started.

Each activity in the network is assigned a number of workdays, which is the time estimated to be needed by using the workers and equipment that are expected to be available. A date then can be given to each of the nodes. In practice, four dates are usually computed: (1) the ESD, or earliest date to start an operaton; (2) the LSD, or latest date to start an operation without delaying overall completion; (3) the EFD, or earliest date to finish an operation; and (4) the LFD, or latest date to finish an operation without delaying overall completion.

Because in construction work so many different operations, or CPM activities, are conducted concurrently, there are in a CPM network many parallel arrows of different lengths crossing any time period and connecting the same nodes. The arrow representing the activity between two

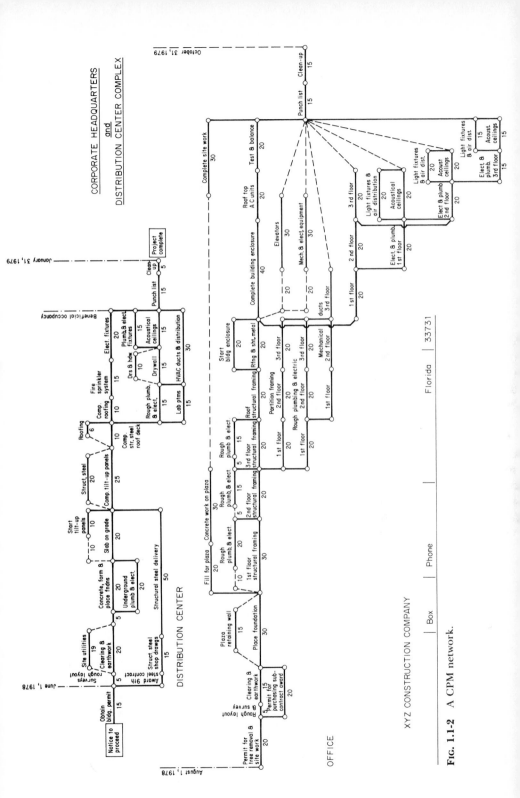

FIG. 1.1-2 A CPM network.

1.1.13

events that requires the longest time for completion is said to be *critical,* and the sequential combination of the longest arrows or activity times from the start of the project to completion is called the *critical path,* hence the term *critical-path method.* The total of these arrows equals the shortest time in which the project can be completed unless some of the individual activities are accomplished in less than their anticipated scheduled times.

Any of the arrows between two events that are shorter than the longest arrow are said to *noncritical,* and the difference between their lengths and the longest length is called *float,* which is the time by which these individual activities could overrun their scheduled times without affecting the overall completion time of the project.

The most important phase in the preparation of CPM schedules is the placing of time estimates on the activities. The accuracy and dependability of this step in the process are the basic key to the dependability of the entire schedule.

CPM scheduling has had wide acceptance on construction work of any appreciable size or scope, and the inspection staff should include personnel familiar with its theory and methods.

Either the bar chart or the CPM schedule can be of great help to an inspector faced with the task of reviewing time-extension requests that stem from ordered changes in the work, from unexpected site conditions, or from changed outside circumstances that are beyond control. The effect of these changes on individual work items or trades can easily be traced through to establish the effect on work progress as a whole. This aspect of the use of bar charts or CPM schedules can be of particular help to the inspector when possible time penalties or delay-cost claims are involved.

PAYMENT REQUISITIONS AND APPROVALS

Most construction contracts, except those for small projects, provide for interim payments to the contractors during the course of the work. The amount of a payment is usually based upon the amount of work that has been completed at the time and, in some instances, upon quantities of material delivered to the site even though some of it has not been installed.

In most large contracts, there is also provision for retention by the owner of a percentage of the agreed-upon payment earned. This is to ensure the contractor's continuing performance, to provide a contingency against the possible development of defects in the work, and in a general way to give the owner an extra factor of control over the contractor. Commonly the retention is 10 percent, and sometimes this is discontinued when the work is half done, so that at the work's termination the moneys held back amount only to 5 percent. Of course on extremely large contracts, for which that amount of retention would work an undue financial hardship, these percentages are often reduced and, in some instances, even completely eliminated.

An important duty of the inspector or the inspection staff is to check these requisition amounts against the quantity of work actually completed on the job. The thoroughness with which this checking must be carried out depends upon the size and character of the work and varies from simple visual observation, as on a small house contract, to detailed quantity calculations and continuous records on larger work. On very large unit-price contracts, payment checking becomes a major periodic task for which a separate survey and accounting section sometimes is set up.

Basic Procedure. On many lump-sum contracts, the contractor is required to furnish to the owner either with the bid or at the start of work a *bid analysis*, a breakdown of the bid into the amounts of money carried for each of the principal subdivisions of the work, i.e., site clearing, excavation, foundation concrete, structural steel, concrete floors, exterior masonry, interior partitions, plumbing, heating, and ventilating, electrical, painting, and so forth through to completion. Often the breakdown is required in greater detail than indicated by this listing. The contractor arrives at the figure for interim requisitions by estimating the proportion of work done in each subdivision or trade, applying it to the amount of money assigned to that work, and adding these results to arrive at the total value of the work completed up to that date.

The inspector must check the amounts of work claimed item by item, and this method is of course more accurate than attempting to evaluate simply the proportion of work completed as a whole. Usually at the end of each month or pay period, the value of all work completed up to that date is calculated, and the sum of the previous payments is deducted in order to determine the amount of payment due for the period in question. (See Figs. 1.1-3, 1.1-4, and 1.1-5a, b, and c.)

Variations. There are many variations of the basic procedure. On most construction, changes in the work which result in additions to or deductions from the contract price are required from time to time. The value of the work done against these change orders must be considered in preparing and checking the requisitions covering the basic contract work.

In unit-price contracts, the inspector's work in the checking and approval of payments is somewhat enlarged, since the payment due is based directly upon the actual quantities of work performed in the various items. These quantities are determined by field measurements, by estimating from plans, or in some cases by an actual work count of materials

APPLICATION FOR PAYMENT

SHEET_____OF_____
DATE PREPARED_____/__/____

CONTRACT NO._____DATED_____/___/_____ PAYMENT NO._____

CONTRACTOR_____ ADDRESS _____
Approximate work performed to_____ 19_____

Item No.	DESCRIPTION OF WORK	UNIT	APPROXIMATE QUANTITIES			Unit Price	AMOUNT
			This Application	Total for Prev. Application	Total to Date		

Less_____% retained as per contract

TOTAL APPLIED FOR, TO DATE $ _____

Balance to date
Less advances under previous applications   _____
To be advanced this application

CHANGE ORDERS (per attached)
    Total to date   _____
    Less: Previously advanced   _____
    Amount to be advanced on this application
TOTAL AMOUNT TO BE ADVANCED THIS APPLICATION (as per copy) $ _____

It is hereby certified that the above quantities of work have actually been performed and that the cost plus compensation above set forth, if any, is computed in accordance with the terms of the above Contract on the basis of work actually performed. This certification, if signed by any person on behalf of the contractor, is made by such person in his individual capacity on the basis of his own knowledge, as well as by the contractor.

PRO/PROJ	ORG	ACT	AREA/ SYST	JOB	AMOUNT

*Individually and on behalf of the contractor

_____
TITLE

Recommended For Payment:

The above estimate of quantities performed is correct and is made from actual inspection and knowledge of work performed:

CORRECT AND IN ACCORDANCE WITH CONTRACT_____

CONSTRUCTION ACCT.

Title:

Approved For Payment:

_____
For Comptroller

Title:

*If contractor is a corporation, certificate must be signed by an officer, and if a partnership, by a partner.

FIG. 1.1-3   An application for payment.

CHANGE ORDER PAYMENT APPLICATION DETAIL

Payment No. _____   Contract No. _____   Sheet _____ Of _____

Approximate work performed to _____ 19 _____

ORDER NO.	TYPE	TOTAL ESTIMATED AMOUNT	ESTIMATE OF WORK PERFORMED		TOTAL AMOUNTS	
			THIS ESTIMATE	TO DATE	THIS ESTIMATE	TO DATE
		AMOUNTS CARRIED FORWARD				

FIG. 1.1-4   An application for change-order payment.

delivered or removed, as, for example, in the case of ready-mixed concrete or excavation. In some cases, the quantity must be determined by survey, as when cross sections of a site are taken, before and after, to determine excavation volumes. In such a case, the inspection staff if it is not a part of the field engineering force would have to be assisted by survey parties.

APPLICATION AND CERTIFICATE FOR PAYMENT AIA DOCUMENT G702

PAGE ONE OF   PAGES

(Instructions on reverse side)

TO (OWNER):

PROJECT:

APPLICATION NO:

Distribution to:
☐ OWNER
☐ ARCHITECT
☐ CONTRACTOR

PERIOD TO:

FROM (CONTRACTOR):

VIA (ARCHITECT):

ARCHITECT'S
PROJECT NO:

CONTRACT FOR:

CONTRACT DATE:

CONTRACTOR'S APPLICATION FOR PAYMENT

Application is made for Payment, as shown below, in connection with the Contract.
Continuation Sheet, AIA Document G703, is attached.

1. ORIGINAL CONTRACT SUM .... $
2. Net change by Change Orders .... $
3. CONTRACT SUM TO DATE (Line 1 ± 2) .... $
4. TOTAL COMPLETED & STORED TO DATE .... $
   (Column G on G703)
5. RETAINAGE:
   a. ____ % of Completed Work $
      (Column D + E on G703)
   b. ____ % of Stored Material $
      (Column F on G703)
   Total Retainage (Line 5a + 5b or
   Total in Column I of G703) .... $
6. TOTAL EARNED LESS RETAINAGE .... $
   (Line 4 less Line 5 Total)
7. LESS PREVIOUS CERTIFICATES FOR
   PAYMENT (Line 6 from prior Certificate) .... $
8. CURRENT PAYMENT DUE .... $
9. BALANCE TO FINISH, PLUS RETAINAGE .... $
   (Line 3 less Line 6)

CHANGE ORDER SUMMARY

	ADDITIONS	DEDUCTIONS
Change Orders approved in previous months by Owner		
TOTAL		
Approved this Month		
Number	Date Approved	
TOTALS		
Net change by Change Orders		

The undersigned Contractor certifies that to the best of the Contractor's knowledge, information and belief the Work covered by this Application for Payment has been completed in accordance with the Contract Documents, that all amounts have been paid by the Contractor for Work for which previous Certificates for Payment were issued and payments received from the Owner, and that current payment shown herein is now due.

CONTRACTOR:

By: _____ Date: _____

State of: County of:
Subscribed and sworn to before me this _____ day of _____ , 19___
Notary Public:
My Commission expires:

AMOUNT CERTIFIED .... $
(Attach explanation if amount certified differs from the amount applied for.)
ARCHITECT:
By: _____ Date: _____

ARCHITECT'S CERTIFICATE FOR PAYMENT

In accordance with the Contract Documents, based on on-site observations and the data comprising the above application, the Architect certifies to the Owner that to the best of the Architect's knowledge, information and belief the Work has progressed as indicated, the quality of the Work is in accordance with the Contract Documents, and the Contractor is entitled to payment of the AMOUNT CERTIFIED.

This Certificate is not negotiable. The AMOUNT CERTIFIED is payable only to the Contractor named herein. Issuance, payment and acceptance of payment are without prejudice to any rights of the Owner or Contractor under this Contract.

Fig. 1.1-5a Application and certificate for payment.

CONTINUATION SHEET

AIA DOCUMENT G703   (Instructions on reverse side)   PAGE   OF   PAGES

AIA Document G702, APPLICATION AND CERTIFICATE FOR PAYMENT, containing
Contractor's signed Certification is attached.
In tabulations below, amounts are stated to the nearest dollar.
Use Column 1 on Contracts where variable retainage for line items may apply.

APPLICATION NUMBER:
APPLICATION DATE:
PERIOD TO:
ARCHITECT'S PROJECT NO:

A	B	C	D	E	F	G		H	I
ITEM NO.	DESCRIPTION OF WORK	SCHEDULED VALUE	WORK COMPLETED		MATERIALS PRESENTLY STORED (NOT IN D OR E)	TOTAL COMPLETED AND STORED TO DATE (D+E+F)	% (G÷C)	BALANCE TO FINISH (C−G)	RETAINAGE
			FROM PREVIOUS APPLICATION (D+E)	THIS PERIOD					

SAMPLE

AIA copyrighted material has been reproduced with the
permission of The American Institute of Architects under
permission number 89044. Further reproduction is prohibited.

This document is intended for use as a "consumable"
(consumables are further defined by Senate Report
No. 94-473 on the Copyright Act of 1976). This document
is not intended to be used as model language (language
taken from an existing document and incorporated, without attribution, into a newly created document), but is a
standard form intended to be modified by separate amendment sheets or by filling in of blank spaces.

Because AIA Documents are revised from time to time,
users should ascertain from the AIA the current edition of
the Document reproduced herein.

Copies of this AIA Document may be purchased from
The American Institute of Architects or its local
distributors.

G703-1983

FIG. 1.1-5b Continuation sheet for application and certificate for payment.

INSTRUCTION SHEET
AIA DOCUMENTS G702a/G703a

A. GENERAL INFORMATION:

AIA Document G702, *Application and Certificate for Payment*, is to be used in conjunction with AIA Document G703, *Continuation Sheet*. These documents are designed to be used on a project where a Contractor has a direct Agreement with the Owner. Procedures for their use are covered in AIA Document A201, *General Conditions of the Contract for Construction*, 1976 Edition.

B. COMPLETING THE G702 FORM:

After the Contractor has completed AIA Document G703, *Continuation Sheet*, summary information should be transferred to AIA Document G702, *Application and Certificate for Payment*.

The Contractor should sign the form, have it notarized and submit it, together with G703, to the Architect.

The Architect should review it and, if it is acceptable, complete the Architect's Certificate for Payment on this form. The completed form should be forwarded to the Owner.

C. COMPLETING THE G703 FORM:

Heading: Complete the information here consistent with similar information on AIA Document G702, *Application and Certificate for Payment.*

Columns A, B & C: These columns should be completed by identifying the various portions of the project and their scheduled value consistent with the schedule of values submitted to the Architect at the commencement of the project or as subsequently adjusted. The breakdown may be by sections of the Work or by Systems. The total amount should remain consistent throughout the Project. Multiple pages should be used when required.

Column C should be subtotaled at the bottom when more than one page is used and totaled on the last page. Initially, this total should equal the original Contract Sum. The total of the column will be adjusted by Change Orders during the project.

Column D: Enter in this column the amount completed for work covered by the previous application. This is the sum of columns D and E from the previous application. Amounts from column F (Materials Presently Stored) from prior payments should not be entered in this column.

Column E: Enter here the value of work completed until the time of this application, including the value of materials incorporated in the project which were listed on the previous Application and Certificate for Payment under Materials Presently Stored (column F).

Column F: Enter here the value of Materials Presently Stored for which payment is sought. The total of the column must be recalculated at the end of each pay period. This value covers both materials newly stored for which payment is sought and materials previously stored which are not yet incorporated into the Project. Mere payment by the Owner for stored materials does not result in a deduction from this column. Only as materials are incorporated into the Project is their value deducted from this column and incorporated into column E (Work Completed-This Period).

Column G: Enter here the total of columns D, E and F. Calculate the percentage completed by dividing column G by column C.

Column H: Enter here the difference between column C (Scheduled Value) and column G (Total Completed and Stored to Date).

Column I: This column is normally used only for contracts where variable retainage is permitted on a line-item basis. It need not be completed on projects where a constant retainage is withheld from the overall contract amount.

Change Orders: Although Change Orders could be incorporated by changing the schedule of values each time a Change Order is added to the Project, this is not normally done. Usually, Change Orders are listed separately, either on their own G703 form or at the end of the basic schedule. The amount of the original contract adjusted by Change Orders is to be entered in the appropriate location on the G702 form.

D. MAKING PAYMENT

The Owner should make payment directly to the Contractor based on the amount certified by the Architect on AIA Document G702, *Application and Certificate for Payment*. The completed form contains the name and address of the Contractor. Payment should not be made to any other party unless specifically indicated on this form.

G702a/G703a-1983   AIA DOCUMENT G702a·G703a • INSTRUCTION SHEET FOR APPLICATION AND CERTIFICATE FOR PAYMENT • 1983 EDITION
AIA® • © 1983 THE AMERICAN INSTITUTE OF ARCHITECTS, 1735 NEW YORK AVENUE, N.W., WASHINGTON, D.C. 20006

FIG. 1.1-5c   Instruction sheet for application and certificate for payment.

On cost-plus contracts, the inspection staff sometimes is relieved of responsibility for payment approval by the presence of a field accounting section, which would include timekeepers, materials checkers, and record keepers. On small cost-plus jobs, however, all this work might devolve upon the inspector, whose job would be to set up the field record system.

Final Payment. The culmination of all the work of checking and approving requisitions comes at the end of the job, when final payment becomes due. At this time, the contract may call for any of a number of formal steps in addition to the payment itself. A certificate of final completion, prepared by the contractor and approved by the engineer or architect, is a fairly common requirement. Another is a statement that all claims outstanding by subcontractors, vendors, or others have been paid or are in process of payment or adjudication. A release document also often accompanies final payment. All these items may come within the purview of the inspector or the inspection staff. (See Fig. 1.1-6.)

Many contracts require that the contractor furnish to the owner certain guarantees and certifications, usually from vendors or subcontractors, such as roofing bonds or elevator warranties. Also, on jobs where changes have been made, it is common practice to require as-built drawings to be furnished for the owner's and designer's files. All these requirements are delineated in the contract or in the general conditions of the specifications, usually with a stipulation that final payment will not be made until they have been met. Assuring compliance with these provisions is one of the important duties of the inspector or inspection staff as a project draws to its conclusion.

CHANGES AND CHANGE-ORDER APPROVALS

A phase of the inspector's activities on most projects, somewhat related to payment-approval responsibility, is the review and processing of change orders (see Fig. 1.1-7 *a, b, c, d, e,* and *f*).

Change Order. *Change order* is the term most often used to designate the document which (1) directs or authorizes the contractor to do work not included in the basic contract, to omit work that the contract does include, or to do work in a different manner from what the plans and specifications prescribe; and (2) establishes the amount of added or reduced compensation to the contractor. Change orders may also provide additions to or deductions from the contract time allowance.

Categories of Changes. The need for change orders can arise from any of innumerable causes. The two broad categories are (1) *changes—changes in plans and specifications* desired by the owner and designer for reasons of their own; and (2) *changed conditions*—necessary changes in the methods and cost of doing the work which arise from site conditions that have turned out to differ from those contemplated by the plans and specifications. Within each category there are many different types of changes, and the procedures for originating, checking, and processing change orders vary with the type and source or cause. In addition, minor changes

RECEIPT AND RELEASE

To Whom It May Concern:

I, We,_____
                                              (SUB CONTRACTOR OR SUPPLIER)

do hereby acknowledge receipts of the full payment for materials, and/or labor, and/or services furnished to

Construction Company, and_____as Owner, in construction

on property known as   (NAME OF OWNER)

(LOCATION OF WORK)

and do hereby release the said Construction Company, and the Owner of said premises from any further liability in connection with the furnishing of said materials, and/or labor, and/or services used in construction and erection of the structure or structures on said premises. and certify that all of the materials, labor, and services performed by me have been fully paid for, and the above described premises can not be made subject to any valid lien or claim by any person, firm, or corporation who furnished to me any material, labor, or services used in the construction of said premises.

IN WITNESS WHEREOF I have hereunto set my hand and seal, this_____day of_____, 19____

_____
                    SUB CONTRACTOR OR SUPPLIER

Witnesses: By_____
                                                            TITLE

_____

_____

AFFIDAVIT

STATE OF_____

COUNTY OF_____

I HEREBY CERTIFY that on this_____day of_____, 19____, before me personally appeared

_____ to me known to be the person described in and who executed the

foregoing Receipt and Release, and he acknowledged the execution thereof to be his free act and deed for the uses and purposes therein mentioned.

WITNESS my signature and official seal at. _____, in the County of_____,

and State of_____, the day and year last aforesaid.

_____   _____
       MY COMMISSION EXPIRES   NOTARY PUBLIC

SEAL

FIG. 1.1-6 Receipt and release.

ENGINEERING DEPARTMENT

TO:

ATT:

REQUEST FOR QUOTATION

FACILITY _____

CONTRACT_____   CHANGE NO._____

TITLE   _____

Please submit an itemized proposal for the change as detailed below by _____

DESCRIPTION:

LIST OF DRAWINGS:

PLEASE SUBMIT PROPOSAL TO: NAME   _____

                                 TITLE: _____

                                 DATE: _____

                                 WORK PERMITTED TO PROCEED PRIOR TO ACCEPTANCE
                                 OF PROPOSAL WILL BE AUTHORIZED ON A TIME AND
                                 MATERIAL BASIS ONLY.

FIG. 1.1-7*a* Change order: request for quotation.

CHANGE ORDER REQUEST

FACILITY _____   CHANGE ORDER NO. _____

CONTRACT _____   CHANGE NO.   _____

TITLE _____

CONTRACTOR _____

DESCRIPTION OF CHANGE:

REASON FOR CHANGE:

COST ANALYSIS

DESIGN _____   / /   ORIGINAL _____   / /

FIELD _____   / /   REVISED _____   / /

REMARKS:

RECOMMENDATION   CONCURRENCE

AMOUNT _____   CONST. DIV. _____   / /

NAME   _____   LINE DEP'T. _____   / /

FIG. 1.1-7*b*   Change-order request.

Contract No. _____

CO	Change	Type	1 CO amount	2 Cumulative amount	3 Balance	4 CO amount	5 Cumulative amount	6 Paid on payment no.	
			Extra work orders			Credits			
1									1
2									2
3									3
4									4
5									5
6									6
7									7
8									8
9									9
10									10
11									11
12									12
13									13
14									14
15									15
16									16
17									17
18									18
19									19
20									20

FIG. 1.1-7c Schedule of change orders (face).

1.1.25

Contract No. _____

CO	Change	Type	1 Extra work orders CO amount	2 Extra work orders Cumulative amount	3 Balance	4 Credits CO amount	5 Credits Cumulative amount	6 Paid on payment no.	
21									21
22									22
23									23
24									24
25									25
26									26
27									27
28									28
29									29
30									30
31									31
32									32
33									33
34									34
35									35
36									36
37									37
38									38
39									39
40									40

FIG. 1.1-7c Schedule of change orders (continuation on back).

1.1.26

Contract no. _____

No.	Description	PACC date	Engineer's estimate	Request for quotation	Contractor's proposal		Verbal notification to proceed	Change-order request			Confirmation copy received
					Date	Amount		Date	CO no.	Amount	

Fig. 1.1-7d Change-order log.

3--CONSTRUCTION ENGINEER'S COPY
OR CONSTRUCTION DIVISION'S COPY

CHANGE ORDER No. __________ CONTRACT No. ________________

FACILITY:
CONTRACT FOR:
TO: , CONTRACTOR
ADDRESS:

In accordance with the above-described Contract:

☐ The following extra is ordered

☐ The time for completion of the contract is extended as indicated below.

☐ The following reduction is ordered

☐ The following change is ordered, at no change in price.

☐ A change is ordered as specifically outlined below.

NOTE to Contractor: Please sign the original and return to the ~~Port Authority's~~ representative whose signature appears in line five (5).

/ / ________ Date ________ (4)

The undersigned has no authority to order any item of extras whose cost, together with the cost of extras previously ordered, will exceed the limit specified in said Contract unless he has been specially authorized so to do by a resolution of the Commissioners. In the event that the above extra is in excess of such limit, the order to perform it shall be effective only if the authorized representative to the owners of the undersigned to order it. (See other side.)

No extension of the time for completion is granted to the Contractor on account of the changes ordered herein unless otherwise specifically stated above.

Dated ____________, 19____ ________________ (5)

Recommended: ________________ (1)

Extra Order Limit $ ________

Issued to Date (Excluding This Item) $ ________

Balance $ ________

EXTRA	Change No.
( ) Unforeseen Field Conditions	(C)
( ) Engineering Dept. Design Change	(D)
( ) Responsible Dept. Design Change	(R)

Construction Committee Action ( ) is ( ) is not Required.
Construction Committee Meeting Date Proposed: ________

APPROVAL RECOMMENDED:

________ (2) Deputy Chief Engineer / / ________ Date

APPROVED: ________ (3) Responsible Dept. / / ________ Date

FIG. 1.1-7*e* Change order.

**CHANGE
ORDER**
AIA DOCUMENT G701

Distribution to:
OWNER ☐
ARCHITECT ☐
CONTRACTOR ☐
FIELD ☐
OTHER ☐

PROJECT:
(name, address)

TO (Contractor):

⌐   ⌐

└   └

CHANGE ORDER NUMBER:

INITIATION DATE:

ARCHITECT'S PROJECT NO:

CONTRACT FOR:

CONTRACT DATE:

You are directed to make the following changes in this Contract.

SAMPLE

AIA copyrighted material has been reproduced with the permission of The American Institute of Architects under permission number 85044. Further reproduction is prohibited.

This document is intended for use as a "consumable" (consumables are further defined by Senate Report No. 94-473 on the Copyright Act of 1976). This document is not intended to be used as model language (language taken from an existing document and incorporated, without attribution, into a newly created document), but is a standard form intended to be modified by separate amendment sheets or by filling in of blank spaces.

Because AIA Documents are revised from time to time, users should ascertain from the AIA the current edition of the Document reproduced herein.

Copies of this AIA Document may be purchased from The American Institute of Architects or its local distributors.

Not valid until signed by both the Owner and Architect.
Signature of the Contractor indicates his agreement herewith, including any adjustment in the Contract Sum or Contract Time.

The original (Contract Sum) (Guaranteed Maximum Cost) was .... $
Net change by previously authorized Change Orders .... $
The (Contract Sum) (Guaranteed Maximum Cost) prior to this Change Order was .... $
The new (Contract Sum) (Guaranteed Maximum Cost) will be (increased) (decreased) (unchanged)
    by this Change Order .... $
The new (Contract Sum) (Guaranteed Maximum Cost) including this Change Order will be ... $
The Contract Time will be (increased) (decreased) (unchanged) by   (   ) Days.
The Date of Substantial Completion as of the date of this Change Order therefore is

Authorized:

ARCHITECT   CONTRACTOR   OWNER

Address   Address   Address

BY_____   BY_____   BY_____

DATE   DATE   DATE

AIA DOCUMENT G701 • CHANGE ORDER • APRIL 1978 EDITION • AIA® • 1978
THE AMERICAN INSTITUTE OF ARCHITECTS, 1735 NEW YORK AVE., N.W. WASHINGTON, D.C. 20006   **G701 — 1978**

FIG. 1.1-7f Sample change order of the American Institute of Architects.

may be covered by an architect's supplemental instructions (see Fig. 1.1-8*a* and *b*).

Payment for Changes.   When the change originates with the owner, architect, or engineer, the contractor is usually notified by the issuance of revised plans or amended specifications, together with a request for a price quotation for effecting the change. When changes of this sort originate well ahead of time so that there is no question of the contractor's being delayed or of the installation of work which would subsequently have to be removed or altered, the contractor is expected to do no work on the change until a price proposal has been submitted, reviewed, and approved. Many contracts include strict stipulations to this effect, and some even state that any work done on changes without previous written authorization and agreement as to price will not be paid for.

Too frequently, however, changes are not decided upon until the work affected is about to start or is already under way, in which case the contractor sometimes is permitted to proceed with the changed work during the time when a cost proposal is being prepared and processed. Under these circumstances, the inspector or the inspection staff must monitor the ongoing work to such a degree that it has recorded knowledge of the actual costs being incurred.

In normal operations when a change is desired, the contractor is notified and a price is requested. On large jobs, the contractor's proposal is sometimes sent directly to the owner or the architect-engineer, who evaluates it and either approves or disapproves it. In many instances, however, it is submitted through the field inspection staff, whose members review it and send it on together with their evaluation and recommendation. Not infrequently a contractor's first submission is judged to be overpriced, and the matter is thrown into negotiation, sometimes informally and sometimes formally by an exchange of correspondence. Because of its intimate knowledge of field conditions, the inspection staff usually is a part of this process.

In many cases, the contractor and the owner or architect-engineer are unable to reach an agreement as to a fair amount for the change, and the contractor is directed to proceed with the changed work on a cost-plus basis. Most contracts contain explicit provisions for this contingency, stipulating the terms for cost-plus change-order work. These provisions cover just which elements of the contractor's organization and forces can be charged to the changed work, what percentages can be added for overhead and profit, and what rates can be charged for equipment rentals. Possibly the most commonly used scale for these items is net cost for materials, labor, and insurance, plus 10 percent for overhead, plus equipment rentals, plus 5 or 10 percent for the contractor's profit. There

---

**ARCHITECT'S
SUPPLEMENTAL INSTRUCTIONS**

Owner ☐
Architect ☐
Consultant ☐
Contractor ☐
Field ☐
Other ☐

AIA DOCUMENT G710 (Instructions on reverse side)

PROJECT:
(name, address)

OWNER:

TO:
(Contractor)

CONTRACT FOR:

ARCHITECT'S SUPPLEMENTAL
INSTRUCTION NO:

DATE OF ISSUANCE:

ARCHITECT:

ARCHITECT'S PROJECT NO:

The Work shall be carried out in accordance with the following supplemental instructions issued in accordance with the Contract Documents without change in Contract Sum or Contract Time. Prior to proceeding in accordance with these instructions, indicate your acceptance of these instructions for minor change to the Work as consistent with the Contract Documents and return a copy to the Architect.

Description:

> AIA copyrighted material has been reproduced with the permission of The American Institute of Architects under permission number 85044. Further reproduction is prohibited.

> Because AIA Documents are revised from time to time, users should ascertain from the AIA the current edition of the Document reproduced herein.

> This document is intended for use as a "consumable" (consumables are further defined by Senate Report No. 94-473 on the Copyright Act of 1976). This document is not intended to be used as model language (language taken from an existing document and incorporated, without attribution, into a newly created document), but is a standard form intended to be modified by separate amendment sheets or by filling in of blank spaces.

> Copies of this AIA Document may be purchased from The American Institute of Architects or its local distributors.

Attachments: *(Here insert listing of documents that support description.)*

ISSUED:

BY
____ Architect

ACCEPTED:

BY
____ Contractor   Date

AIA DOCUMENT G710 • ARCHITECT'S SUPPLEMENTAL INSTRUCTIONS • MARCH 1979 EDITION • AIA®
©1979 • THE AMERICAN INSTITUTE OF ARCHITECTS, 1735 NEW YORK AVE., N.W., WASHINGTON, D.C. 20006   **G710 — 1979**

FIG. 1.1-8a Architect's supplemental instructions.

are of course many variations from these percentages. Very often when time is critical, the contractor is directed to proceed with the change-order work on a cost-plus basis without any effort to reach a lump-sum price. This is customary when the planning and drafting covering the desired changes are incomplete but work can proceed while the information is developed.

INSTRUCTION SHEET
AIA DOCUMENT G710a

A. GENERAL INFORMATION

AIA Document G710 is a new document. It may be used by the Architect to issue supplemental instructions or interpretations or to order minor changes in the Work. It is intended to help the Architect perform the obligations required under Subparagraphs 1.5.9, 1.5.10 and 1.5.14 of AIA Document B141, Owner-Architect Agreement, and Paragraph 12.4 and Subparagraph 2.2.8 of AIA Document A201, General Conditions. None of these should involve a change in Contract Sum or Contract Time.

If the Contractor believes that a change in Contract Sum or Contract Time is involved, different documents should be used. Depending on the circumstances, AIA Document G709, Proposal Request; G713, Construction Change Authorization; or G701, Change Order, may be appropriate.

This document performs many of the functions that AIA Document G708, Architect's Field Order, did before it was withdrawn. If an Architect's Project Representative will be involved in the use of this document, it may be helpful to review AIA Document B352, Duties, Responsibilities and Limitations of Authority of the Architect's Project Representative, to coordinate and verify relationships and responsibilities.

B. COMPLETING THE G710 FORM

The Architect initiates and prepares the form, which is to be signed and accepted by the Contractor.

In the case of a single prime (General) Contractor, the form should be addressed TO: that Contractor only, with the CONTRACT FOR: General Construction identified. Where there are multiple prime contractors, as in a Construction Management or an assigned contract situation, then the appropriate Contractor should be designated along with an identification of the Work involved.

The description of the action required should be carefully prepared after personal investigation or discussions with field personnel or Project Representatives. Many times it will be enough to give written instructions or clarifications, but the objective is to communicate clearly. Drawings or other graphic material should be provided as necessary.

If separate sheets are attached, they should be clearly identified, numbered and dated. It is good practice to have the Contractor initial each attachment at the time this form is signed by the Contractor. The signed form and the initiated copies should be retained by the Architect; other copies should be distributed to the Owner and other interested parties as marked at the top of the form.

AIA DOCUMENT G710a • INSTRUCTIONS FOR ARCHITECT'S SUPPLEMENTAL INSTRUCTIONS • 1979 EDITION
AIA® • THE AMERICAN INSTITUTE OF ARCHITECTS, 1735 NEW YORK AVENUE, N.W., WASHINGTON, D.C. 20006

FIG. 1.1-8*b*   Instruction sheet of architect's supplemental instructions.

Inspector's Responsibility.   The use of cost-plus methods of payment for changes adds appreciably to the workload of the inspector or the inspection staff. The contractor is required to submit daily time slips giving the name, classification, and number of each worker engaged in the change work, the number of hours employed therein, the character of duties performed, and the wages to be paid for the work. Similar information on equipment and material is required.

On large work verification of these daily submissions would be carried out by the field accounting or timekeeping personnel, but on smaller work it frequently devolves upon the inspector, who then needs to make actual head counts periodically and also must be able to differentiate clearly between the basic contract work and the work involved in the change. On large or small work, the inspector's records of labor and equipment costs can be of great importance in a defense against claims that are filed late when there is a question as to whether some work is extra work or is within the contract requirements.

To fulfill responsibilities for both payment approval and change-order approval, the inspector should have a good knowledge of costs. This is not to say that every inspector must be an expert estimator, but a general knowledge of labor costs and materials prices will be of great assistance. In the checking of cost-plus work, this information is available from daily time sheets, payrolls, and the vendor's materials invoices. In checking lump-sum work, the inspector will need some knowledge of production rates in the various trades, which can be acquired by study and systematic observation.

RECORDS AND REPORTS

While field observation of methods, materials, workmanship, and inspection of the finished work may be said to be the inspector's primary function, the record keeping and reporting needed to communicate the results to the owner or the architect-engineer form a secondary duty both demanding and time-consuming. The number and types of reports required from the inspection staff are established by the owner or the architect-engineer in accord with their own organizational procedures.

On small work where one inspector may cover a number of individual lump-sum contracts, these requirements may be very cursory, limited to progress reports and possibly payment approvals. On large work where an inspection staff is employed and work can be both lump-sum and cost-plus, a larger volume of paperwork is required. This volume also will vary with the type of contruction. A relatively simple apartment or office building, for example, will require fewer and simpler reports than a complicated industrial complex, or, say, a nuclear power plant.

Daily Report. All operations, however, require certain basic reports. The most common is the daily report (see Fig. 1.1.-9), which usually includes the date, the weather, a brief summary of what work is being

Date _____

Report no. _____

Sheet 1 of _____

Project _____ Contract no. _____

Weather _____ Temperature Range _____

Prime contractor _____

Subcontractors _____

_____

_____

_____

_____

Major trades	No. of persons	Major equipment
Total		

DESCRIPTION OF WORK PERFORMED AND INSPECTED

Specify:

Location, nature of work by contractor and subcontractors for each operation

_____

_____

_____

_____

_____

_____

_____

_____

FIG. 1.1-9a Inspector's daily report.

Engineering Department

DAILY NARRATIVE

Contractor _____ Contract No. _____

Location _____

_____
_____
_____
_____
_____
_____
_____
_____
_____
_____
_____
_____
_____
_____
_____
_____
_____
_____
_____
_____
_____
_____
_____
_____
_____
_____
_____
_____
_____
_____
_____
_____
_____
_____

Shift _____
Date _____
Counter
Signed _____

Signed _____

FIG. 1.1-9*b*   Daily narrative.

done, the number of workers and supervisors on the job, a list of the equipment in use, and any unusual occurrences such as accidents if anyone is injured, important visitors, and any work stoppages. When a job is so small that even this type of report is not required, the inspector should keep a daily log or diary recording that information. In a general way, it can be said that reports should be sufficiently thorough to establish a record of what transpired on every day, both for use in the planning of future work and for reference in the event that the work results in any form of litigation. A bound daily diary kept by each inspector is the best evidence for use in any claim being resolved, either in court or by arbitration.

Monthly Progress Report.   Probably next in importance to the factual daily reports are reports which record progress. In most construction, large or small, progress is a factor of great and continual interest to the owner. A monthly progress report which compares the status of the work with the planned status as of that date as shown on the progress schedule is a common requirement on work of any size. On some work, progress reports are prepared at weekly intervals, and sometimes when a contractor is racing to meet an important interim date or a critical completion date, as when a power plant is scheduled to be put on line, progress reports of key operatons are transmitted daily. Also many large projects are completed in stages, as, for example, a housing project in which buildings are put into occupancy as they are completed.

Punch List.   Another type of report, used during the period when jobs are nearing completion, is the *punch list.* This is a list of unfinished items of work that are needed for the project to be called acceptably complete. The list usually is prepared by the inspector or the inspection staff working with the contractor's personnel. It is amended daily as new items turn up and as items of work on the list are satisfactorily completed. Eventually the list is reduced to zero, tantamount to project completion.

Accident Reports.   When an accident in which anyone is injured occurs, an *accident report* must be processed. On work large enough to have a separate safety engineer or safety division, this report would be prepared by it. Usually it is prepared by the contractor, though frequently on forms furnished by the contractor's insurance carrier. Copies usually go to the owner, sometimes through the inspector or the inspection staff, which reviews it and attaches its own comments if any seem indicated.

Test Reports.   Contracts sometimes require various tests or inspections of materials going into the work, such as compression tests of concrete cylinders cast at the site, mill tests of structural steel, or Fire Underwriters Laboratory tests of fire-prevention materials. The reports covering these tests usually are channeled through and processed by the inspection staff. The same procedure applies to operating tests such as those of elevators or pressure tests on piping. In many cases, this type of testing is performed by outside testing firms or laboratories that might submit reports directly to the owner or architect-engineer; but when the tests are contract requirements, the inspection staff must follow them up to ensure that the contract requirements are met. (For samples of some of the reports outlined above, see Figs. 1.1-3 through 1.1-7 and Fig. 1.1-9.)

Special Reports. There are other reports covering special situations which may fall within the duties of the inspection staff. For example, on most federal government work in recent years, affirmative-action requirements in connecton with Equal Employment Opportunity regulations necessitate detailed reports from the contractor, the subcontractors, and even materials suppliers, much of which is channeled through the inspection staff. On some projects, materials are paid for before they actually are incorporated in the work. Here delivery receipts, inventories, and bills of sale must be checked to verify that materials and equipment are on site. This is often handled by the field inspection group. From all the above, it will be seen that record keeping is an important part of the inspector's role.

GENERAL PROCEDURES

Concurrent with their primary duties of examining and monitoring the contractor's work and reporting on it, inspectors have a continuous secondary function.

Role as Liaison. Inspectors are the liaison between the architect-engineer or owner and the contractor in many routine matters. The processing of plans, specifications, and other instructions or information in both directions is sometimes handled by them. This is usually the case on projects not large enough for a complete, functionally divided field office. In the same way, inspectors receive and store or transmit the various samples and catalog cuts obtained by the contractor from vendors or subcontractors. Working or shop drawings furnished by the subcontractors to the contractor are routed to the architect-engineer and owner, often through the inspector. (For a record of shop drawings and samples, see Fig. 1.1-10.)

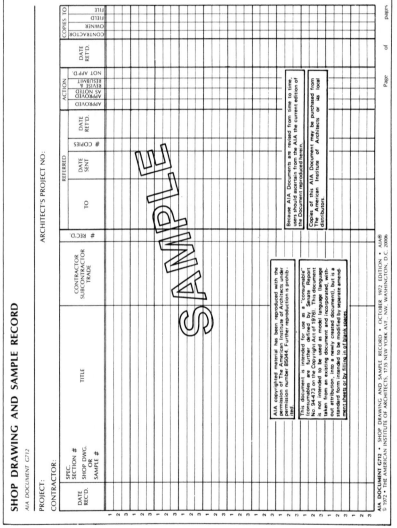

FIG. 1.1-10 Record of shop drawings and samples.

On large work, many forms of off-site inspection are required at cement mills, steel mills, fabricating shops, and factories. Contract provisions covering this work vary. If the inspection arrangements are made by the contractor, the reports may go to the contractor for forwarding to the owner or architect-engineer. If the arrangements are made directly by the owner, the reports might come back to the owner with copies to the field. In either case, they pass through the field inspection staff, which reviews them and collates and files them.

Most contracts contain specific requirements covering the types of insurance that the contractor must carry and the amounts of coverage. Checking the evidence of this coverage is an inspection-staff responsibility, and in some contracts, it is stipulated that work cannot be started until the necessary insurance certificates have been reviewed, approved, and sent to the owner.

In some instances, construction contracts require incorporation in the work of materials not bought by the contractor but furnished by the owner or others. In these cases, the inspection staff has a responsibility for examining this material before it is used and checking its quality, the quantities for the owner's payment purposes, and the contractor's methods of handling and storage.

Compliance by the contractor and the subcontractors with the various codes which control construction is another area in which the inspection staff will be involved. These codes are numerous and vary with the type of work and its location, from building department codes to the elaborate and intricate requirements of the federal government's Occupational Safety and Health Administration (OSHA). In the enforcement of codes, outside inspection personnel sent by the various agencies will often be at the site (sometimes on large work even stationed there), and working with them will be part of the inspection staff's ongoing responsibility. Basic compliance with the governing building code of the location is of course primarily a responsibility of the architect-engineer during the design stages of a project, but in connection with field changes and also in the area of temporary field structures the inspector or the inspection staff may be drawn into code-compliance judgments.

The manner in which an inspector or the inspection staff handles its responsibilities and duties can have much bearing upon both the progess of the work and the quality of the resulting structure. Equally important, it can affect favorably or mar the general sense of satisfaction arising from a well-conducted construction operation creating a quality structure. The inspection staff necessarily represents primarily the owner and architect-engineer as opposed to the contractor, but this need not imply an adversary relationship. Quite the contrary is the case. Both sides share a common goal: a good job done as speedily as possible at as low a cost as possible. The contractor's added objective is the earning of a profit.

Cooperation is the watchword that will assure a successful construction project insofar as relations between the inspection staff and the contractor's forces go. This does not mean any slackening of the standards established in the specifications or required by good practice, but it does mean reasonable interpretations of plans and the acceptance of standard practices in the various trades.

On cost-plus contracts this cooperation is more readily implemented than on lump-sum work, because economy is of the essence for both owner and contractor. On lump-sum work, economy from the contractor's point of view and quality from the owner's point of view sometimes conflict. In these instances, the inspector's role is to ensure that quality prevails but to do this in such a way that progress is not impeded and the owner-contractor relationship is not impaired or needless contractor costs incurred.

Avoidance of Obligation to Contractor.   This subsection would be incomplete without some reference to a most essential element in the inspector-contractor relationship, the complete freedom on the inspector's part from any sort of obligation or indebtedness, however vague, to the contractor or any of the contractor's personnel. This does not preclude working together cordially in the daily business of the job operation or even the development of friendships.

Friendships are not unusual on construction projects at remote sites where the contractor's and the architect-engineer's or owner's field personnel are necessarily thrown together in both their working and their leisure time. But it does mean that members of the inspection staff must refrain from accepting any gifts or favors from the contractor. Here again common sense and reason must prevail.

If a contractor gives a party celebrating a holiday or perhaps the achievement of some significant job milestone, invited inspection people should feel free to attend. If the same occasion was set to include off-site expensive travel and entertainment, attendance by the inspection staff would be improper.

A number of the contractor groups such as AGCA or other contractor associations around the United States conduct annual Christmas parties or summer golf outings to which the architect-engineer and various public agency personnel are regularly invited, and attendance at these has become an accepted practice. Also, it is not uncommon for contractors to distribute gifts at Christmas. If these are trivia, such as pens, small knives, or ashtrays, and particularly if they contain imprints of the firm name and thus are advertising items, they may be accepted. Larger gifts, however, should be declined or returned forthwith upon delivery.

In the past there have been areas, particularly in the public agencies of some large cities, where gifts to inspectors of cases of liquor, clothing items, lavish entertainment, and even cash were not uncommon; and many official eyes were closed to these practices. Such practices are no longer tolerated and, in fact, in many jurisdictions have been made illegal and subject to heavy penalties. All members of the inspection staff must avoid even the appearance of involvement in any of these illegal customs.

Construction Management (CM) Contract.   The observations in this chapter have in general pertained to the inspector's activities and relationships on work where a general contractor is in charge of the project. More recently, large volumes of work are being executed under the construction-management-contract type of administration. In these cases, the duties of the inspection staff will be similar, although there will be some variations in paper processing. These will depend upon whether the field inspection forces are employees of the owner, the architect-engineer, or the CM contractor. Under construction management contracts, inspectors will have more direct dealings with subcontractors than when a general contractor is used and might in fact be the principal liaison between them and the management contractor or architect-engineer or owner.

Preconstruction Meetings.   It is a generally accepted practice to hold a preconstruction meeting before the start of fieldwork on a project. Attending will be representatives of the owner, architect-engineer, public utilities, local governments, traffic-control agencies, resident engineer, clerk of the works, inspectors, and contractor's superintendent and staff.

The general plan for performing the work, coordinating it with utility removals and installations, methods for traffic control, sequence and scheduling of critical operations, and other special project conditions and restrictions will be reviewed. Also, procedures and timing for shop drawings, materials testing, and reporting will be outlined. A list of representatives of each organization with their organization title, specific duty as relating to the project, and mailing address and telephone number to facilitate direct contact will be provided to all concerned.

A well-organized preconstruction meeting sets the stage for an orderly and smooth-running project. Detailed minutes of the meeting will record all actions for future guidance.

Public Relations Role of the Inspector. In addition to carrying out technical and professional functions, the inspector can perform a very valuable service in making a conscious effort to develop and maintain cordial relations with local residents, townspeople, and any who are affected by construction operations. As a friendly source of information about them, the inspector can provide a valuable service to all concerned with and affected by the construction activities. A pleasant, friendly, and cooperative attitude toward the contractor will result in a smoother-running job and need not involve any relaxation in the inspector's professional performance.

Safety in Construction

Louis F. Booth, P.E.
Consultant
St. Petersburg Beach, Florida

Formerly

General Contractor
Manager of Construction
The Port of New York Authority

GENERAL ADMINISTRATION

The duties and responsibilities of the inspector or the inspection staff in the field of safety will vary with the size of the job and with the type of organization supervising it. On very large work, it is a common practice to have a separate safety division headed by a trained safety engineer and staffed with as many trained observers as are needed to cover all the operations. In this situation, the construction inspectors and inspection staff are relieved of much of this responsibility and need only keep their eyes open in a general way for any conditions or methods that seem hazardous and report them to the assigned safety personnel. However, many construction jobs including some fairly large ones do not have this formal safety organization; and the safety observations and accident-prevention measures that they would have handled fall upon the shoulders of the rest of the field supervisory personnel, including to a large degree the field inspection staff. It is to their problems and methods that this chapter is directed. Complete, detailed coverage of safety in construction would require a full volume by itself, so this chapter will cover only the more common and more important aspects of the subject.

The importance of safety provisions and accident prevention on construction work cannot be overemphasized. Aside from the human considerations, accidents can be extremely costly to the workers involved, to the contractor, and eventually to the owner. Apart from the cost of replacing work damaged or destroyed, accident insurance premium rates respond in time to poor experience ratings, increasing a contractor's cost on future work. Moreover, time lost due to accident-caused repairs or replacements often is never regained, so that the owner's use of a project and the income from it are delayed. Thus it behooves the inspector and the inspection staff, whether employed by owner, architect-engineer, or contractor, to be ever conscious of safety considerations.

On large, well-organized construction projects, safety provisions will have been planned long before any fieldwork is started or any inspector or inspection staff is at the site. This advance planning usually includes a review of the plans and specifications to disclose any potentially hazardous conditions or unusual exposures and the establishment of procedures to guard against them and also against the more normal everyday risks. However, on smaller jobs it is possible, in fact probable, that none of this will have been done and the field inspection staff will have a most important secondary duty, the continual observation and study of the construction methods and site organization as they apply to safety. This includes safety of the workers directly engaged upon the work, safety of the public at or near the site, and safety of property from fire or from other accidental damage. In the following pages, the more prevalent hazards and the provisions for handling them are discussed briefly. For a more detailed study of all possible hazards, the various local codes covering a site or the promulgations of the federal Occupational Safety and Health Administration (OSHA) can be reviewed.

As mentioned, the three broad categories of safety monitoring are (1) provisions for the safety of employees, including their own work habits and behavior, (2) provisions for the protection of the public, and (3) provisions against fire, storm, or equipment failures that would result in injuries or property damage. These categories will be reviewed successively in the following subsections.

SAFETY OF THE WORKERS

Among the provisions for the safety of workers, probably the most general and basic are site orderliness and good housekeeping; and this is an area where the inspector's observations and policing can be of great help. Many personal-injury accidents are the result of falls caused by tripping or sliding on debris, nail punctures from scrap lumber, falls on ice in winter, and similar situations. Most of these could be avoided by simple good housekeeping. Rubbish and waste materials should be collected and removed promptly and passageways and work areas kept clear of any unnecessary obstructions. This is an aspect sometimes neglected, particularly on small work, and a tactful inspector's pressure usually can improve it.

Safe Access. Temporary barricades or rails should protect all openings large enough for a worker to fall into or through, particularly on high-rise construction. These should be strong enough and sufficiently braced to resist substantial impacts.

Temporary ladders and stairs must be strong enough for workers and their loads and should be secured into the locations in which they are used. Ladders should extend at least waist-high above the levels to which they lead. When the permanent steel stairways are put into construction-time use, the steel treadpans should be filled level with wood to obviate tripping hazards.

Exterior scaffolds should be erected on firm footings, tied to the structure at frequent levels, and provided with railing at the working levels. Interior scaffolds also must be braced, and rolling scaffolds should be provided with locking devices to keep them stationary when in use. Scaffolding in all its forms requires complicated techniques; and on an operation where it is a major item, such as, for example, beneath a high wide-span roof, the inspection staff should consult appropriate codes or technical texts. See American National Standards Institute (ANSI) standards for ladders and scaffolds.

Protective Clothing.   Protective clothing is an important factor in worker safety. *Hard hats* are of course an elementary item and in recent years have been used on practically all heavy construction where workers may be exposed to falling or flying objects. It is not always easy to enforce the hard-hat rules, and here the inspector's attention can be of help to construction supervisors. Hard hats should be of a quality that will meet at least the minimum requirements of the various codes. (An example is federal specification CGG-H-142 B, Helmets, Construction Workers.) Many contractors provide hard hats, usually with their own company insignia, and also make the wearing of them a condition of employment, with similar stipulations included in their subcontract agreements.

  Goggles for welding, chipping, spray painting, or any work that might endanger eyes are a requirement that should be enforced. *Gloves* appropriate to the workers' task, such as those used by electricians where insulation is important or by iron workers for climbing structural steel, should be worn. *Safety shoes* which protect the workers' feet from lacerations or punctures or against crushing or pinching from rolling or falling heavy objects are available and should be worn by workers exposed to those hazards.

Medical Facilities.   Large projects usually have a first-aid station staffed by a technician or a nurse and, on very large jobs, by a doctor. On smaller work, a first-aid kit, which the inspector must be sure is stocked with adequate supplies, may be available at the site, but outside facilities must be used for serious accidents. Sometimes standing arrangements are made with a nearby hospital and several nearby physicians. The inspector should be familiar with the facilities and locations, names, telephone numbers, and hours of their staffs.

Lighting.   Proper and sufficient lighting arrangements are an important factor in a safe working environment, particularly in underground work or in the interior rooms of structures. Temporary lights are normally installed as fast as work areas are dug or constructed, but in important key locations it is essential that these be supplemented by battery-powered emergency lights so that a power failure will not create intolerable hazard conditions. Warning signs such as "High Voltage" or "Explosives" and "Emergency Exit" location signs should always be well lighted.

Work Habits.   Unsafe conduct by individual workers is an area in which the inspection staff must work only through supervisory personnel. But habitual observation can note practices that are potential accident causes, and attention drawn to them through supervisors can reduce mishaps. Improper equipment operation such as loads swinging without tag lines, workers riding loads, crane operation on unfirm ground without mats, and use of open hooks and other timesaving shortcuts are practices that can be noted and reported. Failure of individual workers to wear protective clothing, operation of power tools without proper grounding, removal of barricades at openings without prompt replacement, and many similar unsafe acts by careless workers are items that the supervisory forces must continually police and items with which the inspector's alertness and cooperation can be very helpful.

Special Hazards. In the other *Handbook* chapters covering individual trades and construction fields much specialized information on safety provisions is included, but a few of the more common precautions in the conduct of excavation work and demolitions are presented here.

Excavations. In trench excavation or pits, any overhanging banks should be removed and undercutting avoided. Sheeting should be amply braced and left in place until backfill or construction reaches its level. Deep pits or trenches should be barricaded when work in them is not in progress. Ramps must be protected with guard curbs adequate for the trucks using them. When rock excavation requires blasting, the explosives used shall be procured, stored, and handled strictly in accordance with the governing codes and the work controlled by a licensed blaster. Adequate blasting mats must protect the shots and a dependable blast-warning system employed.

Demolitions. When manual demolition is employed, barricades should be installed down to floor level at all exterior wall openings. Floor openings and shafts not required for the disposal of debris should be planked over. Exterior wall demolition should proceed from the top downward, though sections may be razed by pulling them inward with care that safe floor loads are not exceeded. Wall demolition should not be carried out adjoining floor openings unless these are planked over. Wreckers should not work on the tops of open walls when weather conditions are dangerous. Floor supports should not be removed until wrecking above that level has been completed and the debris disposed of. When mechanical razing is employed, floor structures should be checked for their ability to support front-end loaders, bulldozers, vibratory breakers, or other equipment. Floor openings or perimeters should have guard curbs to keep equipment on solid areas. When floors are being removed, areas below them should be barricaded to keep out any workers other than those needed for the removal. When steel framing is being demolished, using derricks or cranes, tag lines should be employed and members should be lowered and not dropped. Oxygen or acetylene cylinders should be secured in cradles when they are being raised or lowered. Members should be under no external stress while being cut and should be secured so that they do not fall free. When demolition is done by a clamshell bucket or a swinging ball, no personnel should be within the structure while that work is going on, and the outside area should be well barricaded. The subject of safety in demolition is both broad and complicated, but the foregoing are some of the more common precautions to which a field inspector should give attention.

SAFETY OF THE PUBLIC

Provisions for the protection of the public, particularly on work within cities or along traveled highways, rank in importance equally to measures for the safety of the site workers, and of course the two fields overlap. The public can be divided for safety-protection purposes into two broad groups, those never on the actual site, such as passersby or occupants of adjoining premises, and authorized site visitors who are not site workers, such as sales representatives, public inspectors, news reporters, or sightseers viewing the work with permission of the owner or architect-engineer.

For the first group, the primary caution is to keep outsiders off the site. On work in outlying areas, this is done by means of fencing with guarded gates at entrances needed for workers or materials. In downtown city areas the site can be fenced, and, in addition, a *sidewalk bridge*, a covered walkway, will provide safe passage for pedestrians who must pass close by. Such walkways should be kept clean, free of ice in winter, and free from tripping hazards, nails, or any projections and should be boarded up solidly on the building side. When sidewalk bridges are used for storage, they should be strong enough for the loads, and the checking of this aspect of their use is within the field inspector's duties. When the sidewalk bridges protect demolition projects, the decks should be double-planked and solid rails and wire-mesh flareouts should be installed to protect against falling objects or debris. The passageways should be well lighted, and ample warning signs should be posted at truck entrances, for hydrant locations, or for blasting notices. In the early stages of some city projects when only foundation work below street level is in progress, a stout fence may be used instead of a covered passageway, care being taken to provide stout plank walkways if existing sidewalks are not in good condition. In some cases, contractors provide occasional small framed window openings to permit curious "sidewalk superintendents" to view their work. The publicity value of these openings is doubtful when compared with the disadvantages of having the walkway sometimes partially blocked and also of the possibility of accidents from flying objects, particularly if the excavation work requires blasting.

For both the public outside but nearby and actual visitors to the site, the accident-prevention factor highest on the list is site orderliness, or good housekeeping. Ample passageways should be maintained, well lighted, and free of debris or stored materials and cleaned of mud, ice, loose mortar, or any materials that could cause tripping or slipping accidents. Floor openings in or near these areas should be barricaded or boarded over, and the open perimeters should be railed. Stored materials should be stacked in such a way that no collapse is possible. Any areas of unusual exposure or where hazardous work is under way should be barricaded and visitors barred.

On open types of construction work such as highways or bridges or subway construction, safety provisions to protect the public are usually prescribed in detail in the plans and specifications, and the inspector or inspection staff simply sees to it that those requirements are met. But on smaller work of this type, the specifications may only refer to the appropriate standards or codes and the inspector is left to judge the sufficiency of the measures taken. Where traffic flow actually adjoins the new construction, timber guard curbs, secured firmly to the pavement, should be installed. When traffic is separated from the new work or repairs by a full lane's width or more, it can be controlled by conspicuously colored cones or horses. Repeated signs should warn oncoming drivers well in advance of the start of the work, and extra warning signs should be posted for any special hazards. Flaggers should be posted where equipment operation could in any way endanger either vehicular or pedestrian traffic. After dark, any roadway obstructions should be brightly illuminated.

FIRE PREVENTION

In an appreciable portion of accidents, both personal injury and property damage are caused by or increased by an accompanying fire, and of course in many instances fire *is* the accident. The review of and policing of the measures set up to prevent or control fires are, therefore, among the most important duties of the inspector's program of safety inspection. On large work, particularly in building construction, there are various codes (including that of the Fire Underwriters) which specify fire-prevention measures. On large work that is more spread out such as highways, bridges, dams, or waterfront work, the basic risk is somewhat smaller, but whenever combustible materials are stored or used and processes involving flame or heat are employed, a fire hazard exists. On smaller operations where in many cases the risk is less, fewer precautions are taken, and in these situations awareness and care on the part of the inspector is of even more importance.

Early Installation of Protective Devices.   Fire prevention starts in the planning stage of a construction operation. Preplanned organization of the enforcement of regulations and supervision of fire-dangerous work will prevent many fires from being accidentally started and will facilitate control of any that do. For example, scheduling the very early installation of permanent water-supply service lines and interim temporary lines to hose locations will provide protection from the start of work. On building projects, the sprinkler systems should be installed and connected at the earliest feasible moment. Water-line risers should be carried up as fast as floor installation is completed, with temporary supply connections until the permanent service is available, so that hose-stream protection is operable by the time that large quantities of combustible materials are stored or installed. Materials-delivery schedules can be planned to match installation so that quantities stored at the site are minimized. Workshops and other temporary buildings at a site should be located at safe distances from the structure and separated from each other to reduce possible fire spread.

Fire extinguishers, regularly checked and charged, should be placed at strategic locations on all floors as fast as floor slabs are constructed. In the layout of plant, materials storage, and temporary buildings, consideration should be given to providing easy access by fire-fighting equipment. Standpipe connections should be amply signed and kept unobstructed. If the site is fortunate enough to have nearby fire hydrants, care should be taken that they never are blocked by building materials or construction equipment or trucks.

Winter Hazards.   In winter work, lack of care in the planning and use of the various temporary heat provisions is a source of many construction-job fires. Salamanders, gas heaters, or oil heaters should be of types approved by the code, should be well insulated from the structure, and should be separated horizontally from any built-in or stored combustible material. Charcoal-burning or coke-burning heaters should never be used in enclosed or unventilated spaces, and when any heater type except an electric heater is used, there should be a sufficient supply of outside air to ensure proper combustion and allow breathing by workers. Tarpaulins for enclosing the heated areas should be flameproofed and tightly secured. When heaters with flues are used, the flues should be insulated or well separated from the structure. Local heating equipment in temporary buildings should be approved types and be regularly checked. When propane is used, the tanks should be installed outside the heated building.

Construction-Process Hazards. The various construction processes which entail fire hazard such as cutting and welding, operation of tar kettles, blowtorch work, soldering, and pouring hot joints should be accompanied by definite fire-protection measures. Combustible fluids should be stored off the site except for the minima needed for a day's supply, which should be in approved containers. Gasoline should be kept in safety cans not to exceed 10-gal (37.85-L) capacity. Any gasoline-powered or diesel-powered equipment should be shut down during refueling. Gas cylinders should be stored away from heat sources or hot sunlight and in small groups with the fuel gases separated from the oxidizing gases. Valve covers should be kept in place and tanks protected from falling or damage. Flammable paints should be stored in limited quantities and protected from heat. At some point in this general subject, smoking must be mentioned. While control of smoking on construction sites admittedly is difficult, there are hazard areas where its prohibition can and should be enforced. Fuel-storage and painting areas are two of them.

Temporary wiring is another not-uncommon source of accidental fire. All wiring should be placed out of reach of traffic or inadvertent worker access and protected from physical damage, water, or weather. All circuits should be adequately fused with outlets located in safe positions. Complete information on the location and operation of cutoff switches should be in the hands of appropriate electrical and supervisory personnel during working hours and of the security staff during nonwork time.

Security Staff. Coverage by the security staff should include well-planned tours with regular time intervals and the necessary clocks or stations to record that the tours have been made. Everyone should be completely familiar with the locations of extinguishers or other fire-fighting equipment and with the alarm procedures.

As with all other aspects of safety, good housekeeping is a prime element in fire prevention. Prompt removal of scrap lumber, packing materials, and combustible debris reduces the amount of materials to feed flames and makes all areas more accessible. Neat storage in limited, separated piles of the more combustible building materials reduces the chance of fire spread. All these aspects of site orderliness are items that an inspector habitually should observe.

SAFETY INSPECTIONS

On large work where the supervisory force includes a safety division, continuous safety inspection is its major role. On smaller work where there is a general responsibility, field inspectors will perforce bear much of this load. General safety awareness concomitant with other inspection duties is a required attitude, but, in addition, periodic pure safety inspections are advisable. Such inspections would detect potential hazards and expose unsafe practices earlier than would only casual attention and would uncover shortcomings in site housekeeping (accumulations of rubbish, improperly stored materials, inadequate barricades, and defective protection of openings) in time for prompt correction. They would pick up unsafe methods of doing work or handling materials and any improper operation of equipment. They would check on the use of protective clothing or gear by both construction workers and site visitors. They would monitor general code compliance. These inspections should be periodic but varied to check on any special operations and on off-hour security coverage. Sometimes nonscheduled safety inspections without foreknowledge by the groups to be covered have salutary benefits.

In well-planned construction projects of any magnitude, it is customary to hold one or more preconstruction safety meetings attended by the contractor and such subcontractors as have by then been selected and by representatives of the architect-engineer and the insurance carrier. Here questions of construction methods to prevent fire or accidents and the safety equipment needed for the job are resolved, and formal safety agenda are prepared. The inspection personnel, whether in the employ of the owner, the architect-engineer, or the contractor, should be present at these meetings so that in the course of safety inspections during the work they can see whether or not all the planned safety provisions are being carried out. In addition, they can detect and report on hazards which were not anticipated and can identify any unforeseen items of heavy exposure and see that they are controlled.

Safety checklists are a tool useful to the inspector in monitoring safety performance. Usually these checklists are prepared during the preconstruction planning phase and are amended as the work develops or as critical operations are begun. Sometimes individual safety checklists are prepared for the different trades or operations, such as for electrical work, steel erection, exterior wall-panel installation, and demolitions or perhaps for work in confined areas. Often a basic list covering normal exposures on the site is supplemented by a special checklist to cover overnight and weekend periods when work is shut down. The last would particularly involve the adequacy of security coverage.

Safety inspections during nonwork hours are by necessity largely the function of the security service. This service should include frequent tours recorded at sealed check-in stations. Security staff should be trained for emergencies and should be in good condition both physically and mentally. When the security service is contracted out, minimum standards in this respect should be specified. Probably the most important items in the off-hours security safety checklist are those pertaining to fire prevention, and this is best assured by frequent and dependable coverage of all the areas.

ACCIDENT INVESTIGATIONS AND REPORTS

When accidents do happen—and they will despite the most thorough prevention planning and safety-rules enforcement—the investigation is generally conducted by the supervisory forces of the contractor or the architect-engineer, or both, though on major mishaps involving loss of life a public agency might also be involved. The field inspector, with continuous and concurrent knowledge of the operations and methods, should be able to make valuable contributions both in the determination of cause and in the establishment of methods to prevent repetition. On large work where supervision includes a safety engineer or a safety division, those personnel would lead the investigation, sometimes implemented by representatives of the insurance carrier.

When a major accident involving loss of life or extensive damage occurs, the investigation takes on certain legal aspects and a field inspector's contribution must be carefully considered and accurate. The collection of facts in detail becomes most important, and these should be duly reported. While drawing conclusions from these facts is within the inspector's province, formally stating them should take place only in conjunction with the employer, owner, architect-engineer, or contractor.

On minor accidents in which individual injuries result, particularly if these involve lost working time, the accident report is prepared by the worker's employer, though the insurance carrier's representative might prepare the report if one is at the jobsite. In either case, a field inspector who is aware of the facts and circumstances can make a contribution of value. (See Fig. 1.2-1 for a typical agency-type personal-injury accident report and Fig. 1.2-2 for a form used for a personal report filed by the injured party.)

It is also within the province of the inspector to be sure that the first-aid kit is in a readily accessible location. Most frequently this will prove to be the contractor superintendent's field office if the job is of such size that this office is within or adjacent to the work. Particularly in high-rise or widely spread projects, however, additional first-aid kits should be placed on upper floors or in the more widely spread locations, prominently marked, so that they are quickly available when a need for them arises. The field inspector should periodically check the kits to be sure that they are adequately stocked for minor-injury treatment.

FIRST REPORT OF INJURY

CARRIER
FILE NO.

REPORT ALL DEATHS BY TELEPHONE OR TELEGRAM WITHIN 24 HOURS

1. EMPLOYER'S FIRM NAME	2. EMPLOYEE'S NAME (First, Middle, Last)	3. SOCIAL SECURITY NUMBER	
MAILING ADDRESS AND TELEPHONE NUMBER	EMPLOYEE'S HOME ADDRESS	4. DATE OF ACCIDENT	HOUR
		5. LAST DATE WORKED	

6. NATURE OF BUSINESS	7. AGE	8. SEX	9. RACE	10. HOW LONG EMP.	DO NOT WRITE IN THIS COLUMN
11. NAME OF WORKMEN'S COMPENSATION INS. CO.	12. OCCUPATION		13. DEPARTMENT NAME		EMP. NO.
	14. Inj. First Reported Date and Hour		15. SUPERVISOR'S NAME		
16. WAS EMPLOYEE PAID FOR DATE OF INJURY ☐ YES ☐ NO	17. DID EMPLOYEE LOSE TIME FROM WORK? ☐ YES ☐ NO	18. IF YES DATE RETURNED OR PROBABLE DATE			CARRIER NO.

	19. HOURS WORKED ☐ PER DAY ☐ PER WEEK	20. NO. DAYS PER WEEK	INDUSTRY NO.
WAGE INFORMATION (ANSWER APPLICABLE SECTIONS)	21. RATE OF PAY ☐ PER HOUR ☐ PER DAY ☐ PER WEEK		LOC. NO.
22. IF PIECE WORK OR COMMISSION ENTER AVERAGE WEEKLY AMT. AMOUNT	23. If Board, Lodging or other advantages were furnished in addition to wages state estimates	WEEKLY AMOUNT	

24. PLACE OF ACCIDENT (Street, City, County)		EMPLOYER'S PREMISES ☐ YES ☐ NO	AGE
25. HOW DID ACCIDENT HAPPEN? (State fully what the employee was doing and whether the worker was struck, fell, etc. Give all factors contributing to accident, use separate sheet if needed)	FOR DATE STAMP ONLY		SEX
			ACC. TYPE
			AGENCY INJ.
			AGENCY PART
			BODY LOC.
26. NAME THE OBJECT, SUBSTANCE OR EXPOSURE WHICH DIRECTLY INJURED THE EMPLOYEE.			NAT. INJ.
27. DESCRIBE THE INJURY OR DISEASE AND INDICATE PART OF BODY AFFECTED. (E.G. AMPUTATION OF RIGHT INDEX FINGER AT SECOND JOINT, FRACTURED RIBS, LEAD POISONING, ETC.)			INIT. HAND,
28. NAME AND ADDRESS OF PHYSICIAN	29. NAME AND ADDRESS OF HOSPITAL		TIME CHARGE
			TYPE DIS.
30. WAS PHYSICIAN AUTHORIZED BY EMPLOYER ☐ YES ☐ NO	31. IF DEATH CASE, GIVE DATE	TOTAL MEDICAL PAID TO NEAREST DOLLAR	PAY LAG.
32. FOR CARRIERS AND SELF-INSURERS	If no Permanent Injury – To close no lost time - File this Report including Medical Costs. To close one to seven day lost time - File SF-2 and this Report showing Medical Costs.		STATUS
33. PREPARED BY	34. OFFICIAL POSITION	35. DATE	
			WEEKLY WAGE
THE LAW PROVIDES A PENALTY OF $100.00 FOR FAILURE TO FILE THIS REPORT WITHIN 10 DAYS AFTER KNOWLEDGE OF INJURY			POLICY YEAR

FIG. 1.2-1   A typical public agency personal-injury accident report.

EMPLOYEE'S OCCUPATIONAL DISEASE OR INJURY REPORT

Instructions: 1. Employees will complete Part I and forward to Supervisor. 2. Supervisor will send photocopy of completed Part I to Workmen's Compensation Agent, immediately. 3. Supervisor will complete Part II and send original P.A. Form 360 to P.A. Medical Clinic. 4. P.A. Medical Clinic will complete Part III and send original of fully completed report (Parts I, II, and III) to Inspection and Safety Division.

PART I – PREPARED BY EMPLOYEE IN OWN HANDWRITING

Name		Home Address (Street, No., City, State, Zip Code)		Area Cd.	Home Tel. No.

Employee No.	Social Security No.	Date of Birth	Sex M ☐ F ☐	Marital Status: ☐ Married ☐ Divorced ☐ Single ☐ Widowed ☐ Separated	Job Title

Fac/Div.	Org. Unit No.	Telephone Ext.	Date of injury	Time ___M	Shift/duty Hrs.	Did it occur on P.A. premises? ☐ Yes ☐ No	Weather Conditions:

Date injury reported	Date disease diagnosed	To whom reported – Name/Title

Location where injury took place or disease was contracted	State in which injury or disease occurred ☐ N.Y. ☐ N.J.	Name of Witness

Was medical treatment received? ☐ Yes ☐ No	If yes, check: ☐ First Aid ☐ P.A. Clinic ☐ Hospital ☐ Private Dr.	Date of treatment	Name and address of doctor or hospital

Describe injury or disease in detail – use right or left to indicate side of body affected

Describe how injury or disease occurred. Indicate what you were doing at that time. Name the object, substance or condition which directly caused injury or disease.

What could have prevented your injury or disease? Describe any corrective measures that should be taken to avoid its recurrence.

Signature of person other than employee completing this form.	Employee's Signature	Date

PART II – HANDWRITTEN BY IMMEDIATE SUPERVISOR OF EMPLOYEE

Describe how injury or disease occurred. Indicate cause.

Comment on the preventive suggestion given by the employee above. What action have you taken to prevent recurrence?

Immediate supervisor's signature	Print immediate supervisor's name and title	Org. unit head's signature

PART III – TO BE COMPLETED BY MEDICAL DEPARTMENT

Is the injury or disease expected to be disabling	☐ Yes	☐ No	☐ Unknown

Will the injury or disease involve the employee in any of the following?

a) Permanent transfer to another job or termination after lost work days	☐ Yes	☐ No
b) Temporary transfer to another job	☐ Yes	☐ No
c) Working at a permanent job less than full time	☐ Yes	☐ No
d) Working at a permanently assigned job, but cannot perform all duties assigned to it	☐ Yes	☐ No

Additional Comments:

Medical Department – Signature	Title	Date

FIG. 1.2-2　Report to be filed by an injured employee.

In summary, *safety is everybody's business*. The inspector should monitor unsafe practices and bring them to the immediate attention of the proper person, i.e., the unsafe worker or the supervisor as appropriate to the time and circumstances of each safety violation.

CHAPTER 1.3

Construction Surveying

Lystre L. Sutcliffe, Jr., P.E.
Vice President and Manager of Construction Engineering
Services Department
Parsons Brinckerhoff Construction Services, Inc.
Trenton, New Jersey

F. A. Jarrett, L.S.
Chief of Surveys
Parsons Brinckerhoff Construction Services, Inc.
Trenton, New Jersey

Construction surveying covers a wide range of tasks, from verifying existing controls from which construction projects are to be built to furnishing an as-built survey to verify a construction project's final location. This chapter will provide a step-by-step process of construction surveying from preconstruction through construction and postconstruction phases. Marine surveying is described at the end of the chapter. Many of the surveying methods described throughout this chapter can supplement the marine-surveying methods described. It is assumed that the reader has a basic working knowledge and familiarity with surveying instruments, techniques, and terminology as well as a basic knowledge of the applications of surveying to a construction project. A glossary of miscellaneous terms is provided at the end of the chapter.

PLANNING THE FIELD SURVEY

The importance of sufficient planning to minimize field problems prior to a field survey cannot be overstressed. One method of minimizing field problems is mentally to run through the survey tasks to be performed prior to the field survey to determine what will be needed. Planning a survey course with checkpoints, calculating offsets, angles, and geometric data for vertical and horizontal curves, establishing centerlines, planning a grid for a topographical survey, and the many other tasks associated with the field survey can be augmented through the use of sketches or drawings, if necessary, to show anything from one complex feature of a field survey to an entire survey plan with intricate details. Organized calculation sheets can be particularly useful as a check during a field survey when problems arise.

PRECONSTRUCTION SURVEY

The preconstruction survey is performed to review and refine existing horizontal and vertical controls which have previously been established during the design phase of the project. During this phase, review accuracy requirements for the primary horizontal and vertical controls designated by the designer to assure that the controls are accurate enough to provide the tolerance required by the project. Tolerance requirements will vary with the type of project. For example, route surveys for highways and railroads require second-order Class II surveys, i.e., horizontal control that is 1 part in 20,000 and vertical accuracy of 1.3 mm $\sqrt{K}$ (K is the distance in kilometers between points). Major structures such as viaducts and water crossings require second-order Class I surveys, i.e., horizontal control that is 1 part in 50,000 and vertical accuracy of 1.00 mm $\sqrt{K}$.

Review construction-contract plans to determine whether or not the existing control is in a location that can be used during construction and will not be destroyed during construction. If it cannot be used without being disturbed, provisions for additional control points in safer places must be made. All additional control points must be provided with reference ties (see Fig. 1.3-1) so that they can be easily recovered at any time

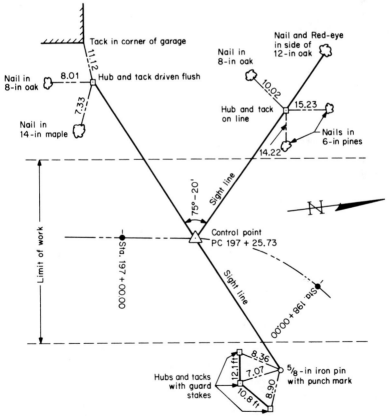

FIG. 1.3-1 Typical construction reference ties (1 in = 25.4 mm; 1 ft = 0.3048 m).

during construction. Once the control points have been established, horizontal control in areas deemed necessary is run by one of three methods: traversing, trilateration, or triangulation. The required accuracy for these methods is a function of the type of project and as dictated by the designer.

Vertical control (bench mark) is handled similarly to horizontal control. First, determine whether or not the existing control is sufficient in both supply and accuracy for the project. If necessary, get additional bench marks in areas where they will not be disturbed, and run level circuits through the existing and new points to the accuracy required. The primary control is now adequate to proceed with the preconstruction stakeout.

1. Establish the centerline or control line of the project, compute stations and offsets or angles and distances from the control baseline to key points on the centerline such as PCs, PTs, TSs, SCs, etc. (see Fig. 1.3-2), and lay these points out. Compute the deflection angles and chord length for curves, and proceed to run in the actual centerline using 50-ft (15.2-m) stations.

All the major control points noted above, plus any additional points that may be necessary to maintain sight distances, should be referenced so that they can be easily recovered or replaced when destroyed by construction equipment. This can be done by one of several methods, the most effective and reliable being intersection ties. Place the transit or theodolite on the control point, and obtain a sight on a well-defined object outside the limits of work. This can be a nail and red ribbon in a tree, a pin driven flush with a punch or crosscut, etc. If a pin is used, it should be positioned so that a target can be placed over it (see Fig 1.3-1).

After the sight has been obtained, at least two additional points can be placed on line. The points placed on line should then be referenced with swing ties. When this step has been completed, another sight point as near as possible to 90° from the first line should be obtained and the above process repeated. You now have a reliable set of reference points.

To replace the original point, simply set an instrument on one of the intersection lines, backsight on the sight point, and set straddle points on each side of the original-point location. Set the instrument on the other line, backsight to one of the sight points, and intersect the straddle line. The original point is thus reestablished.

2. Set offset stakes 10 or 15 ft (3.05 or 4.57 m) outside the limits of work where possible, usually at intervals no greater than 50 ft (15.2 m). These stakes should be set perpendicular to the centerline or control line and radial on a curve. Record the offset distance to the centerline and an elevation at the top of each stake (Fig. 1.3-3). Grade sheets (Fig. 1.3-4)

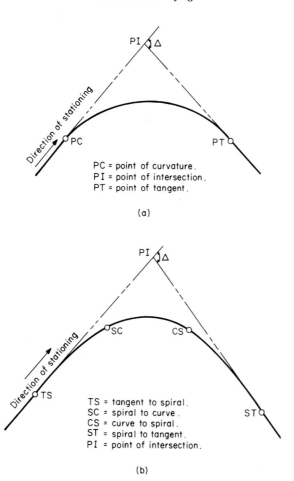

PC = point of curvature.
PI = point of intersection.
PT = point of tangent.

(a)

TS = tangent to spiral.
SC = spiral to curve.
CS = curve to spiral.
ST = spiral to tangent.
PI = point of intersection.

(b)

FIG. 1.3-2 Computation with curves. *(a)* Simple curve. *(b)* Simple curve with spiral transitions.

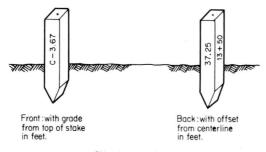

Front: with grade
from top of stake
in feet.

Back: with offset
from centerline
in feet.

Side: shows station.

FIG. 1.3-3 Typical grade stakes: 2 by 2 in (50.8 by 50.8 mm) with survey tack (1 ft = 0.3048 m).

Station, + ft	Cut or Fill, ft	Offset left, ft	Offset right, ft	Cut or Fill, ft	
902 + 00			51.25	C-2.35	
+ 50			50.80	C-3.22	
903			53.62	C-	
+ 50			55.40		
904			52.20		
+ 50			52.75		
905			56.41		
+ 50			55.08		
906					
+ 50					
907					
+ 50					
PC + 73.20			50.00		
908			↑		
+ 50					
909					
+ 50					
910					
+ 50					
911			↓		
PT + 02.80			50.00		
+ 50					
912					

FIG. 1.3-4   A typical grade sheet (1 ft = 0.3048 m).

should then be made showing the offset distance from the centerline or control line to the stake and the depth of the cut or fill from the top of the stake to the finished grade at the centerline.

3. For calculating earthwork cut or fill quantities, cross sections should be run at a maximum of 50-ft (15.2-m) intervals. At this stage, the position of the slope stakes can be computed and set at the toe and top of slopes. When laying out the side-slope lines for a roadway section, offset and elevation calculations should be made and stakes set with the appropriate accuracy. Similarly, offsets from the centerline of the roadway for pavement and shoulders should maintain the same level of accuracy for calculation and stake placement.

Also at this point, centerlines that cut off or match those of the roadway should be determined, for example, when ramps leave the main line, intersecting side road, or streams. Careful records of these field surveys must be made in order to check postconstruction or as-built cross sections against the survey data laid out with respect to the design data. Final earthwork quantities will be easier to calculate when initial survey data have been properly recorded.

4. At bridge structures, it is necessary to stake the centerline of each pier and the centerline of bearings at abutments (Fig. 1.3-5). It is usually convenient to double-stake each line on both sides of the structure and far enough apart [20 to 30 ft (6.1 to 9.14 m)] on both sides of the structure to provide adequate sight distance when the columns are being constructed. The offsets on the stakes should all be measured from the centerline of the bridge. It is very important that this stakeout be checked, double-checked, and cross-checked to assure correct alignment, skew, and span length. A good rule of thumb for the surveyor to use when staking structures is that tolerances are ± 0.0. This will avoid all alignment problems as construction progresses. The double set of stakes will be used to establish alignment control for pile layout, footings, columns, pier caps, and anchor bolts.

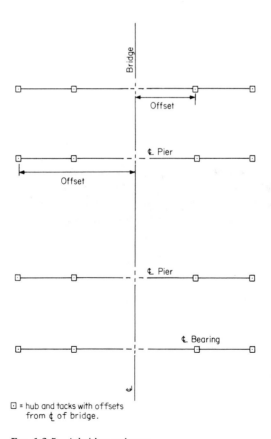

☐ = hub and tacks with offsets
   from ₵ of bridge.

FIG. 1.3-5 A bridge stakeout.

Depending on the size of the structure, at least two stable bench marks should be established nearby. These will be used to control the elevations of the structure at various stages, such as top of footing, top of columns, top of bearing pads, and bush-hammer grades.

Cross sections may be run along the centerline of each pier and the centerline of bearings at the abutments to facilitate earthwork cut-and-fill calculations in these areas.

5. Drainage structures, water mains, sanitary sewers, and electrical-conduit structures are laid out by placing a stake at each end of the pipe. Intermediate stakes are usually placed at intervals of 25 to 50 ft (7.6 to 15.2 m) along the centerline of the pipe and offset beyond the limits of the work to prevent them from being disturbed during construction. Stakes are also placed on the centerline, extended beyond each end of the pipe. Cross sections of the existing ground are taken and will be used in computing excavation quantities.

Elevations on the top of each stake are taken at this time. The depth of the cut is to be marked on the stake to coincide with the invert grade of the pipe. Headwalls, catch basins, and manholes must also be staked at this time, with the pipe invert and top elevations of the structure noted on the stake. Where catch basins or manholes will match up with curblines, care must be taken in determining the location and alignment of the curbs.

Occasionally during fill operations, sufficient quantities of earth are not readily available on the project site. In this instance the required quantities of earth are obtained from a borrow pit. Generally there is an agreement to pay a fee for the borrowed earth to the owner of the land where the pit is located.

Therefore, careful measurements, calculations, and survey work at the borrow pit must be made along with accurate records in order to provide a fair accounting of the actual quantities of borrowed earth. Borrow-pit baselines should be laid out so that the cross sections can be run perpendicular to the proposed face of the cut. Enough baseline should be laid out so that it can be referenced for easy recovery at completion of the excavation. Reference ties should be placed outside the limit of work so as not to be destroyed during the excavation. At least two bench marks should also be placed well outside the limit of work. An assumed elevation may be established on one of the bench marks. A level run should be made back to the first assumed bench mark to verify the assumed elevation.

The cross sections should be run far enough beyond the proposed limits of excavation so that a check on original ground can be made when running the final sections. If possible, determine where the vertical cut faces, if any, will be, and lay out preliminary cross sections perpendicular to the vertical cut faces.

Buildings should be laid out by placing a set of offset stakes at each corner and along the building line extended to a point beyond the limits of work (see Fig. 1.3-6). These stakes will be used as control points for footing excavation and foundation placement as well as checkpoints during construction. Most buildings are square or rectangular. To assure that the building to be constructed is either square or rectangular, determine what the diagonal distance should be between corner points and measure the distance between the corner points. If the two diagonal distances are equal, the points laid out will produce a building that is either square or rectangular. For buildings that are shaped like a parallelogram, the method just described for checking the accuracy of the shape can be employed. When a building is of an irregular shape, such as an L shape, an octagon, or a combination of regular and/or irregular shapes, a system of triangles can be used to check the building's shape by employing the same method on the various shapes that make up the building.

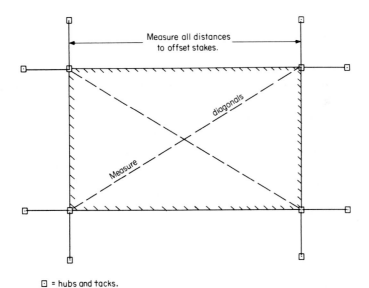

☐ = hubs and tacks.

FIG. 1.3-6 A building stakeout.

SURVEY DURING CONSTRUCTION

Once the primary horizontal and vertical controls have been set during the preconstruction phase, working controls and offsets can be established for a convenient reference. As in all phases of construction surveying, accurate planning and record keeping are of paramount importance and cannot be overstressed.

Roadway Subgrade.   When preparing a roadway subgrade, the contractor can use the control offset stakes placed during preconstruction to determine how much cut or fill is required. The cut or fill information is shown on the grade stake. A mark is placed on the grade stake as a reference elevation, and the cut or fill quantity is noted, for example, C 3.67 ft (1.12 m) for a cut of 3 ft 8 in (1.12 m) and F 0.5 ft (152.4 mm) for a fill of 6 in (152.4 mm).

Frequently, when moving earth, a contractor will encounter unsuitable earth material and will have to remove and replace it with suitable earth material. During this process, quantities of unsuitable material must be obtained because a contractor may be entitled to additional compensation for the additional work and material, particularly if this condition was unforeseen. The method used for determining quantities can be the same or similar to that described for borrow pits under "Construction Survey."

Roadway Centerline.   Once the road subgrade has been placed by the contractor, the roadway centerline can be reestablished by resetting the control points from the previously set reference ties. The centerline can be run, and offset stakes placed from the centerline or the offset line may be run directly from the previously set reference ties. In either case, the offset stakes are usually set at least 2 ft (0.61 m) outside the gravel or base-course line. Grades are placed on the offset stakes, usually at an even foot (0.305-m) increment above either the subgrade elevation or the finished grade. Grade sheets will be supplied to the contractor and will include such information as the distance from the proposed grade down to subgrade at the centerline and lane lines and edge-of-pavement locations. This information will vary depending on the cross section of the roadway and on whether the roadway is a curve, an intersecting ramp, or a side road or on many other conditions.

Finish Grades.   After the subgrade has been completed and checked and the base course placed, it will again be necessary to rerun the centerline or an offset line to provide fine-grade stakes. These are similar to the stakes placed for the subgrade, but they will be used to grade the subbase as well as placing the finished pavement.

A number of methods for setting finish grades can be used. Among them are (1) finish-grade stakes with keel marks denoting a convenient increment of measure to the finish-grade elevation and (2) small reinforcing steel bars with the top edge of a strip of masking tape wrapped around the rebar to denote a convenient increment of measure to the finish-grade elevation. Among the quickest and most accurate methods of setting finish grades is by using a Lenker rod, an instrument from which the elevations are read directly.

Structure Layout. Structure layout consists in providing enough information so that a structure can be constructed in its proper location and elevation. This may be accomplished by using offset stakes or by providing lines, usually of lime, on the ground that actually show the shape of the structure to be built. Typical structures include piles, footings, columns, pier or pile caps, anchor bolts, box culverts, catch basins, storm-drain inlets, manhole structures, and so on.

Pile locations can be determined by referencing from preconstruction offset and control stakes by laying out the pile cap or footing and then proceeding to lay out the piles in relation to the actual footing. The actual pile layout should be verified to assure that all piles fall within the limits of the footing concrete.

Preconstruction offset and control points serve as reference points when laying out footings, pile caps, or piers. When piles are used in a foundation system, extreme care must be taken to assure that they are correctly located within the pile-cap layout and then checked when pile-driving operations are completed. It is important to report to the designers any significant deviations of actual piles from required pile locations. Generally, when timber or steel piles are used, the piles are longer than necessary to prevent pile splicing. When necessary, timber or steel piles can be spliced. Once a pile is driven to refusal, the point at which the pile is bearing on rock to provide the necessary bearing for the structure, the excess pile material must be cut off at the *pile-cutoff elevation*, usually noted on the plans, in order to integrate the pile with the pile cap. Therefore, sufficient pile-cutoff-elevation marks should be made on each pile.

After the piles have been driven and cut off, the actual footing limits must be laid out on the ground. When the forms are in place, a check should be made to confirm that the footing is in proper position and that the top of footing elevation is accurately established on the forms. The next operation is locating the centerline of the pier and column for proper location of dowels and reinforcing steel.

Several possibilities exist for structures directly above the footing, among them concrete or masonry walls or foundation walls, reinforced-concrete, steel, or wood columns, and reinforced-concrete pedestals or piers, short concrete columns on top of which steel columns bear. As stated previously, extreme care must be taken in locating and coordinating these structures with the footing to assure conformance with the design documents.

Reinforced-Concrete Walls or Foundation Walls.   Establish the centerline of the footing (either continuous or individual) by establishing an offset reference system, as described earlier. A convenient and simple offset line can be a taut string line in conjunction with a piece of wood long enough and marked to indicate the limits of the footing, location of dowel reinforcing lines, form lines, or any other feature that is part of the foundation system. Once this offset system has been set up, construction workers can use it with little or no assistance from the surveyor. Of course, occasional checks on the offset line and foundation should be made to assure accuracy. A final form-line alignment, plumbness, and elevation check should be made prior to concrete placement. Remember that it is easier to adjust forms prior to concrete placement than it is to demolish a solid concrete wall. At the top of reinforced-concrete walls or foundation walls, bearing elevations must be established and verified for other components of the structure.

Reinforced-Masonry Foundations or Walls.   The same process for establishing and maintaining a centerline used for a reinforced-concrete foundation wall can be used for a reinforced-masonry foundation. Precast masonry units come in assorted shapes and sizes, either solid, semisolid, or hollow. Semisolid or hollow units are used for a reinforced-masonry foundation to allow for reinforcing-steel placement. Accurately lay out the dowel reinforcing steel so alignment of the masonry-unit voids coincides with the bars to allow them to be threaded through the voids. Outside- or inside-corner points are generally set at corners, on extremely long walls, or at other convenient locations to aid in the accuracy of construction. Alignment, plumbness, and elevation checks should be made periodically and at completion of the work. At the top of masonry foundations or walls, bearing elevations must be established and verified for other components of the structure.

Reinforced-Concrete Columns or Pedestals.   Using previously described offset control methods, establish the centerline of the column to assure proper placement of dowel reinforcing prior to footing-concrete placement. After concrete placement, form lines should be checked to assure proper alignment, plumbness, and top-of-column elevation.

Steel or Wood Columns.　These columns generally bear directly on bearing plates on footings or reinforced-concrete pedestals. Using previously described offset control methods, establish the centerline of the column and lay out the anchor bolts in accordance with the plans. Anchor-bolt templates are helpful in placing anchor bolts accurately. Once the footing or pedestal has been poured, a thin steel leveling plate must be grouted in place to assure a level bearing surface for the column at the correct elevation. Once the columns have been placed, a plumbness check should be made.

Hammerhead Pier Caps.　When constructing a hammerhead pier cap, used in highway construction, it is necessary to assure that the cap is placed at the proper elevation and superelevated, when necessary, at the required angle. Proper placement of anchor bolts, bearing pedestals, and bearing pads is essential. The bearing elevation is usually set ¼ in (6.35 mm) higher than noted on the plans to allow for concrete shrinkage. This also allows for bush hammering, a process used to obtain a smooth surface for bearing placement.

Anchor Bolts.　After bush hammering, if the anchor bolts have not been poured in place, lay them out directly on the bearing pads. This is critical owing to the tolerances provided by the fabricators which supply the beams. Again keep in mind that surveyor tolerance is ±0.0. When laying out anchor bolts, it is helpful to construct an anchor-bolt template, noting the centerline of the pier and the centerline of the bridge with a chalk line. Carefully measure the distance from the centerline of the bridge to each centerline of stringer along this line. Then place the template on the line, and mark the anchor-bolt locations for drilling. At this time make a careful check of the span length. After the anchor bolts and bearing plates have been placed and the beams erected, elevations are taken along the top of each beam at the ends and quarter points. This will determine the amount of camber in each beam so that haunch and final grades may be computed.

Decks.　When the deck forming is in place, the elevations at the joint headers and screeding finished grades are established. After the deck concrete has been placed, a final alignment and grade are established for the parapet walls and railings.

POSTCONSTRUCTION SURVEY

The postconstruction survey is necessary to compute final quantities and to provide as-built plans. When checking final roadway cut or fill quantities, it is first necessary to rerun the centerline of the project, usually at 50-ft (15.2-m) stations or as previously established in the preconstruction phase (the notes made during this phase will be very helpful). Rerun the cross sections at all previous positions plus any additional stations that may be necessary. At these additional stations it will be necessary to interpolate an original ground section between known cross-section lines. The original notes should be available when running the final sections to check the original ground elevations at the limits of work. This procedure also applies when running final sections at a borrow pit using the procedures described earlier.

Measurements of pavement are taken directly on the surface, not by holding the tape horizontally to the pavement. This is necessary because actual areas are required. Odd areas of pavement such as turnouts for ramps, etc., are usually broken down into a series of triangles to determine their area. In all cases, clear, concise field notes should be kept so that office personnel will have no problems in deciphering them.

Seeded areas will have to be measured in the same way that pavement areas are taken to determine the final areas of topsoil and seeding. These measurements are also measured flat on the surface and not horizontally.

All lengths for drainage pipes, etc., are measured at this time if they have not been measured by the inspector at the time of installation. All items that are bid by linear foot, square foot, cubic yard, etc., will have to be measured to determine final quantities. Special surveys will be required for major water crossings.

MARINE SURVEYING

When surveying over water, establish land-based points for the primary baseline. To establish a strong triangulation network, place towers in the water or at near predetermined locations. Care should be taken in determining the location of these points so that they can be used for positioning the piers for bridges or tube sections for tunnels. These points will also be helpful in positioning a boat while running the soundings.

The primary horizontal control can be run either by triangulation or by trilateration. With the accuracy of electronic distance-measuring (EDM) equipment now available, a great deal of time can be saved by measuring the legs of triangles. The network can then be computed and adjusted and a few sets of angles turned to verify the results.

Vertical control can be established by running reciprocal levels between points. Tide gauges can then be established from these new bench marks to be used for soundings and dredging.

A great deal of time should be devoted to planning all operations for this type of survey. Make sure that all equipment is in good working order; theodolites, levels, and EDM equipment have all been calibrated; and communications equipment and boat motors are working properly. All personnel should be well versed in the operation of each piece of equipment and the methods to be used. These items are essential because much time can be lost in transporting personnel and equipment by boat to remote stations.

Weather is also a major factor that must be considered when working on water. Conditions can be very hazardous when wind and salt spray interfere with operations. It is also difficult to obtain the required accuracy under these conditions.

GLOSSARY OF MISCELLANEOUS TERMS

Bench marks Permanent points set with known elevations, usually a large spike in a tree, a square cut on solid concrete, etc.

Borrow pit Offsite area used to provide additional fill for a project.

Control points Primary working points that are established to control the survey on a project.

Deflection angles Angle from the back tangent or chord extended to the next chord.

Grade sheets Sheets set up with the stationing stake offsets and cut or fill.

Lenker rod Level rod with an endless tape where elevations are read directly after setting the proper reading from the bench-mark elevation.

Reference ties Points set outside the work area which are used to replace control points destroyed during construction.

Straddle points Points set on either side of a line to prepare for an intersection.

Theodolite Modern version of a transit with all angle readings taken internally (within the instrument).

Transit Instrument designed to sit on a tripod and turn horizontal and vertical angles.

Traverse   Method of extending control by using a baseline consisting of angles and distances. It can be either an open traverse, which begins on known or assumed stations and does not tie to anything, or a closed traverse, which begins and ends on known control points or stations.

Triangulation   Method of extending control with a series of triangles beginning and ending on a baseline, usually measured with a high degree of accuracy.

Trilateration   Method of extending control with a series of triangles in which the sides are measured in place of the angles.

Public Works Special Requirements

Lt. Gen. John W. Morris, U.S. Army (Ret.)
J. W. Morris, Ltd.
Construction Consultants
Arlington, Virginia

Construction Management Professor, University of Maryland

Formerly

Chief of Engineers, U.S. Army Corps of Engineers

Public works construction involves facilities similar in many ways to those built in private enterprise. There is a great variety of facilities built by public works, ranging from large monumental-type buildings to small rest and comfort stations, from interstate highways to small mountain trails, from plumbing repairs to major complete utilities systems, from small drainage structures to major flood-control and navigation projects, and from small maintenance and repair jobs to construction of major complex military facilities, locks and dams, navigation channels and harbors, spacecraft facilities, and major transportation and communications systems. There is as much variety in locations as there is variety of facilities with sites, from the central cities to remote sites and even to foreign countries.

The supervision and inspection (S&I) of public works projects are also similar in many ways to those required in private enterprise, but there are some differences caused by the nature and scope of some projects, location, requirements in contracts dictated by statute, limitations imposed by law, and the owner's being the general public, with financing through public funds. This chapter deals with these differences.

Just as each contractor and architect-engineer have a unique mode of operation, so also do the various government agencies have different ways to approach the construction of facilities. Some facilities are provided by grants to state or local governments for construction by local governmental agencies, while other facilities are built by various federal agencies themselves. Government agencies have their own rules and ways of accomplishing construction, depending upon the professional resources inherent in the agencies. Most public works construction is actually performed by contractors from private enterprise who may or may not be acquainted with the requirements, statutes, and procedures for public works or with the agency involved. Just as the facilities to be built are unique for each project, S&I may also be unique, and the inspector must understand the requirements for the specific job.

Consideration is given in this chapter to contract requirements, responsibilities and relationships which differ from those of private enterprise, and an inspection approach which can be effective for public works.

AUTHORITY AND RESPONSIBILITY OF THE PUBLIC WORKS INSPECTOR

The inspection organization may consist of individuals on the payroll of the construction agency, architect-engineer Title II contract, or a construction management firm. Authorities delegated to the inspector could be different and unique for each project. For public works, authority rests with the contracting officer, who may delegate certain authorities to varying degrees. As a rule some delegation of authority is made to the resident engineer, for whom the inspector normally works. It is incumbent on the inspector to be aware of the specific authority delegation which has been made for the specific job and to be aware of the exact authority that has been given. Delegation of authority by the contracting officer is issued by written document.

The contracting officer's representative at the site has certain responsibilities which are inherent in the position. Being at the site as the representative of the government gives the inspector the responsibility to assure that the quality of work produced is that which was designed, no more and no less. This responsibility is dual both to the government agency represented and to the government's ultimate user of the facility being constructed. It is not the inspector's responsibility to determine what is good, better, or best by way of quality, as this is a function of design. The inspector is responsible for seeing that the designed quality has in fact been produced by the builder and that the progress being made will in fact comply with time requirements of the contract. Because the agency must fulfill its time commitments to the user and minimize the cost to the public which could result from added overhead caused by late completion of the work, the inspector must take action or provide information to one who has authority to take action to assure completion on time.

In addition to the dual responsibility to the public agency and the user, the on-site representative of the contracting officer has a responsibility to the contractor. For example, all inspection, approvals, and disapprovals should be accomplished so as to avoid delay in the contractor's work. The inspector must investigate and determine the facts surrounding delays or alleged delays so that equitable adjustments can be made as appropriate in time requirements in the contract for completion. When excusable delays such as strikes, unusually severe weather, or changes ordered by the contracting officers occur, verifying whether the incident occurred and ascertaining its impact on the progress of work, what it affected, and how much effect it had are part of the job. Since public contracts contain provisions for equitable adjustments in time for certain excusable delays which are not the fault of the contractor, the contracting officer must rely upon the on-site staff to determine (1) whether or not delays are the fault of the contractor, (2) the facts surrounding the delays, and (3) the impact on operations in progress. Adjustments are to be "equitable," or fair, to the contractor as well as to the government. The inspector must keep the contracting officer informed concerning progress and work conditions. Some public works projects can involve public safety with serious consequences in life and property damage in the event of failure. For example, failure of a large dam or bridge could be a major disaster; therefore, the public works inspector must exercise extreme care to assure compliance with contractual requirements. The finest design is worthless if it is not followed during construction.

Required documentation includes the public works inspector's own findings and activities, the contractor's activities, and any conditions which could affect the quality or progress of the work. These records become very important for reports to the contracting officer and for establishing the facts in the event of disagreements or claims at a later date.

CONSTRUCTION QUALITY CONTROL AND ASSURANCE

In some public works contracts, there are formal provisions for *contractor inspection system* or *contractor quality control*. The responsibility and methods of inspection have been debated in symposia and seminars by professional societies and government organizations for the past few years. There arise such questions as these: "Who is ultimately responsible for quality?" "Who can best control the quality?" "Should the fox be put in charge of the henhouse?" "Are such requirements appropriate in a construction contract?"

First, let us consider some undeniable facts. A contractor who accepts a contract agrees to build the facility according to plans and specifications and in fact agrees to control the work and operation in a manner that will produce the specified quality. Accomplishment of the work necessitates management to produce the quality of work required by the contract. Management is *control*; therefore, the contractor is legally responsible and liable for *quality control* whether or not it is separately stated in the contract. Control implies prospective action to cause things to happen in the future and to regulate while work is in progress.

On the other hand, it is the government's, or owner's, responsibility to assure that it is obtaining the quality purchased; therefore, *quality assurance* is a responsibility of the government on a public job. Assurance, or "to make sure," implies verification, which could be accomplished after the fact. The contractor could not expect the government to exercise quality control without giving up the contract, nor could the government expect the contractor to perform quality assurance in the government's interest. Each party to the contract must play a separate role, and neither can perform for the other. Some actions involved in both roles could be similar, but the timing could differ.

This condition demands that each party to the contract have a system for accomplishing its own purpose. Both systems could include, but not be limited to, some inspection and testing. The contractor's quality-control system must be geared to preventing mistakes and minimizing costs by doing the work right the first time, while the government's system must assure that the work is done correctly for acceptance purposes.

Acceptance inspections occur daily as work which will be concealed later by other work is accomplished. Therefore, quality control and quality assurance proceed simultaneously throughout the job, but for different purposes, in different frequencies, and in different manners and procedures.

There have been many misunderstandings of the separate clauses in Department of Defense contracts. Some have concluded that the government has delegated all inspection and testing to the contractor. Such a conclusion is incorrect, as just explained. The clauses are intended to emphasize the responsibility to control operations and to document actions for accomplishing this end, for which the contractor is *already* responsible. Usually the contractor is required to furnish the documentation to the government for surveillance.

When the government's inspection force can assure itself, through surveillance of the contractor's quality control, that the required quality has been produced, the amount of the government's inspection effort can be adjusted to apply its resources where most needed for the accomplishment of its mission. Surveillance activities could involve observance of the contractor's quality-control actions, witnessing the contractor's tests, verification of test results by independent testing when appropriate, independent inspection of the work, reviewing the contractor's quality-control reports and comparison of findings with government inspection reports, and checking calibration of the contractor's laboratory equipment.

The contractor's quality control and the government's quality assurance should not be a mere duplication of effort. The two parties should work together cooperatively to produce and verify the quality of work required by the contract.

Quality-control inspection is most effective when performed in a three-step systematic manner.

1. Preparatory Inspection. Prior to actual start of a new operation in the field, some preparatory checks and actions can be taken to avoid mistakes which could be costly to correct later or result in an inferior-quality product. Shop drawings should be carefully checked prior to purchase of materials to assure that the correct materials are ordered. When materials are delivered to the job, they should be inspected to assure receipt of the correct materials ordered and to discover any damage in shipment. These materials should be inspected periodically during storage, prior to use, to assure that they are protected so as to preserve their quality until time for use on the job. Manufacturer's certifications should be checked for materials received and checked against specified requirements.

2. Initial Inspection. As a new type of operation such as concrete place-ment, masonry, or roofing is started, a recheck of specified requirements for that work should be made. Workers have a tendency to perform work as done on the last job, but requirements may differ for this one. By assuring that the materials furnished are the correct ones for this job, that they have not been damaged in handling and storage, that the workers understand the specific requirements for workmanship, the work can be started correctly. This procedure is much more practical than discovering at a later date that wrong-size joints were used or that tooled joints were specified but were actually struck flush. When mistakes are discovered after a wall is half-built, correction is expensive in both time and money and could result in a patched-up job rather than a new one. When work is started right, it has a good chance of continuing in the same way. When new workers are brought on the job, additional effort is needed to assure that they understand the requirements for this job even though the operation on which they are employed may already be in progress.

3. Follow-up. While work which starts right has a good chance of con-tinuing right, many factors can affect the work as it progresses, such as change of personnel, weather, arrival of additional materials, accidents, or apathy. Periodic follow-up inspections can assure that the work contin-ues correctly and can disclose mistakes early enough for them to be corrected at the least expense. Continuous inspection may not be neces-sary during the follow-up stage if the work is visible for later inspection. Spot inspections may then suffice if preparatory and initial inspections have been effective. On some types of work, however, compliance can-not be checked later because work is concealed soon after placement. Such is the case in earth embankments, for example, where each lift is quickly covered by the next, and density must be assured as the work progresses. Requirements for the individual job must be determined by the unique design of each project. Inspection and quality control should be carefully planned in advance so that the work is performed with mini-mum effort, avoiding mistakes rather than having to correct them later and correcting early at minimum expense any mistakes which may occur.

CONSTRUCTION SCHEDULES AND NETWORK ANALYSIS SYSTEMS

Most public works contracts require a contractor to schedule operations and to furnish the schedule to the contracting officer for approval. Not only should such schedules be carefully checked for compliance with contract requirements regarding time, breakdown, value, and being reasonably attainable and practical, but they should also be checked to ascertain that the sequence of operations will result in the quality of work specified. For example, adequate time must be allowed for curing concrete, structural steel should be erected and plumbed before adjacent masonry is scheduled, and interior finish work should not be scheduled until the building is enclosed enough to protect it from weather damage, etc. For some public works projects, network analysis systems such as the program evaluation and review technique (PERT) or the critical-path method (CPM) may be specified for the schedule. The public works inspector should be familiar with the use of these techniques. Since their appropriate use usually involves an understanding of the system and experience in the use of data from a computer, special instruction in the practical application of network analysis systems is very beneficial. Even when it is not specified, some contractors use network analysis for scheduling and controlling the progress of work. To monitor the progress and management of the work, the inspector must understand the system being used.

OTHER SPECIAL REQUIREMENTS OF PUBLIC WORKS

Four additional requirements that affect the inspector's responsibilities must be considered on many public works jobs:

1. Proprietary Specifications. Such specifications are usually forbidden on public works projects in order to allow competition by the public. This condition results in a technical description of the product rather than specification by brand name and model number; therefore, a closer, more careful review of shop drawings than would be required for a brand name is necessary. This condition also results in larger volumes of specifications and more submittals and approvals prior to purchase of equipment and materials.

2. Value Engineering. This approach is frequently found in public works contracts. Since value engineering is a systematic team approach to optimize the cost, it must be employed early enough so that intolerable delays will not result. Since the contractor usually participates in the savings from these value-engineering efforts, the inspector should be aware that an incidental request for substitution of materials or equipment is not necessarily value engineering. The public works inspector should be aware of agency policy and procedures for value engineering when such provisions appear in the contract.

1.4.8 General Construction

3.   Unit-Priced-Bid Items.   These are frequently found in public works contracts. When they are included in the contract, the inspector must be aware of measurement and payment provisions for these items so that measurement can be made in the specified manner at the appropriate time.

4.   Code of Conduct.   The code of conduct for a public works inspector may differ from that in private enterprise. On a federal government project, for example, inspectors or other government personnel are forbidden by law to accept favors or gratuities of any kind from a contractor. Meals, tickets to ball games, and other gifts which may be offered should be refused to avoid breaking laws whose infraction could result in serious penalties. An inspector must not get in a position of obligation to a contractor doing business with the government agency.

In summary, inspection of public works can be similar to inspection in private enterprise, but there are many special considerations. Some, but not all, have been listed in this chapter. The inspector must be completely familiar with the requirements of the individual contract and the procedures of the particular government agency.

Construction Disputes and Claims Avoidance

Donald R. O'Hearn
Manager, Program Control
Parsons, Brinckerhoff, Quade & Douglas, Inc.
New York, New York

Construction claims are potentially one of the most troublesome aspects of managing construction inspection projects. Many professionals are now devoting their entire careers and staffs to preparing, presenting, and litigating claims for a contractor. Several legal firms handle only claims cases and find this work very profitable for both their clients and themselves. The resident engineer and inspectors, as representatives of the owner, must understand the causes of claims, how to avoid them, and, if they arise, how to handle them.

A simple definition is "A claim is an unresolved dispute." It can result from differing interpretations of unclear or confusing plans and specifications. It can be a dispute over tight tolerances as to whether or not they are achievable (buildable) with current best construction techniques. It can be an allegation that the geotechnical information in the contract is not representative of the actual soil encountered. The contractor may claim that progress was delayed or interrupted by the owner (or a representative of the owner), the resident engineer, weather, other contractors, etc. In short, claims can originate from many and numerous causes. Historically, the most costly claims have been either for delays or for alleged changed conditions.

A dispute is not considered a claim until it becomes impossible or impracticable to resolve between the parties. All reasonable efforts should be made to come to an agreement on the dispute and to settle the time and cost issues. The dispute can then be concluded by a modification to the contract. The *reasonable-man rule* applies to a dispute; that is, "What is the judgment a reasonable man would have made with the best information available to him at the time?" Do not be afraid to make a judgment or a decision to resolve a dispute as long as you can show that it was thoroughly researched and that it was based upon the best information and was reasonable.

If the decision is to deny part or all of the disputed request, then the contractor has the legal right to go to court for another decision. At the point at which the dispute cannot be resolved, it becomes a claim.

Contractor claims are expensive to process to their ultimate conclusion through the courts or arbitration and are often detrimental to the best interests of both client and contractor. Claims, therefore, are best avoided or at least settled, if possible, at an early stage.

CLAIMS AVOIDANCE

Claims avoidance is the responsibility of all parties concerned: the designer, the owner or client, the resident engineer's staff, and even the construction contractor. The contractor must desire to avoid having the dispute being carried to litigation and must make a reasonable effort to settle it at the earliest possible stage. Remember that a contractor who decides to go to court has the legal right to do so even with no chance of winning the case. It is, therefore, impossible to avoid claims completely. The best that can be done to reduce claims to a minimum is either by settling a dispute as a change order or by mitigating the dispute through persuasive arguments to such an extent that the contractor withdraws it.

The resident engineer and inspectors must use all practical means to anticipate, identify, and mitigate those conditions that could lead to disputes. During the performance of the work, problems or potential problems should be addressed promptly. It is important to maintain open communications between the contractor, the owner, and the resident engineer. With prompt communications, problems will be identified early and resolved quickly to minimize disputes and/or delays relating to disputes.

The use of change orders in a fair and timely manner is recommended as a primary claims-avoidance measure. Requests for change orders should be investigated with the intent that the contractor be given just and reasonable compensation for all adjusted work items, imposed long-term suspensions of work, and unavoidable delays. This does not imply that the resident engineer should recommend that the owner execute contract modifications simply to avoid possible claims but rather to use the negotiation process to promote the best interests of both the owner and the contractor. For example, if the contractor was delayed because the designer was unreasonably late in approving a shop drawing and this tardiness caused the contractor to fall behind schedule, the contractor is due a time extension to the extent of the impact or for that portion of the delay which was unreasonable. This example may appear to require judgmental, subjective decisions, but a number of techniques have been developed to identify and quantify impacts and to aid the field inspection staff to make objective decisions.

The elements of claims avoidance which precede construction include:

- Integration of plans and specifications; avoidance of ambiguities
- Constructibility review
- Risk sharing
- Disclosure of information
- Review of claims procedures
- Alternative bids
- Provision for arbitration

- Preliminary construction plans in bid documents
- Realistic schedules and interfaces
- Bidder prequalification
- Review of contractor's bid unit cost

The elements of claims avoidance during the construction phase include:

- Schedule control and update
- Timely actions by owner
- Fair and timely change-order process
- Good communications with contractor
- Avoidance of adversary relationships
- Negotiation in good faith

Two of the earlier approaches which constitute a major step toward claims avoidance are (1) the constructibility review discussed in the next subsection, coupled with (2) a realistic, achievable construction sequence plan.

CONSTRUCTIBILITY REVIEW

The assurance of the constructibility of the engineering design of the project rests primarily with the designer and the owner. Knowledgeable construction engineers, however, can contribute to the constructibility of the bid documents by bringing their long-term field experience gained on similar projects. A constructibility review is a key claims-avoidance measure. The review is done when the design has passed the conceptual stage or is between 15 and 35 percent complete and again at about the 95 percent complete stage. The review should be performed by a group of multidisciplined construction-engineering professionals whose combined background and experience would permit them to review all completed or partially completed documents to verify the following:

- Reasonableness of work sequences, interface relationships, and period of performance
- Adequacy of lead times for materials and equipment procurement
- Accuracy of jobsite description and depiction of conditions
- Availability of subsurface and design background data for contractor's use

- Degree of site restrictions and adequacy of access, work areas, and disposal sites
- Availability of utilities connections for construction
- Consideration of the impact of adverse weather on the work plan and milestone schedule
- Adequacy of specialized data, such as traffic maintenance or waterway traffic, and procedures to cope with it

It is important to purge contract documents of disclaimers and furnish all available data to provide a better bidding for the contractor. For example, any soils information available to the designers should also be made available to the bidders. The entire burden of risk should not be placed upon the contractor but be shared equitably with the owner. Real estate should be available to the contractor at award to avoid unforeseen delays. Documents must be written in technical language but should be simplified when possible to generally understandable language.

In addition, the constructibility review group should review the bid documents and assess them for clarity, integration of plans and specifications, and absence of ambiguities. A written report of the findings should be furnished to the owner and the designer.

REALISTIC CONSTRUCTION PLAN (SCHEDULE)

A realistic, achievable construction sequence plan, more commonly called a *schedule*, should be done in several phases: (1) prebid phase, (2) construction phase, and (3) as-built phase. The construction sequence plan is the basis for overall contract duration and for interim milestones. It should be made part of the construction documents "for the bidders' information only." Any special assumptions such as multiple shifts, crew sizes, special production rates, etc., should be clearly indicated to the bidders. The prebid schedule should prevent an allegation that "The contract duration was too short to perform the work."

The purpose of scheduling is to establish reasonable, orderly, and achievable objectives and then to provide adequate tools for measuring the attainment of those objectives. Inherent in any successful scheduling approach must be the flexibility to modify significant interim objectives, called *milestones*, in the face of changing internal conditions while still achieving the overall objectives of constructing an affordable project on time.

Scheduling, in general, should be discussed to make it possible to understand its role in claims avoidance. Currently in the United States construction industry two types of schedule techniques are commonly used: (1) the bar chart or Gantt chart and (2) critical-path-method (CPM) scheduling.

Bar Chart.   The bar chart is a chart showing work activities on a time scale. It is commonly used for relatively small projects ($2 million or less). A bar chart may or may not show the cost of each work activity.

Each bar shows the planned start and completion of each activity. It does not show the planned progress rate or the interrelationships between work activities. For example, electrical wiring cannot be installed until the electrical conduits have been installed, but the bar chart will normally show "electrical work" as one activity. An example of a bar chart is shown in Fig. 1.5-1.

Bar charts are used as a minimum scheduling effort. The left edge of the bar is the time when the activity starts; the right edge, the time when the work is finished. Between the two edges is a solid connecting bar, indicating that work is occurring. The total time difference between start and finish of the work is called *duration*. Additional work activities are shown on the chart by additional bars. Normally a bar chart is limited to no more than 25 significant activities, but together they represent over 90 percent of the work. The remaining activities are either combined into a miscellaneous bar or simply are not shown. The purposes of bar charts are to show a logical sequence of construction, the time (duration) it will take

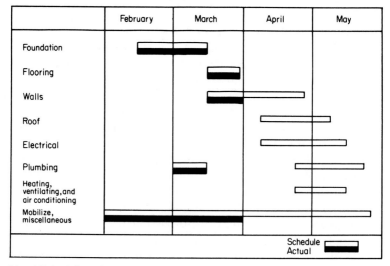

Fig. 1.5-1   A bar chart.

to perform each activity, and the planned start and completion dates for the activities. In any schedule, the sequence of construction must be followed once it has been approved by the resident engineer. The contractor has the right to make minor adjustments to the start, duration, and finish of each activity provided that, in doing so, contract completion is not delayed. If the contractor desires to revise the sequence of construction after approval, the resident engineer should have the authority to approve the revision. The contract specifications must be written to bind the contractor to obtain the approval of the resident engineer for the bar-chart schedule.

The schedule is the contractor's work plan. The fact that the resident engineer approves or disapproves the contractor's schedule does not take responsibility away from the contractor. This point must be made clear in the contract specifications, at the prebid conference, and throughout the course of the project. Simply stated, the schedule belongs to the contractor. The resident engineer has the right to ascertain that the schedule meets all contract requirements and times and that the contractor has planned adequate crews and materials to perform the work. If the contract schedule is not achievable, then additional crews, equipment, shifts, etc., must be added to complete the work on time. The bar chart tells the on-site inspection staff limited information about the significant work items. It does not show the relationship of one work item to another, how much of one work activity must be completed before another can start, what production rates are anticipated, the rate of spending, and many other significant items.

To overcome some of the basic deficiencies of the bar chart, inspection forces have cost-loaded the work activities and added additional information. An example of a modified bar chart is shown in Fig. 1.5-2. The modified bar chart has a significant additional management tracking item: cost. The bars on the bar chart are assigned a cost percentage relative to the total cost of the contract. For example, walls may represent 18 percent of the total cost of the contract. If the walls are 35 percent complete, they represent 0.35×18 percent $= 6.3$ percent of the total cost of the contract. An S curve, representing cumulative cost, can then be plotted. The scheduled cost is shown as one curve, and the actual cost of work performed also is plotted. Actual cost should approximate scheduled cost if the contractor is on schedule.

The modified bar chart provides, in addition to some schedule information, some cost information. This may be all that is required for managing small, short-term construction contracts. It is also useful in confirming or disputing requests for payment based upon progress. It is recommended that any construction project be managed by a modified bar chart as a minimum.

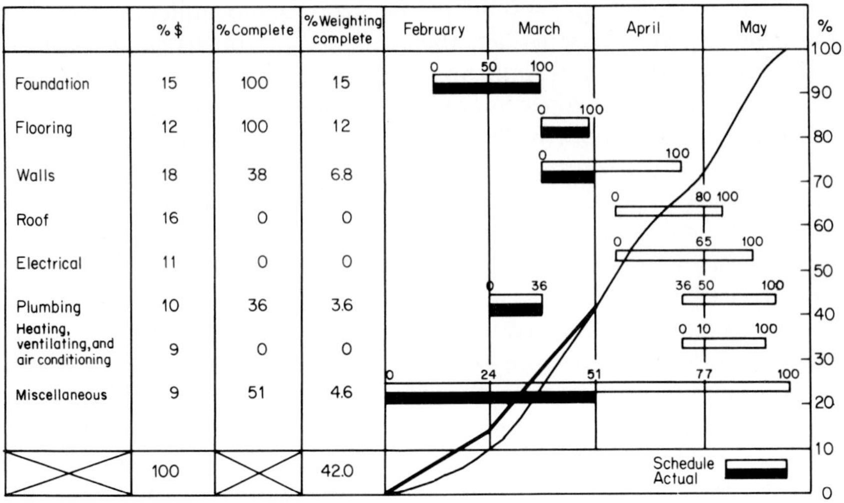

	% $	% Complete	% Weighting complete	February	March	April	May	%
Foundation	15	100	15	0 50 100				100 — 90
Flooring	12	100	12		0 100			80
Walls	18	38	6.8			100		70
Roof	16	0	0			0 80 100		60
Electrical	11	0	0			0 65 100		50
Plumbing	10	36	3.6		36	36 50 100		40
Heating, ventilating, and air conditioning	9	0	0			0 10 100		30
Miscellaneous	9	51	4.6	0	24	51	77 100	20 — 10
	100		42.0				Schedule Actual	0

FIG. 1.5-2 A bar chart with estimated and actual progress in value of completed work.

Critical-Path-Method Schedule. For complex or expensive projects a critical-path-method (CPM) schedule is commonly used. The CPM schedule overcomes many of the deficiencies of the bar chart, going into much greater detail about how the contractor plans to perform the project. The CPM ideally should portray the contractor's actual work plan. It should be time-scaled for ease of understanding and should show a sufficient, but not excessive, level of detail to manage the work completely. Each work activity is assigned the cost, crew size, major equipment, and production rates associated with that activity. The work plan does not merely include on-site work. It includes significant office work such as shop drawings, working drawings, and procurement activities. Also, off-site procurement, fabrication, and deliveries are clearly identified. The contractor's work plan would normally be prepared by a prudent contractor for internal control. The inspection staff deserves no less information to permit it to represent best the owner's investment and interest.

The contractor's work plan improves the inspection staff's ability to provide:

- Early warning of schedule problems
- Early identification of special problems, (i.e., crew size, equipment, etc.)

- Identification of high-cost areas for special management attention
- Change-order evaluation and negotiation
- Claims-avoidance information
- Claims-evaluation assistance
- Identification of work-around opportunities
- Improved probability of on-time, on-budget performance

The CPM schedule should be prepared by the contractor and approved by the resident engineer as a *baseline schedule*; that is, it should represent the contract plans and specifications as bid. It should not be adjusted in any way to recognize potential changes which may have occurred after the contract was awarded. This stipulation is crucial to claims evaluation. Subsequent updates of the CPM schedule may show changes, but the baseline schedule is just that: it represents a baseline on which all changes may be measured for schedule impact.

After approval of the baseline CPM schedule by the resident engineer, only minor changes may be made by the contractor without approval. Any changes to logic or to significant duration must be approved by the resident engineer. (If the contractor has misjudged a duration, additional crews or shifts may be indicated to recover actual or probable lost time.) Any changes to the approved CPM schedule should be made only after careful deliberation and approval of the resident engineer and, if applicable, the owner.

The work-plan CPM schedule and costs, original schedule, and monthly updates should become a "living picture" of the latest status of the project until completion. They also should be capable of being measured against the baseline cost schedule approved by the resident engineer.

What is a CPM schedule and how does it work? The answer to the first part of this question is simple: read the Associated General Contractors' manual *CPM in Construction*. It will also answer a portion of the second part of the question. The rest will be learned through use of CPM and experience. An alternative is to hire a CPM scheduling engineer for your staff or as a consultant. A brief explanation of the CPM of construction scheduling follows:

The critical path is the shortest path of work activities between the start of the contract and the completion of the work. It may be demonstrated on a scale of time or without it. It shows that some work cannot start before other work is finished and that some work can be performed concurrently with other work.

The basic graphical representation in CPM is an arrow, which represents a work activity, thus:

On each end of the arrow (activity) is a circle called a *node*:

$$\circ\!\!-\!\!\!-\!\!\!-\!\!\!-\!\!\!\rightarrow\!\!\circ$$

To the activity, a description and duration in working days are given:

$$\circ\!\!\underset{\text{FRP Col.17}}{-\!\!\!-\!\!\!-\!\!\!-}\!\!\!\rightarrow\!\!\circ$$

When work activities are put together in a logical sequence, they may look like the example in Fig. 1.5-3.

An actual CPM schedule will show an activity level of between 500 and 4000 activities. Below 500 activities, a bar chart will normally suffice. Above 4000 activities, the computer system begins to control the project, not the project personnel the computer system. There have been numerous examples of construction projects going sour because the CPM schedule was made so complicated that control was lost. The key to successful CPM scheduling is that it should be able to be understood by both the highest and the lowest level of decision maker (i.e., owner, construction supervisor, inspector, etc.). A CPM should be developed in sufficient

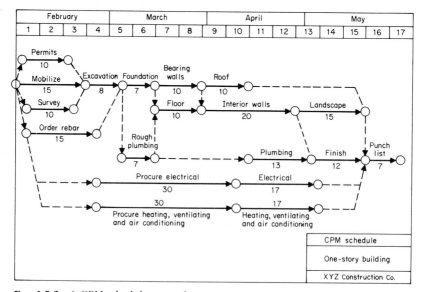

Fig. 1.5-3 A CPM schedule network.

detail for the work to be performed but not in excessive detail that will turn people away from using it as an effective planning tool.

There are two types of critical-path schedules: activity-on-arrow (called I-J) diagrams and precedence (called PDM) diagrams. The differences between the two types are best left to the specialists. For the inspection staff it is sufficient to understand that PDM diagrams are useful for designers and for construction contractors. I-J diagrams (e.g., Fig. 1.5-3) are useful for contractors and resident engineers. As representative of the owner, the resident engineer should insist that I-J diagrams be specified. The reasons for this stipulation are complex, and this conclusion is based upon court decisions.

The reason that a CPM diagram should be time-scaled is that it begins to look like a bar chart and therefore is more likely to be used by field personnel. A "today line" can be struck on the diagram and will identify at a glance every activity where work is currently scheduled. Key milestone dates, particularly those which define points of interface among contracts and/or agencies, are highlighted on the schedule. The contractor should be required to update the schedule monthly, reflecting actual starts and completions of work activities, approved change orders, and agreed changed conditions. If delay has occurred, the contractor should provide a plan to make up the lost time or provide documentation to show that the lost time cannot be recovered. An assessment can then be made as to who was responsible (liable) for causing the delay. The resident engineer must then either grant a time extension or alert the contractor to the possibility of liquidated damages. However, never threaten the contractor with liquidated damages as this may be construed as intimidation.

DAILY MONITORING

The inspector is the front line of claims avoidance. The inspector's daily reports, coupled with the resident engineer's diary and reports, must record what work actually occurred or did not occur. The reports must be complete, factual, and objective. Personal remarks should not appear in the reports. Properly prepared, the daily reports can provide an irrefutable record of actual events and the time of those events.

Documentation and record keeping should be maintained with the following basic considerations:

- Documentation should be literate.

- Unnecessary or inappropriate comments, either oral or written, should not be made, as they later could indicate prejudice.

- Documentation should contain too many rather than too few facts.

- All observable conditions, including hour, day, or week time frame to support issues accurately in case time is in dispute, should be recorded.
- Learn what is effective and allowable evidence in a courtroom and what is not.
- Documentation called for in the contract should be followed exactly.
- The importance of answering all correspondence must be stressed.
- Files must be complete and in chronological order.

EARLY ACTIONS REGARDING DISPUTES

The resident engineer should instruct the contractor in writing to address all intents to claim to the owner through the resident engineer's office. Upon receipt from the contractor of an intent to claim, the resident engineer should immediately take the following steps:

1. Forward the original letter of intent to claim to the owner, retaining a copy for the job file.
2. Acknowledge in writing, without commitment, receipt of the intent to claim. (Care must be taken that no indication of the resident engineer's opinion regarding the contractor's allegations is either given or implied.)
3. Assemble any and all documents regarding the dispute. (These may include, but not be limited to, all pertinent reports, diary entries, photographs, and correspondence.)

On all disputes submitted by the contractor, the resident engineer must prepare a factual analysis with detailed citations to the evidence that will either support or rebut the contractor's position, using daily reports, diary entries, photographs, etc. After making the factual analysis, the resident engineer will forward it with recommendations to the owner.

If the dispute is determined to be meritorious by the owner, the resident engineer will evaluate the costs or time durations and initiate an appropriate modification of contract. If the dispute is determined to have no merit and the owner concurs, the resident engineer will so inform the contractor. More frequently, the dispute will have some merit, but the amount of time and cost will be in dispute. The resident engineer should evaluate the amount of time and cost objectively and with full documentation supporting the conclusions.

After an intent to claim has been presented by the contractor, the resident engineer should request in writing that the contractor submit detailed documentation in a timely manner, say, within 60 days, or as provided in the contract. It may not be possible to submit the documentation until after the disputed work is done. Both sides should continue to document the dispute until a resolution is reached.

Upon the first indication that a dispute exists, the resident engineer should direct the office engineer to collect a complete file of all correspondence and reports which may relate to the dispute. The resident engineer then assigns a task force of key personnel which may include the project engineer, the chief inspector, and several inspectors to evaluate the dispute. Often, several specialists in geotechnical, estimating, or scheduling departments may be involved. The evaluation should be approached in three phases: (1) evaluation phase, (2) responsibility phase, and (3) quantification phase.

Evaluation Phase.   This phase is to determine only the facts. What was the contractor's plan? Was it consistent with the plans and specifications? Did the contractor follow or deviate from the plan? Did the contractor's allegations have any truth or merit in whole or in part? During the evaluation phase no opinions should surface. If a member of the task force expresses an opinion before the facts are established, that person should be removed from the team. The resident engineer cannot permit the evaluation to be influenced by a preprejudiced opinion, as this will ultimately work against the best interest of all concerned. The evaluation task force should prepare a report which includes a chronological summary of all related correspondence and an as-built schedule for related work. Examples of these reports are shown in Figs. 1.5-4 and 1.5-5.

Responsibility Phase.   This phase is the assignment of responsibility (fault) once the resident engineer has determined that the claimed dispute has merit. Merit may be in whole or in part. Claims will result in one of the following actions by the resident engineer:

1. Deny claim.
2. Grant time but no money.
3. Grant money but no time.
4. Grant both time and money.

When the dispute is clear-cut, it can be promptly settled as a change order. More often, the dispute is not clear-cut. For example, the resident engineer requests the contractor to hold back on the pouring of a retaining wall because a design change is being prepared (resident engineer's responsibility). Concurrently the contractor has failed to submit for approval the concrete design mix (contractor's responsibility). Both parties have separately caused a delay, but the delays were concurrent. Who

---

CHRONOLOGICAL SUMMARY OF KEY CORRESPONDENCE

CLAIM NO. 2

1. March 3 letter, Simmons to Bradly.

   Revised drawings coming for CIP beams. May affect forms.

2. March 5 letter, Bradly to Simmons.

   Acknowledge March 3 letter. Need revised drawings by March 10 or will cause delay.

3. March 9 transmittal, Simmons to Bradly.

   Three revised drawings, CIP beams.

4. March 12 letter, Bradly to Simmons.

   Drawings moved steel, will affect lifting bars, blockouts, forms. Require change order and time extension.

5. March 18 minutes of meeting.

   Simmons suggests no-cost, no-time change order. Bradly says unacceptable.

6. March 19 letter, Bradly to Simmons.

   Will proceed but intend to claim.

7. March 21 letter, Simmons to Bradly.

   Acknowledge receipt of March 19 letter. Keep accurate records of extra cost, if any.

Fig. 1.5-4   Report of key correspondence.

should be assigned the responsibility? In a case like this, it is proper to deny the claim or, if circumstances dictate, to share the responsibility. The services of an outside expert are normally called upon by one or both parties when shared responsibility is indicated.

Quantitative Phase.   This is the period when the resident engineer calculates the amount in terms of time and money. This phase presumes that it has been determined in the responsibility phase that the contractor's claim has total or partial merit. To assist in quantifying, the services of an estimating engineer, auditor, and other professionals are recommended.

The burden of proof for time and money is the responsibility of the contractor. All documentation provided by the contractor must be objectively reviewed and either confirmed or refuted. The resident engineer

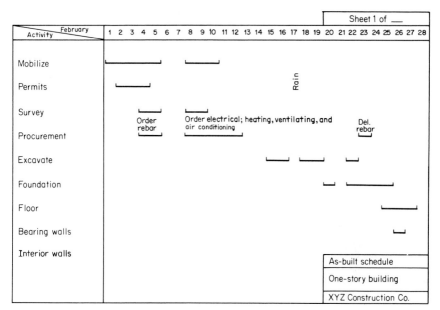

Fig. 1.5-5　An as-built bar chart.

has the right to request additional supporting documentation if the records do not support the contractor's conclusions.

Upon objective review of all the supportable documents and estimates, it can be determined how much time and money should be offered to settle the dispute. By showing the contractor that there is solid justification for the resident engineer's position and that the resident engineer has sufficient documentation to go to litigation, the dispute can often be quickly resolved.

Resident Engineer's Responsibility Regarding Alleged Delays.　Whenever an event occurs or a situation arises which has the potential of delaying the contractor with respect to the contract completion date and it can be demonstrated that the cause of the potential delay is beyond the contractor's control (i.e., strikes, unusually severe weather), the resident engineer, in conjunction with the scheduler and the contractor, will make a determination of the extent of the potential delay. *No time extensions can or will be granted to the contractor at this time.* The actual duration of the delay expressed in days will be placed in a "pool" and will be taken into account only with respect to assessment of liquidated damages.

An example of the use of a pool of delay time would be an unseasonably wet month that is followed by an unseasonably dry month, the cumulative effect being normal number of bad-weather days. Good weather does not automatically negate the effects of bad weather. The impact upon the specific construction work at the time of the bad weather must be considered.

If and when it is determined by the contractor that the contract completion date cannot be met, the contractor may present for the resident engineer's review and analysis a request for an extension of time in the form of a claim for delay. This request should demonstrate the reasons behind the failure to meet the contract completion date and present practical alternatives such as resequencing items of work and/or methods of accelerating the work, with time and dollar values assigned. No request will be entertained prior to the approval of the contractor's CPM schedule.

After detailed scrutiny and analysis by the resident engineer in conjunction with the scheduler, the owner, and the contractor, a determination will be made as to the following:

1. What is the actual impact in time on the contract completion date? This evaluation is made after unused float time, etc., is taken into account.
2. What impact does the request for time extension have on other prime contractors who are working adjacent to this contractor?
3. What, if any, remedial action can be taken to compress the schedule and allow for on-time completion? What will this action or actions cost in terms of time and dollars? To whom?
4. What would the impact on the contractor be if the time extension were disallowed and liquidated damages were assessed? How would accumulated pool time serve to mitigate this impact?

After these determinations have been made, the request for an extension of time with the resident engineer's analysis will be forwarded, along with recommendations, to the owner. Figure 1.5-6 is a sample form to assist in the analysis of a contractor's request for a time extension.

If the owner has recognized the contractor's request as having merit, the owner will direct the resident engineer to issue a notice of proposed modification for a time extension. If the owner denies the request for a time extension, the resident engineer will so notify the contractor.

It is essential that the owner be kept informed in writing of any and all steps taken with regard to the foregoing procedure.

NEGOTIATING MODIFICATIONS

A negotiation team should be established to review all available information which has been gathered by the resident engineer and the engineer's

---

ANALYSIS OF CONTRACTOR'S REQUEST FOR A TIME EXTENSION

(Format only)

Contract no. _____   Contractor _____
Requested time extension _____   Claim no. _____
Date of request for TE _____   Dates of delay _____
Reference to other claims _____
Construction work involved _____
Type of work: original work, changed work, or extra work
Relationships of the work to the latest approved CPM schedule _____

Contractor's statement of the event causing the delay and substantiating data __
_____

Resident engineer's analysis that the completion of the contract was or was not delayed solely and directly by the event _____
_____

Contractor's statements of responsibility by the owner or the resident engineer
_____
_____

Contractor's action to prevent or minimize delays caused by the events
_____
_____

Contractor's activities during the period of delay _____
_____

Resident engineer's recommendation for an extension of time _____
_____

_____   _____
Resident engineer   Date

Contract no. _____

Concur: _____   _____
Owner's representative   Date

FIG. 1.5-6 Analysis of request for a time extension.

staff. The team should consist of those people closest to the nature of the dispute (i.e., the resident engineer, project engineer, office engineer, chief inspector, estimator, cost engineer, and scheduler). Additional personnel may be added to the team, but if this is done, others should be dropped. Too large a negotiating team becomes unwieldy.

The team should develop a negotiating strategy and decide who will be the principal spokesperson for the group. If the dispute differences are relatively small, negotiations can usually be concluded in one session with the contractor. If the differences are large, it is wise to proceed methodically.

At the first meeting between the negotiating teams of the resident engineer and the contractor, each side presents its arguments and conclusions and presents its rebuttals to the other side. Care should be taken to avoid an adversary relationship. Each side should then retire to consider the arguments and to present additional information supporting its views. If the contractor can provide additional supporting documentation, the resident engineer should review it objectively. This is not the time to lock in on an uncompromising position. The purpose of negotiations is to arrive at a settlement which is fair and reasonable to both sides.

Agreement can usually be reached in a few negotiating meetings. When it is reached, the resident engineer must fully document the agreement and the reasons for the final decision. The documentation should include an audit trail to permit the owner to follow the logical development.

If it becomes apparent that agreement cannot be reached, the resident engineer prepares a *final finding of fact* for the owner to send to the contractor, fully detailing the resident engineer's position and refuting the contractor's position. If the resident engineer recommends that some time and money be awarded to the contractor but this is less than the contractor believes justified, the engineer issues a *unilateral contract modification* and makes payment to show good faith. The contractor may then exercise the arbitration option of the contract or resort to the courts if no arbitration is provided to attempt to recover the difference.

In summary, regardless of who is right and who is wrong, timely and factually complete documentation by both sides will greatly expedite dispute resolution. While disputes are inherently adversary matters, adopting an equitable approach to their resolution is generally in the best interest of all parties.

SECTION 2

Heavy and Specialty Construction

CHAPTER 2.8

Electrical Construction / 2.8.1

CHAPTER 2.9

Vertical Transportation: Elevators and Escalators / 2.9.1

CHAPTER 2.10

Horizontal Transportation: Automated People Movers
Substructures and Guideways / 2.10.1

CHAPTER 2.1

Excavation and Embankment

Monroe M. Johnston, P.E.
Consultant
Ormond Beach, Florida

<u>Formerly</u>

Chief of Geotechnical Branch
Engineering Division
Office of the Chief, U.S. Army Engineers

PART 1

This chapter provides embankment inspectors with guidelines, construction techniques, quality-control procedures, and soil-testing methods for embankment construction. The principles of inspection are presented in simple language, and technical terms are defined as they appear in the text.

The emphasis is on construction control for earth and rock-fill dams, but the techniques are applicable to other types of embankments such as fills for highways, railroads, and foundations of buildings. The sections have been arranged to follow the logical sequence of construction, from initial training of the inspector through step-by-step construction of the project.

Engineers have recognized that the embankment inspector is the last line of defense against poor-quality construction. No design, regardless of how well conceived, will result in a successful project unless each construction phase is executed in accordance with the plans and specifications. Because inspection and control are more art than science, the concepts in this chapter must be applied with sound judgment and proper caution. Some aspects of embankment construction and control fall within that category of problems for which there are no universally accepted solutions.

ROLE OF THE EMBANKMENT INSPECTOR

Purpose and Importance of Inspection.   A significant number of embankments such as earth dams, levees, and highway fills have required expensive remedial measures because of poor construction practices or undetected adverse conditions. The purpose of inspection is to ensure compliance with the plans and specifications and to recognize unusual and unforeseen conditions during construction. The design of an embankment is not really completed until construction is over and the project is functioning as intended by the designer.

Construction projects are supervised by an engineer who is responsible for all phases of the work and generally has the title *project engineer*. The construction supervisor keeps this "overall" supervisor informed of construction progress, results of testing and inspection, and all unexpected conditions that may concern the project. Thus, timely progress reports may result in corrective measures, if necessary, before the problems become too costly. The embankment inspector, one of the key personnel on the construction supervision staff, has the basic responsibility of helping to ensure that the intent of the designer is fulfilled.

Training of the Inspector.   The most important phase of the inspector's career is training. Before construction begins, novices must be instructed by experienced inspectors (or by engineers) who have participated in actual construction. Such training should be given at a center designed for this purpose. New inspectors must become thoroughly familiar with the latest testing techniques, equipment, and inspection procedures. Training then should be continued during actual construction, with the novice inspector working closely with experienced ones.

Size of Inspection Force.   Because there are many types and sizes of embankment projects, only general guidelines can be given concerning the optimum size of an inspection force. At a project where only a few thousand cubic yards of fill are placed daily, 1 or 2 inspectors may be adequate. On the other hand, at a large project where 20,000 yd^3 (15,000 m^3) of fill may be placed each day, 8 or 10 inspectors may be required. An efficient inspection force should include a chief inspector as well as an adequate number of fill-placement and borrow-area inspectors and laboratory testing technicians. Preconstruction planning meetings are usually held to determine the size of the inspection team.

Relationship between Inspector and Contractor.   Generally, the highest-quality and best-constructed embankments are those supervised by an inspection team not hired by the contractor. In these cases, the relationship between the inspectors and the contractor can become controversial.

Some contractors may, on occasion, feel that shortcuts and expedients are necessary to meet schedules or increase profits. Inspectors sometimes are subjected to pressures from contractors to accept construction that is substandard. Here inspectors must be fair but firm and insist on full compliance with the intent of the plans and specifications. Even an inexperienced inspector may recognize that a certain construction operation may lead to results that are not in accordance with the contract documents. Effective inspection is based on the concept that the inspector will be firm in enforcing the plans and specifications but will be fair and cooperative with the contractor. Before construction begins, the contractor should meet with the project engineer and the construction supervision staff to establish the ground rules of inspection and the action that will be taken in instances of nonconformance with contract documents.

THE FIELD LABORATORY

Physical Plant.   During construction, much of the control testing is performed in a field laboratory adjacent to the project. The size of the laboratory depends on the magnitude of testing required. The floor space needed generally ranges from 400 to 1000 ft^2 (37 to 93 m^2); the larger the laboratory, the more efficiently can the testing technicians work without the overcrowding and confusion so common at many projects.

The structure should be free of excessive vibrations caused by machinery or traffic. Air-conditioning and heating facilities, ample workbenches, storage bins and cabinets, work sinks, and proper lighting are essentials for any laboratory. A separate room should be provided to house dust-producing activities such as sample processing and sieve analysis; such a room should contain an exhaust vent.

Testing Equipment.   All testing apparatus should be as specified in the test procedures outlined in the subsection "Soil Test Procedures and Equipment." A stockpile of spare parts and standby equipment will prevent delays if the regularly used apparatus becomes worn, breaks, or is lost.

Soil-test results are only as accurate as the procedures and equipment used to produce them. Regular inspection and calibration of all testing apparatus will help ensure test accuracy. A record should be kept of the calibration date, the method of calibration, and the personnel who made the calibration.

For some large projects, where the basic field laboratory is remotely located with respect to the test area, it is usually necessary to provide a pickup truck or a van to serve as a mobile field laboratory.

SOIL DEFINITION, SYMBOLS, AND RELATIONSHIPS

General.   Geotechnical engineers (specialists in the field of soil mechanics and foundation engineering) generally define *soil* as a natural aggregate of mineral grains that can be separated by such gentle mechanical means as agitation in water. Soils exist in an enormous variety and include sands, silts, clays, and mixtures of these three basic classifications.

While soil has been used for thousands of years as a construction material, only in the twentieth century has there developed a systematic group of mathematical relationships that are used to define soil properties and enable the engineer to predict soil behavior.

Some Fundamental Soil Relationships.   A soil mass is composed of a multiphased system consisting of *solids* (the soil particles), *liquids* (generally water), and *gases* (generally air). If the void, or empty, spaces between the solid particles are completely filled with liquid, the soil mass is said to consist of a *two-phase system.* If the void spaces are partially filled with liquid, the soil mass consists of a *three-phase system* (air, water, and solid particles). The volumes and weights of the different phases of matter can be represented by a graph, termed a *block diagram*, such as Fig. 2.1-1. Block diagrams of this type can be used to define the basic relationships of any soil mass and the separate components within the mass. The values that

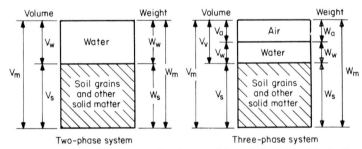

FIG. 2.1-1   Block diagrams and volume-weight relationships. Block diagrams of this type can be used to define the basic relationships of any soil mass and the separate components within the mass. The components are defined as follows:

Volume relationships	*Weight relationships*
V_m = total volume of a soil mass	W_m = total weight of a soil mass
V_s = volume of solid matter	W_s = weight of solid matter
V_w = volume of water	W_w = weight of water
V_v = volume of voids	W_a = zero

can be determined in the laboratory by actual measurement are the weight and volume of a wet soil sample, the weight of the same sample after it has been dried, and the specific gravity of the solid particles. With these measured values, the mass or bulk weight, the water content, the dry unit weight, the degree of saturation, the void ratio, and the porosity of the soil mass can be computed. The relations between volumes and weights are important in many types of soil calculations such as those to determine the degree of compaction necessary to construct a proper earth fill. In Table 2.1-1 are given the equations for determining some basic relationships. In Fig. 2.1-2 is shown the correlation between dry unit weight and void ratio for several values of specific gravity.

PREPARATION OF EMBANKMENT FOUNDATION AND ABUTMENTS

Soil Foundations and Abutments. The foundation area of a dam is the valley floor and terraces on which the embankment is to be constructed. The abutments are the walls of the valley, ravine, or canyon and are simply extensions of the valley floor. Inspection during preparation of these features of construction is of high importance because the foundations and abutments will be hidden by the embankment and be inaccessible forever. Many problems with embankments have been traced to improper treatment of foundations and abutments. The inspector should determine the intent of the designers as to the proper foundation preparation to be able to carry out inspection responsibilities more intelligently.

TABLE 2.1-1   Volume and Weight Relationships

Value required	Equation	Expressed as*
Mass unit weight γ_m	$\gamma_m = \dfrac{W_m}{V_m}$	lb/ft^3
Water content w	$w = \dfrac{W_w}{W_s} \times 100$	Percent
Dry unit weight γ_d	$\gamma_d = \dfrac{W_s}{V_m}$	lb/ft^3
Degree of saturations	$S = \dfrac{V_w}{V_v} \times 100$	Percent

*1 lb/ft^3 = 16.02 kg/m^3.

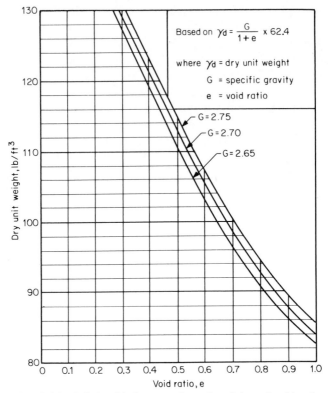

FIG. 2.1-2   Relationship between dry unit weight and void ratios.

This may entail several on-site conferences with the designer, the project engineer, and the inspection staff so that there is no doubt as to the method of foundation and abutment preparation.

A good design office will provide the project engineer with special instructions concerning any special treatment or procedures dictated by exposure of existing conditons in the foundation. These special instructions should be coordinated with the plans and specifications to implement construction better.

The first step in preparing a soil foundation for the placement of an embankment consists of clearing (removing trees, undergrowth, and all existing structures), grubbing (removing stumps and large roots), and stripping (removing sod, topsoil, rubbish fills, large boulders, miscellaneous objects such as water mains, and similar undesirable materials). Next, all stump holes or other large depressions are filled with select material and compacted with power-driven hand tampers in zones where it is not practical to use sheepsfoot or pneumatic-tired rollers. Then the entire foundation is proof-rolled with at least one pass of a heavy roller to detect undiscovered soft zones and to help restore the disturbed upper foot of the stripped foundation to an adequate density.

For embankments that will be used as water-retaining structures, an inspection trench at least 4 ft (1.2 m) deep should be opened along the embankment centerline from abutment to abutment. This trench will aid in locating abandoned utility pipes and pervious or organic pockets overlooked in earlier subsurface exploration. The trench should be wide enough to facilitate thorough compaction of the backfilled material. Earth abutments should be cleared, grubbed, and stripped as carefully as the valley foundation, and any caves or constructed adits should be reported so that they can be treated.

Rock Foundations and Abutments.   Foundations and abutments of rock often pose great difficulties in treatment before embankments can be constructed on them. Certain types of rock must be protected against mechanical or chemical erosion by seeping water. The finer embankment materials must be prevented from migrating into rock joints or fissures, and excessive seepage pressure through jointed rock must be anticipated and corrective action taken.

Under the entire core, transition zones, and filter zones of the embankment, the rock surface must be cleaned of all loose rock fragments including semidetached blocks of rock. Projecting rock knobs must be removed by hand wedging; to minimize damage to intact rock, blasting with light charges should be used only as a last resort. Exposed cracks and crevices should be cleared of soil or loose rock. Cleaning is usually carried out with air or water jets and hand picks. All fissures are then filled with an approved grout mix, and a grout pipe is sometimes inserted near the bottom of deep cracks to permit the grout to be pumped in under low pressure.

For shallow cracks the grout may be broomed and brushed into the voids, but the treatment must not result in layers of grout covering surfaces of sound rock. Potholes and other large depressions should be filled with lean concrete vibrated in place. This "dental treatment" of rock surfaces should result in a foundation that will be smooth enough to permit compaction of fill material on it by using pneumatic-tired rollers.

At rock abutments, the area beneath the embankment core (and in many cases, the transition zones) must be given similar dental treatment. All irregularities such as rock knobs and overhangs should be trimmed back to form a reasonably uniform slope up to the embankment crest. There should remain, after treatment, no vertical surfaces in the abutment higher than 10 ft (3.05 m).

Before placing any embankment fill on the treated rock foundation or abutment, the project should be inspected by the staff geologist and geotechnical engineer.

Cutoffs. The term *cutoff* encompasses a wide range of methods for reducing underseepage through the foundations of dams, dikes, and levees. Cutoffs are often extended through the more pervious strata and keyed into more impervious underlying strata. A widely used seepage barrier is an excavated trench cut through the pervious strata and backfilled with compacted impervious soil. The trench is excavated from abutment to abutment (and sometimes into the abutments) and is located under the embankment centerline or somewhat upstream of the centerline. When the trench is below the water table and water seeping into it cannot be controlled by sump pumps, dewatering by means of well points is employed to permit the trench to be backfilled with soil compacted at a controlled water content.

Surface erosion that may wash undesirable material into the excavation is controlled by placing shallow drainage ditches along the top of the slopes. After the trench has been excavated, the inspector should determine whether or not the side slopes and base width are as specified and examine the trench for evidence of bulging, cracking, or other signs of instability. Extreme care must be taken to ensure that the trench extends the specified depth into impervious strata.

Other types of cutoffs include sheet piles (more rarely used), cast-in-place concrete walls, and *slurry trenches* (comparatively narrow, vertical-walled trenches held open by a special slurry during excavation). Rock foundations containing fissures, joints, or solutioned voids usually are treated by grouting, a technique in which a special concrete mixture is forced into the voids under controlled pressure.

EXCAVATION EQUIPMENT AND METHODS

Excavating Equipment. There are five basic types of excavators: power shovels, draglines, clamshells, side-delivery loaders, and scrapers. Each type offers certain advantages, and in most cases several types are used on the same project.

Power shovels provide the best means for mixing and blending soils of different properties and water content in the excavation. The depth of cut can be varied, and the open bucket can be run through the soil mixture several times before loading the material. Typical rates of excavation range from 150 to 350 yd^3/hour (114.7 to 267.6 m^3/hour) for shovels with dipper capacities of 3 yd^3 (2.3 m^3) (excavation rates depend on the type of material being excavated). Excavation faces of 8 to 15 ft (2.4 to 4.6 m) in height are considered most efficient.

Draglines and clamshells have dipper capacities about the same as those of power shovels, are operated from cranes, and are effective in moving earth that is below the water table. They will excavate about 75 percent as much as a power shovel of the same size, are not as satisfactory as a power shovel for mixing soils in a vertical cut, and cannot excavate harder material as well as can a shovel.

Side-delivery loaders provide a rapid means of excavation in areas having a flat topography and uniform soil conditions. Their rate of excavation has been as high as 1200 yd^3/hour (917.5 m^3/hour). These loaders make a cut 3 to 6 ft (0.9 to 1.8 m) deep and, therefore, are not as satisfactory as power shovels for mixing horizontal strata of soils having different properties.

Scrapers are combination excavating and hauling units pulled either by slow-moving crawler tractors or by rapid-moving rubber-tired tractors. The rubber-tired scrapers are used more often than trucks as hauling units, especially at projects where main highways do not have to be traversed. They have an added advantage over trucks in that they spread material on the embankment surface in a layer which is close to the correct thickness for compaction. Scrapers are not efficient mixers of soil layers and therefore work best for borrow pits where the soils are uniform or where selective excavation of thin horizontal layers is desired. Scrapers work well in stiff clays because they excavate in relatively thin strips and remove the material in a finer form than the large chunks so often excavated by using power shovels.

Hauling Equipment. In addition to scrapers, fill material may be transported from the borrow area to the embankment in bottom-dump, end-dump, or side-dump trucks. If the material to be hauled is sand, gravel, or reasonably dry earth, the use of bottom-dump trucks will reduce the time required to unload the units. Truck capacities range from 5 to 50 tons (4.5 to 45 metric tons).

In areas of rough topography, where the cost of building haul roads is high, electrically operated conveyor belts are used to haul materials. The belts may be several hundred feet long with transfer points from one belt to another, permitting haul distances up to several miles.

BORROW AREAS

Evaluation. Embankment-fill borrow areas are those sources of suitable material located as close as possible to the site. Borrow material may be taken from upstream or downstream valley areas adjacent to the embankment site or from more remote locations depending on the results of preconstruction evaluations. Suitable areas are selected in the design stages by geologists and soils engineers on the basis of their interpretation of the results of subsurface investigation and materials testing. When a large volume of excavation is required during construction of such features as cutoff trenches, spillways, and diversion channels, the excavated material is often used to build part of the embankment. A material-usage chart should be provided so that the inspector can become familiar with the source, quantities, and type of materials that will be incorporated into the various zones of the embankment.

Before fill operations begin, the inspector should review all soils borings and test data concerning the borrow areas to become knowledgeable about the classification of the proposed fill material, its in-place or natural water content, the depth to the water table and to rock, the proposed depth of cut and the range of maximum dry unit weights, and optimum water content. To supplement the original test data, additional representative samples should be obtained from various depths and subjected to classification, compaction, and natural-water-content tests. Any basic difference between the new test data and the design data should be resolved before any fill is placed. In some cases, new data gathered just before construction have required changes in specifications. For example, the proposed borrow materials may be wetter or drier than anticipated, parts of the borrow area may contain soils of different classification than that determined during design stages, and actual excavations in the borrow pit may reveal that the rock line is higher than earlier explorations had indicated.

If these or similar deviations from original design assumptions are reported immediately to the design office, timely corrective action can be taken.

Preparing the Borrow Area.   The borrow area must be cleared, stripped, and grubbed in a manner similar to that used in preparing the embankment foundation. Some borrow areas may be far too dry to produce material that can be compacted properly in the fill. This may be corrected by ponding water over the areas by means of low dikes surrounding the borrow area. Irrigation is sometimes accomplished by using a pressure sprinkler system. The length of time required to bring the soil to the desired water content depends on the soil's permeability and the depth of soil being moistened.

In regions of high rainfall or where the borrow area is low and adjacent to a river or lake, the soil deposit may be too wet for proper compaction. Wet borrow areas can sometimes be dried out by cutting a series of drainage ditches leading to lower ground or to a sump where the excess water can be pumped well away from the area. Drying by sun and wind can be accelerated by disking, harrowing, and plowing, particularly if the soil is silty.

EARTH EMBANKMENT CONSTRUCTION

Types of Embankments

Embankments are of two basic types: those that are constructed to impound water, such as dams, dikes, and levees; and those that are constructed to support traffic or structures such as highway and railroad fills, bridge abutments, and fills under buildings. The construction and construction control of all types of embankments, regardless of the ultimate use of the embankment feature, are similar. That is, the same principles of soil mechanics, the same construction equipment and methods, and the same basic testing and quality-control techniques are used throughout the world to complete an embankment project. The only differences in construction and quality control are the degrees to which these fundamental principles are applied during the building of the project. For example, the failure of a water-retaining structure such as a dam, with perhaps a reservoir having a depth of 200 ft (61 m), would result in such a catastrophic loss of life in a highly populated area that construction of extremely high quality is mandatory. On the other hand, the distress of a highway embankment after completion might cause, at most, the loss of a few lives and, at least, inconvenience to traffic while repairs are being made.

The construction methods and control techniques that follow are applicable to earth dams and dikes, but the concepts can be applied equally, with a little judgment, to the construction of any embankment.

Earth Dams.   Embankment dams range from the nearly homogeneous type to the more complex zoned dams containing many different materials located in specific parts of the embankment section. In constructing earth dams, drainage zones of comparatively free-draining material are placed in downstream portions of the embankment to control seepage. These drainage zones are composed of sands or gravelly sands that are usually 10 to 100 times more pervious than the material in the core of the dam. In Fig. 2.1-3 are shown four types of seepage-control drains.

Whenever possible, dams are constructed of materials available locally to reduce hauling costs. Engineers have determined which types of material function most efficiently when compacted properly in various zones of the dam section. Through intelligent zoning, great economy of material utilization will result without sacrificing the safety of the embankment. The more impervious materials should be placed in the upstream zone of the dam; the more pervious materials, in the downstream zone. Many dams are built with a central *core* of impervious soils sandwiched by upstream and downstream *shells* of pervious soils or rock. Transition zones of material of intermediate permeability are placed between the

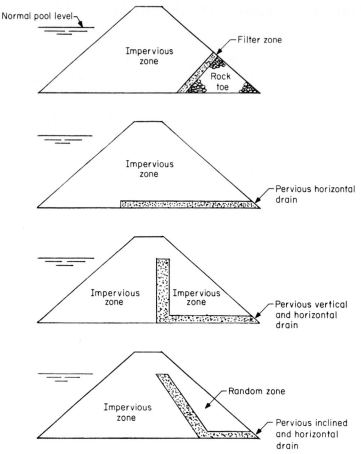

FIG. 2.1-3 Typical drains used to control seepage through embankments (not to scale).

core and the shells to prevent migration of finer particles into the coarser ones. There is no standard design for earth dams, and no two dams are alike, although many are similar in zoning. For most dams, the design section using the identical slopes and zones is extended from abutment to abutment. Occasionally, when foundation conditions vary across the valley, different zoning or outer slopes are used in different reaches of the same dam. At present, there are over 50,000 earth dams in the United States. Typical zoned dams are shown in Fig. 2.1-4.

Compaction Equipment

The two most common types of compaction used in fill construction are the sheepsfoot, or tamping, roller and the pneumatic-tired roller (Fig. 2.1-5). Each type compacts soil layers by a kneading action, in that the

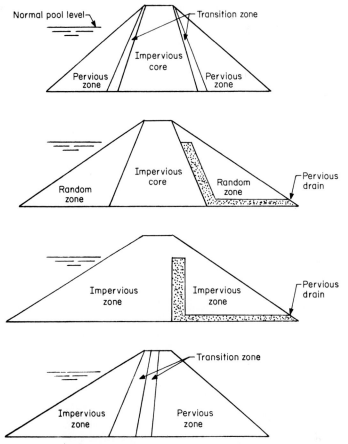

FIG. 2.1-4 Typical earth-dam sections (not to scale).

pressure from the roller varies from zero to a maximum and then to zero again as it passes over the soil.

The sheepsfoot roller (Fig. 2.1-6) consists of a hollow steel drum with projecting steel lugs or "feet" of a special shape. The most effective utilization of the compactive energy occurs when the roller drum lifts off the soil surface ("walks out") for the last few passes. Sheepsfoot rollers may be made heavier by adding water or a mixture of water and sand inside the hollow drum. The unit pressure exerted by the feet may also be increased by reducing the size of the feet; unit pressure may be decreased by increasing the foot size. Foot pressures generally range from 100 to 500 lbf/in² (psi), or 689.5 to 3447.4 kPa, and the speed of roller is generally about 3 to 5 mi/hour (mph), or 4.8 to 8 km/hour, although some self-propelled rollers can attain speeds up to 10 mi/hour (16 km/hour).

Sheepsfoot rollers may be used to compact impervious, semi-imper-

FIG. 2.1-5   Compacting earth fill with sheepsfoot and pneumatic-tired rollers.

FIG. 2.1-6   Compacting a clay fill with a heavy sheepsfoot roller.

vious, and semipervious materials. They can produce a good bond between compacted layers, break down large pieces of soft rock, and crush
and blend into the soil mass most large clods of earth and compact soils
having a wide range of water contents without bogging down. Tractor-
drawn rollers may consist of a single drum, two drums pulled in tandem,
or two drums one beside the other and pulled by the same tractor.
Self-propelled rollers have become popular because their direction can be
reversed without turning them around. As shown on Fig. 2.1-7a, the dry
density of the material being compacted increases as the number of roller

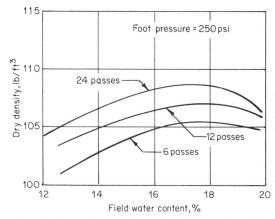

FIG. 2.1-7a Influence of number of sheepsfoot-roller passes on dry density. (1 lb/ft³ = 16 kg/m³; 250 psi = 1723.4 kPa.)

passes increases if the material is at or below the optimum water content. If the material is compacted at water contents that are 3 or 4 percentage points higher than the optimum water content, the influence of the number of roller passes is lessened significantly. For soils this wet, little extra density is obtained after about six passes of the roller.

For a soil layer having a loose-lift thickness of 8 in (203 mm) and a water content near the optimum, satisfactory densities can usually be obtained with 6 to 12 passes of a sheepsfoot roller having foot pressures of 250 to 300 psi (1723.4 to 2068.4 kPa).

The pneumatic-tired roller applies the force of the pressurized tires at the surface of the soil layer. The pressure is slightly lower for the first one or two passes because the tires sink deep into the initially loose soil. After additional passes the soil layer is densified enough so that the tires press on the surface. Tire pressures usually range from 50 to 200 psi (344.7 to 1378.9 kPa), depending on the soil type and the placement water content.

Pneumatic-tired rollers may be used to compact impervious, semi-impervious, semipervious, and pervious materials, although they are not as effective in densifying pervious materials as other types of compactors. Pneumatic-tired rollers can travel faster, can compact soil in thicker layers, and require fewer passes than sheepsfoot rollers. Further, they tend to locate soft spots in the underlying layers, and the tires leave a tight, sealed surface which protects the fill from penetration by rain. But in certain types of high-plasticity clays, pneumatic-tired rollers do not provide a good bond between soil layers, particularly if the soil is several percentage points wetter than the optimum water content.

As shown in Fig. 2.1-7b, an increase in the number of passes results in an increase in the dry density of the material as long as the material is not significantly wetter than the optimum water content.

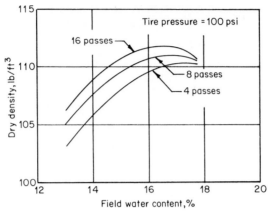

FIG. 2.1-7*b*   Influence of number of pneumatic-tired-roller passes on dry density. (1 lb/ft^3 = 16 kg/m^3; 100 psi = 689.5 kPa.)

Frequently, both sheepsfoot and pneumatic-tired rollers are used in combination in compacting fills so that advantage can be taken of the best features of each type of equipment. One of the prime responsibilities of the embankment inspector is to ensure that the compactors used are exactly as specified.

Construction Testing and Control for Impervious and Semi-impervious Materials

The soil tests required to control the placement of impervious and semi-impervious materials in any fill are (1) standard compaction, (2) Atterberg-limits, (3) grain-size-distribution, or sieve-analysis, (4) water-content, and (5) in-place-density. Detailed procedures for performing these tests are presented in the subsection "Soil-Test Procedures and Equipment."

Standard Compaction Test.   For a given impervious or semi-impervious soil there is a specific maximum density to which the soil can be compacted by using a specific amount of compactive energy. To obtain this maximum density, the soil must be at a specific water content. The water content existing at the maximum dry density is termed the *optimum* water content. The maximum dry density and the optimum water content are determined by a test in which specimens of the same soil at different water contents are compacted in cylindrical steel molds using a specific amount of compactive energy provided by a free-falling rammer. The most commonly used test for field control of embankment construction is called the *standard* compaction test (sometimes called, erroneously, the Proctor test).

The standard compaction test is made by using a mold of 1/30 ft^3

(0.00094 m³); the soil is compacted in three equal layers with a 5.5-lb (2.5-kg) hammer (or rammer) dropped from a height of 12 in (305 mm) 25 times on each layer. The resulting compactive effort is 12,375 ft·lb of energy per cubic foot of compacted soil (475.1 J/m³). The results of a compaction test are plotted on arithmetic graph paper, with water content as the abscissa (horizontal coordinates) and dry density as the ordinate (vertical coordinates). The results of such tests are shown in Fig. 2.1-8. A

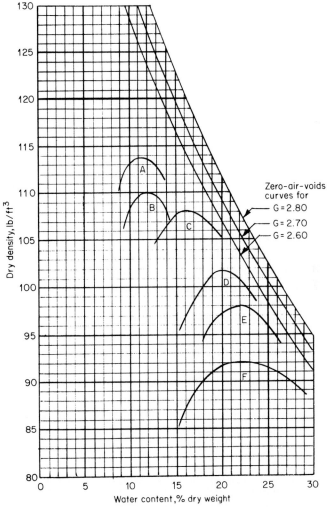

FIG. 2.1-8 Typical results of laboratory compaction using standard compaction effort. From the bottom curve, *F*, upward, the clay content and plasticity of the soil decrease (1 lb/ft³ = 16 kg/m³).

horizontal line extended from the peak of the curve denotes the maximum dry density; a vertical line extended downward from the same peak will intercept the value of the optimum water content.

Atterberg-Limits Test.　The consistency of a remolded, cohesive soil can be changed by increasing or decreasing its water content. A test method called the Atterberg-limits test has been developed to establish criteria for the boundaries between the limits of soil consistency. Depending on the water content of a given soil, there are five distinct stages of consistency. In the order of increasing water content they are:

1. Solid stage (soil is completely dry).
2. Semisolid stage (soil has the consistency of stiff putty).
3. Plastic stage (soil has the consistency of soft putty).
4. Semiliquid stage (soil will flow when shaken).
5. Liquid stage (soil particles are held in suspension).

The water contents that correspond to the stages of consistency are called the Atterberg limits (boundaries between the stages of consistency). The consistency stages may be represented in a diagram, as shown in Fig. 2.1-9. The liquid limit and the plastic limit are the upper and lower limits, respectively, of the plastic range of a given soil. In other words, the water content of a soil *just* as it passes from its plastic to its semiliquid stage is its liquid limit. The water content of the same soil *just* as it passes from its semisolid to its plastic stage is its plastic limit. The numerical difference between the liquid limit and the plastic limit, termed the *plasticity index*, represents the range of water contents through which the soil is in the plastic stage. The lower the value of the plasticity index, the lower the plasticity of a given soil.

　The Atterberg limits, together with the grain-size distribution of a soil, are employed to classify the material when using the system presented in the subsection "Unified Soil-Classification System."

Grain-Size-Distribution Test.　The grain-size-distribution test (usually called *sieve analysis*) is a process in which the proportion of material of each grain size present in a given soil is determined by a laboratory test. For grain sizes no smaller than 0.074 (particles which will not pass through the

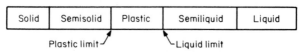

FIG. 2.1-9　Atterberg stages of soil consistency.

openings of a No. 200 sieve), a grain-size distribution can be determined by passing a specific weight of dry soil through a set of sieves having progressively finer openings. The quantity of material retained on each sieve is weighed, the grain-size distribution is computed, and the results are plotted on a grain-size graph as shown in Fig. 2.1-10.

Water-Content Determination. The water content of a soil mass is computed by dividing the weight of water in a given mass by the dry weight of the particles in the mass. The weight of water in a soil specimen is determined by weighing a specific sample in its natural state, drying the specimen, and finding the difference in the two weights. The most accurate method for determining the weight of water in a soil specimen is to use a controlled-temperature oven, but the drying time for many types of soil is 16 to 24 hours. To expedite the drying time, a device called *moisture teller* is often used. In this rapid method, a soil sample is placed in the apparatus, and hot air is forced through the sample for 1 or 2 hours to dry the soil. Sands may be dried in less than an hour in containers held over open flames or seated on hot plates, but this method should never be used to dry materials containing clays or organic matter because the extremely high temperatures tend to drive off absorbed water and false values result.

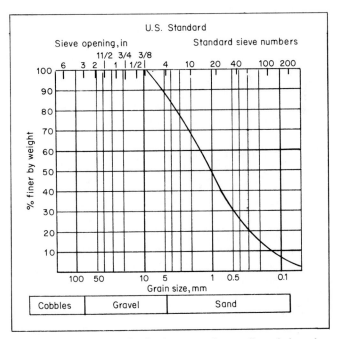

FIG. 2.1-10 Grain-size-distribution curve for a well-graded sand.

Sand-Displacement Method for Determining In-Place Density. A standard procedure for determining the in-place density of fill material is the sand-displacement (sand-cone) method. The procedure consists of digging a sample of material from the fill and, by use of calibrated sand poured into the hole, determining the volume of the hole from which the sample was removed. The water content of the sample is determined, and the dry density is computed.

This method is very accurate, can be used for all types of soils, and requires inexpensive apparatus. However, the field portion of the test takes about 15 to 30 minutes and sometimes interferes with fill operations.

Water-Displacement Method for Determining In-Place Density. In this method, the steps to be followed to determine in-place density are similar to those in the sand-displacement method except that water is used to determine the hole volume. A rubber membrane connected to a calibrated cylinder containing water is forced by low pressure into the hole from which the soil has been removed. The membrane fills the hole, and the volume of water required to fill the membrane is measured by use of calibrated markings on the glass cylinder.

When properly used, the procedure is as accurate as the sand-displacement method. The membrane can be punctured by sharp particles that may be in the material being tested.

Use of Piston and Drive Samplers for Determining In-Place Density. The drive sampler is a thin-walled cylinder with a beveled cutting edge that is driven into the soil with a drop hammer to obtain a sample of uniform dimensions. The piston sample is similar to the drive sample with respect to the type of cylinder used, but the tube is pressed slowly into the fill to recover the sample.

While the piston sampler recovers a less disturbed specimen than does the drive sampler, no sample obtained by either device is completely undisturbed. Therefore, the use of devices of this type may result in erroneous values for in-place density.

Determining In-Place Density by Using Nuclear Devices. Because nuclear devices can be used to determine, by indirect methods, the fill water content and "wet" density very rapidly (within 1 or 2 minutes), many more determinations can be made each day than by any other procedure. The three basic types of nuclear devices are the direct transmission, the back-scatter, and the air-gap apparatus. All three types use gamma rays emitted into the soil mass being tested, with the results of the average wet density of a small mass near the surface determined by calibration curves. These calibration curves are formed by comparing the known densities of different soil types with the readings on the gauge of the nuclear device. Measurement of the soil water content is based on the principle of measuring the slowing of neutrons emitted into the soil from a fast-neutron source within the nuclear equipment. Results obtained by using these devices should be checked frequently against results obtained by using the sand- or water-displacement methods.

Well-calibrated nuclear devices can be valuable adjuncts to more conventional methods for finding the values of in-place densities and result in better control of fill placement. The embankment inspector should attend one of the training centers available for instruction in the use of nuclear devices.

Location and Frequency of Control Tests. Before fill placement begins, a systematic sampling and testing program must be established for all zones of the proposed embankment. This program should be laid out on plan views and cross sections of the embankment, with the location and type of test to be performed indicated by a symbol such as an open circle. As the tests are completed, a brief summary of the test data should be added to the chart. In Fig. 2.1-11 is an example of such a fill-control chart.

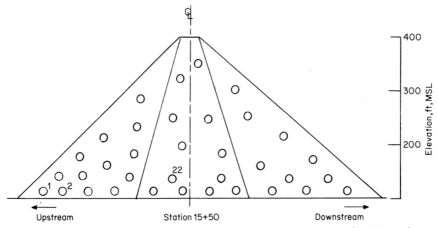

Fig. 2.1-11   Fill-control chart (for one section only). (1 ft = 0.3048 m; 1 lb/ft³ = 16 kg/m³.)

Test no.	Type of test	Test location		Dry, lb/ft³	Water content, %	Passed	Failed
		Elevation	Offset from centerline				
1	In-place density	2.0	570 ft U/S	102.3	16.1	√	
2	In-place density	2.0	510 ft U/S	98.1	18.7		√
22	In-place density	6.0	70 ft U/S	104.6	15.8	√	

Test frequency should be high at the beginning of construction when the borrow areas are first utilized. After rolling requirements have been well established and as the inspection team becomes more familiar with the properties and behavior of the material being placed, test frequency may be reduced. Typically, in-place density, water-content, and Atterberg-limits tests, grain-size analyses, and standard compaction tests are made for each 2000 to 3000 yd^3 (1530 to 2290 m^3) of material placed for the first three or four lifts being placed. Then, depending on the type of material and its water content, the frequency of this set of control tests may be reduced to one set for every 4000 to 5000 yd^3 (3060 to 3820 m^3) of fill placed. If at any time during the construction life of the project the number of tests showing failure of the fill to meet specifications becomes excessive (more than about 10 percent failures), the frequency of testing must be increased until the reasons for the failures are determined and corrective action is taken.

The locations of the field tests should be at random but representative areas on the fill as well as at areas where special techniques, such as hand compaction against abutments or around structures, are used. The results of tests on suspect areas are used to decide whether or not to require additional compaction of low-density material or removal of material that is too wet or of incorrect classification. After corrective action has been taken, check tests are made before the fill area is approved for placement of the next lifts.

Field control tests become part of the legal documentation of construction. It is essential that all test locations be specific as to station number, offset, and elevation. Test-data sheets become even more valuable records if they include weather conditions, compaction procedures used, and any unusual circumstances concerning the fill placement.

Correlating In-Place Density and Water Content to Laboratory Compaction Tests. In the design stages, assumptions are made concerning the properties of the proposed fill materials. These properties include the shear strength, permeability, and deformation characteristics of the material and are derived from laboratory tests made on borrow materials. Such tests are made on representative specimens which are remolded to dry densities and water contents that the designers envision will result when the fill is completed. Thus, for the final project to function properly, it is imperative that all parts of the embankment be compacted as nearly as possible to the density *and* water-content ranges assumed by the designers.

Most embankment designs are based on dry densities that are no less than 95 percent of the density derived from the standard compaction test (in some cases, design assumptions may be based on 90 or 100 percent of laboratory values, but these assumptions are exceptions to the rule). Further, designers usually predicate their assumptions on the basis that the water content of the fill will be reasonably close to the optimum water content determined from the standard compaction test. For example, a specification for embankment fill may call for the material to be compacted with equipment and procedures which will produce a dry density that is no less than 95 percent of the maximum dry density derived from the laboratory compaction test. If the maximum dry density based on the laboratory test is 108 lb/ft^3 (17.3 kg/m^3), then the specifications are, in effect, requiring this particular material to be compacted to no less than 0.95×108 lb/ft^3 $= 102.6$ lb/ft^3 ($0.95 \times 17.3 = 16.4$ kg/m^3). In addition, the specifications usually require that the water content of the compacted fill be within a narrow range of values that fall above and below the optimum water content based on the laboratory compaction test. Thus, if the optimum water content for the same material is found to be, for example, 18 percent, then the designer may call for the compacted fill to have a water content within plus or minus 2 percentage points of this value, or to range between 16 and 20 percent. Another way that fill water-content requirements may be specified is to call for a water-content range that is no greater than 100 percent and no less than 90 percent of the optimum water content.

Recognizing that it is difficult to ensure that all fill materials are compacted to the dry densities and within the water-content range specified, a certain quantity of test values that fail to meet the requirements is permitted without reworking the "failed" areas. Realistic specifications may allow 10 or 12 percent of the *total* fill to contain areas that fail to meet requirements *if* these areas are not concentrated in one location or zone within the embankment.

In Fig. 2.1-12 is shown a typical standard compaction curve superimposed on a hatched zone that delineates the range of acceptable dry

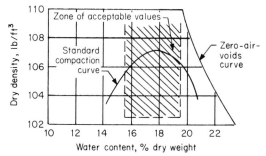

FIG. 2.1-12 General range of acceptable in-place densities and water contents for a typical sandy clay. (1 lb/ft^3 = 16 kg/m^3.)

densities and water contents for compacted fill forming a typical embankment.

In performing a standard compaction test, it is normal practice to prepare and compact four or five specimens of the same material at water contents that bracket the estimated value of the optimum water content. These four-point or five-point compaction tests provide sufficient data to develop a well-formed curve from which accurate results can be read. If such a compaction test were performed on fill material taken immediately adjacent to each in-place-density and water-content test, a very good comparison could be made between field and laboratory values. In actual practice, it is not always feasible to do this because testing cannot always keep pace with the rate of field placement unless there is a very large inspection team. Therefore, expedient methods have been developed for relating field and laboratory test results.

One such method is to perform the standard compaction test by using only three specimens of the same material prepared at three different water contents (one specimen near the optimum water content, one drier than the optimum, and one wetter than the optimum). The results are used to plot a so-called three-point compaction curve. If such a curve is superimposed on a family of five-point compaction curves developed from tests on similar materials, the *shape* of the three-point curve can be better defined, as shown in Fig. 2.1-13.

Attempts have been made to compare the results of in-place densities and water contents with maximum dry densities and optimum water contents derived from two-point and even one-point compaction tests. Such expedients have led to significant errors, and these methods should not be used for fill control.

In Fig. 2.1-14 is shown a useful correlation between the Atterberg limits and maximum dry density and optimum water contents. The results of standard compaction tests and companion liquid and plastic limits on 972 soil samples were used to form the chart. Using the same data, the correlation shown in Fig. 2.1-15 relates the liquid limit and plasticity index to the maximum dry density.

The Bureau of Yards and Docks of the U.S. Navy developed the following empirical equations for estimating the maximum dry density and optimum water content when the Atterberg limits are known:

$$\text{Maximum dry density (lb/ft}^3) = 130.3 - 0.82 \text{ liquid limit} \\ + 0.3 \text{ plasticity index}$$

$$\text{Optimum water content (percent)} = 6.8 + 0.43 \text{ liquid limit} \\ - 0.2 \text{ plasticity index}$$

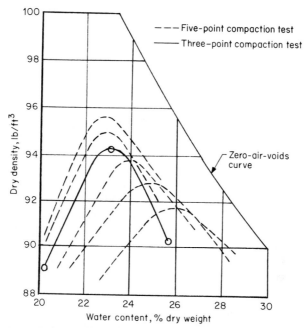

Fig. 2.1-13 Fitting a three-point compaction curve by using a family of five-point compaction curves. (1 lb/ft³ = 16 kg/m³.)

For soils having liquid limits ranging from 20 to 40 and plasticity indices less than 15, M. M. Johnston developed the following empirical equation for estimating the standard maximum dry density:

Maximum dry density (lb/ft³) = 132 − liquid limit + plasticity index

All these charts and equations may be used to check for gross errors in compaction-test values and to supplement control procedures.

A convenient way to present comparisons of in-place dry densities and water contents with laboratory values of maximum dry densities and optimum water contents is shown in Fig. 2.1-16. Percentages of maximum dry densities are plotted versus the variations of field water contents from the optimum water content.

Visual Control during Filling Placement. To supplement actual control testing, visual methods to control fill placement have been developed. An experienced inspector can estimate the water content of fill material by the feel and appearance of a handful of soil. A simple, rapid technique is to roll out about 10 g of the material on a clipboard to form the threads of

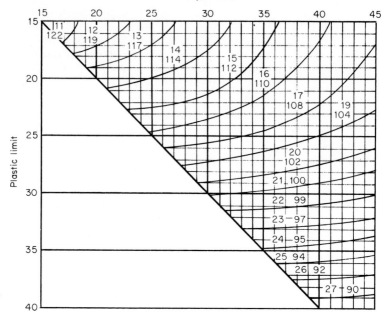

FIG. 2.1-14 Correlation of liquid and plastic limits and maximum dry density and optimum water content. Numbers between curves identify zones of optimum water content and maximum dry density. (*After E. G. Yemington, who developed the correlation presented in a chart by G. R. Ring and W. H. Collins of the Bureau of Public Roads in* Correlation of Compaction and Classification Test Data; *chart modified by Monroe M. Johnston.*)

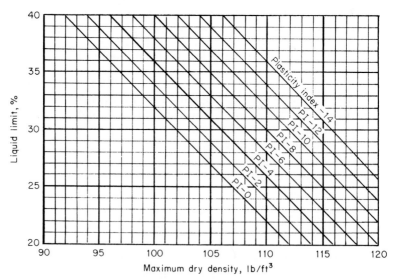

FIG. 2.1-15 Liquid limit and plasticity index related to maximum dry density. (1 lb/ft³ = 16 kg/m³.) (*After Monroe M. Johnston; based on a correlation of E. G. Yemington.*)

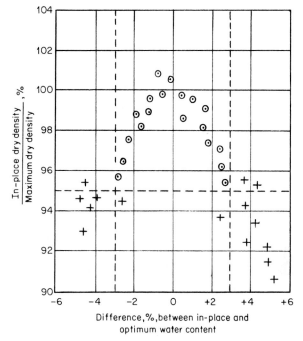

FIG. 2.1-16 Graphical presentation of field-control-test results.

its plastic limit [the soil is at its plastic limit when the thread crumbles into ¼- to ⅛-in (6.35- to 3.175-mm) lengths at a diameter of ⅛ in (3.175 mm)]. If the fill specimen forms the plastic-limit threads after less than 20 or 30 seconds of rolling, the soil is near its optimum water content and ready for compaction. If it takes more than 2 or 3 minutes to form the plastic-limit threads, the soil is usually much wetter than its optimum water content.

Proper lift thickness before compaction may be estimated visually once the judgment of the inspector has been calibrated by actual measurement. A surer method is to measure the loose-lift thickness with a flat, stiff metal foot rule pushed vertically through the uncompacted material to the underlying layer. Grade stakes are sometimes used, but these interfere with compaction equipment. Because there is a tendency to place loose lifts in thicker layers than specified, the inspector should be especially alert to check this feature of construction.

By observing the action of compaction equipment, a trained inspector often can detect whether or not the fill material is at the proper water content. When pneumatic-tired rollers are used, any of the following indicates that the material is at a water content that is too high for efficient compaction:

1. Tires sink into the loose lift by more than half of the tire width.
2. The soil ruts excessively after the first three passes.
3. The fill material undulates in waves ahead of the tires.
4. The fill material shears out from under the tires.
5. There is excessive springing or rebound of the fill during the last few passes.

When sheepsfoot rollers are used, any of the following indicates that the material is much wetter than its optimum water content:

1. Large amounts of soil cling to the roller feet.
2. The roller drum does not walk out during the last few passes.
3. The soil is churned up behind the roller during the last few passes.

In areas of the fill where it is suspected that the fill is being placed at a water content that is too high or at a dry density that is too low, the frequency of control tests should be increased so that the need for corrective treatment can be shown.

Treatment of Fill Areas That Fail to Meet Specifications.   When tests show that the fill has not been compacted to the specified dry density and within the required range of water contents, the area must be reworked and retested. The in-place density may be increased by increasing the number of passes of the compaction equipment, by increasing the foot or tire pressure, by decreasing the loose-lift thickness, or by using a combination of these corrective measures. If the fill material is wetter than specified, the soil may be disked, harrowed, or plowed, air- or sun-dried down to an acceptable water content, and then recompacted.

As a last resort, soil that is too wet for any of these treatments should be removed from the fill.

Compaction of Pervious Fill

Material for the construction of pervious fills includes sands, gravelly sands, sandy gravels, and, occasionally, slightly silty sands. An important characteristic of materials of these types is that they are comparatively free-draining. For this reason they are used in embankment zones such as toe drains, inclined drains, and filter layers to control seepage. In Fig. 2.1-4 are shown several embankment cross sections having zones of pervious materials.

The degree of drainability of pervious materials is a function of particle sizes and grain-size distribution. The quantity of water which can pass through a given mass of soil under a particular head differential can be determined by the coefficient of permeability, the value of which depends on several factors including the dry density, the size and shape of the particles, and the viscosity of the water.

Pervious materials must be compacted to a dry density that is high enough to prevent the fill from deforming under any expected loads, including seismic loads.

Equipment for Compacting Pervious Fill. While pervious fill may be compacted with pneumatic-tired rollers and crawler tractors, the most effective equipment for producing high densities is the vibrating steel-wheeled roller (see Figs. 2.1-17 and 2.1-18). This type of roller, developed in Europe and used in the United States for two decades, usually has a total weight ranging from 2 to 5 tons (1.8 to 4.5 metric tons). It may be either self-propelled or towed by a crawler tractor. Pervious fill is compacted best when the steel drum is vibrating on the fill surface at frequencies between 1100 and 1500 cycles/minute and the forward speed is between 1 and 1.5 mi/hour (1.6 and 2.4 km/hour). The highest degree of compaction is attained when the layer of fill being densified is completely saturated at the time of compaction. Saturation has been accomplished on some projects by use of water-spraying equipment flooding the fill just ahead of the vibrating roller. A comparatively high dry density can be attained by four passes of the roller over a loose layer 12 in (304.8 mm) thick.

FIG. 2.1-17   Koehring Bomag double-drum vibratory units compact the sub-base of a road shoulder after a utility line has been put in. These units rely on high impact for compaction, provided by rotating weights. One drum is always in the impact mode.

FIG. 2.1-18   A single-drum vibratory roller, BW213 (BW210D), is furnished with a drum drive for traction in granular, loose materials in which other units would normally bog down.

In constricted areas where it is not practicable to use large rollers, hand-operated vibrating plates have been found effective in compacting pervious materials.

Relative Density.   When a mass of pervious material is at its loosest state, it is said to be at its *minimum density;* when the material is at its densest state, it is at its *maximum density.* The maximum and minimum densities of a pervious material can be determined by laboratory tests if the maximum particle size in the soil mass does not exceed about 3 in (76 mm). The test procedures for determining maximum and minimum dry densities have not been standardized universally, but a commonly used set of procedures is presented in the subsection "Soil-Test Procedures and Equipment."

An equation has been developed that defines the state of density of a given pervious material. This equation gives the *relative density* of the material and is as follows:

$$\text{Relative density (percent)} = \frac{(D_{max}(D - D_{min})}{D(D_{max} - D_{min})} \times 100$$

where D_{max} = dry density of soil in its densest state
D_{min} = dry density of soil in its loosest state
D = dry density of soil in place

As can be seen by application of this equation, when the in-place density of a given pervious material is equal to its maximum density, its relative density is 100 percent. When pervious fill is dumped on a surface such as a foundation or an embankment, it is in a loose state and has a low relative density. After the material has been spread and compacted, it attains a denser state and is at a high relative density. The following gives a commonly used set of adjectives for defining the *state of denseness* of pervious materials:

Relative density, %	State of denseness
0–15	Very loose
16–33	Loose
34–64	Medium
65–87	Dense
88–100	Very dense

In Fig. 2.1-19 is shown a chart for the rapid determination of relative density when maximum, minimum, and in-place dry densities are known.

Construction Testing and Control for Pervious Materials

Specifications may require that all pervious zones of the embankment be compacted to a relative density of, for example, no less than 70 percent. To ensure that the fill is compacted to dry densities equal to or greater than that specified, the inspector must first determine the in-place dry density by using one of the methods outlined under "Construction Testing and Control," the sand-displacement method, the water-displacement method, or the use of nuclear devices. This value must then be related to the values of the maximum and minimum densities of the *same* material for which the in-place density was determined. Clearly, the most accurate approach is to perform a maximum- and a minimum-density test on a soil specimen taken immediately adjacent to the area in which the in-place-density test was made. If all material in the entire embankment had the same particle size and shape, grain-size distribution, and specific gravity, it would be necessary to perform only one or two maximum- and minimum-density tests to have enough data to control the placement of the embankment. But in view of the variability of pervious material, many values of maximum and minimum dry densities are needed because the equation for relative density is sensitive to small changes in these values.

Correlations between maximum and minimum density and the coefficient of uniformity may be used to detect gross errors in laboratory determinations of maximum and minimum density. The method for determining the coefficient of uniformity using the grain-size distribution curve is shown in Fig. 2.1-20. For pervious soils, the value of both maximum and minimum dry densities increases as the value of the coefficient of uniformity increases. In other words, as the material becomes better graded or as the particles cover a wider range of sizes, the soil mass can

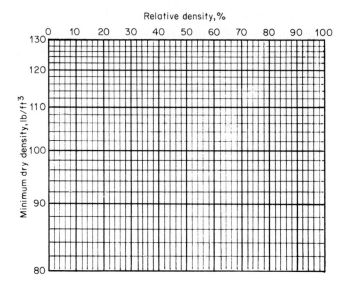

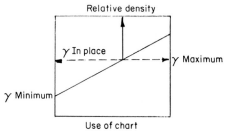

FIG. 2.1-19 Graphical determination of relative density. To determine relative density, plot maximum and minimum density on their respective scales and draw a straight line between the two values. For any intermediate density, the corresponding relative density is read directly from the chart as shown. (1 lb/ft^3 = 16 kg/m^3.)

more readily become more tightly packed as the smaller particles fill the voids between the larger sizes.

An empirical relation between the coefficient of uniformity and maximum and minimum density is shown in Fig. 2.1-21a. Such correlations may be formed for each project in the early stages of construction by performing a series of sieve analyses and maximum-minimum-density tests and plotting data derived from the test results. If the scatter of values is not too great, the plots can be used to supplement the laboratory test results. As construction progresses, these correlations should be updated.

It should be kept in mind that, theoretically, no pervious material can

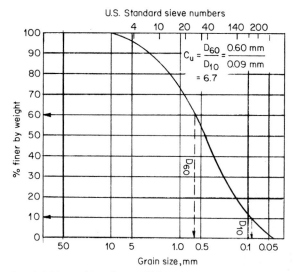

FIG. 2.1-20 Uniformity coefficient for a well-graded sand.

be compacted to a value higher than 100 percent relative density. If test results show that a given material has been compacted to a relative density that is significantly higher than 100 percent, an error probably has been made. The error could be caused by relating the in-place density to incorrect values of maximum and minimum density or by an incorrect determination of the in-place density. Occasionally, field compaction equipment *will* compact fill to a dry density that is higher than the laboratory value of "maximum" dry density, but this is an exception to the rule.

When a pervious fill fails to meet specification densities, the dry densities may be increased by reducing the lift thickness, by increasing the number of compaction passes, or by using a heavier vibratory roller.

Protection of Pervious Fill against Contamination

At projects where inclined or vertical drainage zones of pervious fill are incorporated into the embankment (such as shown in Fig. 2.1-3) hauling equipment may cross the pervious zone. The tires of the equipment will transport material from the surface of the impervious fill to the surface of the pervious fill. Sometimes as much as several inches (1 in = 25.4 mm) of impervious fill is "tracked" in this manner over the surface of the pervious zone and forms a partial seal to restrict drainage when the project is in operation. The inspector must see that this impervious coating or contamination is removed from the top of the pervious fill before the next lift is placed.

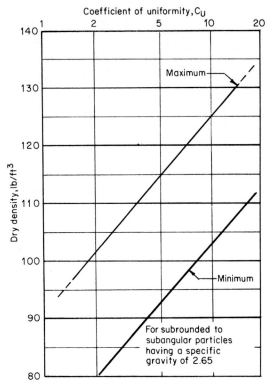

Fig. 2.1-21a Empirical relationship between maximum and minimum density and the coefficient of uniformity. (1 lb/ft^3 = 16kg/m^3.) *(After Monroe M. Johnston.)*

Compaction of Earth-Rock Fill

Any embankment fill material which includes in its composition a significant quantity of particle sizes larger than ½ in (12.7 mm) in diameter may be termed *earth rock*. Materials such as gravelly sands, sandy gravels, silty gravels, clayey gravels, and silt-clay-gravel mixtures are in this category. A good example of an earth-rock material is *till* (an unstratified glacial deposit of clay, silt, sand, gravel, and boulders).

Because it is the only embankment material available in many parts of the United States, hundreds of dams, highway fills, and other types of embankments have been constructed of earthrock. Owing to its erratic nature and heterogeneity, the proper control of its placement is very difficult.

In an earth-rock mixture, the maximum dry density increases and the optimum water content decreases as the percentage of coarse particles increases *until* a point is reached where there are insufficient fines to fill the voids in the total mass. When this point is reached, the maximum dry density of the mixture begins to decrease. As shown in Fig. 2.1-21*b*, maximum dry density is attained for most rock-soil mixtures when the rock content of the total mass is about 40 to 50 percent by weight. The percentage of coarse particles in the total mixture also influences the maximum dry density of the matrix of fine particles (the soil itself) surrounding the rock in the mass. For a given compactive effort, the maximum dry density of the fine fraction is not affected significantly if the total mass contains less than about 20 percent coarse particles. As the percentage of coarse particles increases above about 20 percent, the maximum dry density of the fine fraction (or matrix) decreases rapidly. These trends are valid regardless of the water content of the fine fraction.

The best earth-rock fill is one that has been compacted so as to provide a rock skeleton surrounded by a matrix of soil which is at a high dry density.

Laboratory Compaction Tests. The standard compaction test using a 6-in- (152.4-mm-) diameter compaction mold gives valid values of maximum dry density and optimum water content when the specimen being tested contains less than 10 percent by dry weight of particles no greater than ¾ in (19.05 mm) in diameter. For earth-rock mixtures containing more than 10 percent by weight of coarse particles having a maximum size of 2 in (50.8 mm), a special standard compaction test has been developed. In this test, the compaction mold has a diameter of 12 in

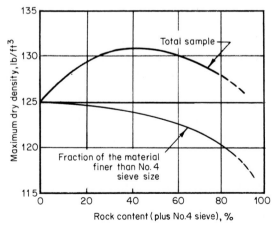

FIG. 2.1-21*b* Relationship between maximum dry density and rock content for a typical earth-rock mixture using the same compactive effort. (1 lb/ft³ = 16 kg/m³.)

(304.8 mm), and the compaction rammer weighs 11.5 lb (5.2 kg) and has a rammer face of 4 in (101.6 mm) in diameter.

Field Compaction Equipment.   To achieve a dense, well-knit earth-rock fill, it is usually necessary to increase the field compactive effort above that used for fine-grained soil masses. This may be done by increasing the tire pressure or foot pressure of the rollers. During the design stages, a test section of the proposed fill is built (if the magnitude of the project justifies the cost) so that the most efficient type of compaction equipment can be evaluated before actual construction begins. It has been found that loose-lift thickness should be about 1.5 times greater than the diameter of the largest rock particle in the fill. Cobbles and boulders that are too large to permit proper compaction [generally, rocks larger than about 1 ft (0.305 m) in diameter] should be removed from the fill before the compaction equipment passes over the loose lift.

Determining In-Place Densities.   The most accurate method for determining the in-place density of an earth-rock mixture is the sand-displacement test procedure. Because of the presence of large particles, the volume of the hole excavated must be greater than that used for fine-grained materials. When the percentage by dry weight of coarse particles in the total sample ranges from 5 to 10 percent, the hole volume should be no less than $\frac{1}{10}$ ft^3 (0.0028 m^3). For material containing more than 10 percent coarse particles, the hole volume should be no less than $\frac{1}{5}$ ft^3 (0.0056 m^3). Large-scale sand-cone devices are available for testing earth-rock materials.

Correlating In-Place Density and Water Content to Laboratory Compaction Tests.   For fills containing less than 10 percent by dry weight of coarse particles smaller than $\frac{3}{4}$ in (19.05 mm) in diameter, in-place dry density and water content should be compared with the results of a standard laboratory compaction test. When the fill contains less than 35 percent by dry weight of coarse particles and a 12-in- (304.8-mm-) diameter compaction mold and special rammer are not available, an expedient fill-control technique is sometimes used. The method is based on the concept that if the dry density of the *fine* particles in the fill is high enough, then the dry density of the total earth-rock mixture is satisfactory. The dry density of the fine fraction can be calculated by using the following equation:

$$D_f = \frac{(F)(D_t)(G)(62.4)}{(62.4)(G) - (C)(D_t)(1 + A)}$$

where D_f = dry density of fine fraction, lb/ft^3
  F = proportion of fine fraction in total sample expressed as decimal fraction
  D_t = dry density of total field sample, lb/ft^3
  G = bulk specific gravity of coarse particle
  C = proportion of coarse fraction in total sample expressed as decimal fraction
  A = absorption of coarse particles

1 lb/ft^3 = 16 kg/m^3.

The water content of the fine fraction can be calculated by using the following equation:

$$W_f = \frac{W_t - (C)(A)}{F} \times 100$$

where W_f = water content of fine fraction, percent
  W_t = water content of total field density sample expressed as decimal fraction

The term *coarse particles* refers to those particles in the field sample larger than the maximum size allowed when using a given compaction mold. These sizes are shown in Table 2.1-2.

The adsorption of the coarse particles is equal to the saturated surface dry weight minus the oven dry weight divided by the oven dry weight.

The following example illustrates the application of these equations to earth-rock material containing particles too large to be tested by laboratory compaction equipment.

Given: An earth-rock fill specimen having an in-place dry density of 120 lb/ft^3 (1922 kg/m^3) and a field water content of 15 percent and containing 30 percent coarse particles [in this case, particles larger than 0.75 in (19.05mm)] having a bulk specific gravity of 2.50. The adsorption of coarse particles is 10 percent.

Find: The dry density and water content of the fine fraction (in this case, particles equal to or smaller than 0.75 in).

$$D_f = \frac{(0.70)(120 \text{ lb/ft}^3)(2.50)(62.4)}{(62.4)(2.50) - (0.30)(120)(1 + 0.10)} = 112.6 \text{ lb/ft}^3$$

and $W_f = \dfrac{0.15 - (0.30)(0.10)}{0.70} \times 100 = 17.1$ percent

TABLE 2.1-2   Mold Diameter and Maximum Particle Size

Diameter of compaction mold, in (mm)	Maximum particle size permitted, in (mm)	Particle sizes, coarse fraction, in (mm)	Particle sizes, fine fraction, (in mm)
4 (101.6)	0.19 (4.83)	Larger than 0.19 (4.83)	Smaller than 0.19 (4.83)
6 (152.4)	0.75 (19.05)	Larger than 0.75 (19.05)	Smaller than 0.75 (19.05)
12 (304.8)	2 (50.8)	Larger than 2 (50.8)	Smaller than 2 (50.8)

Charts such as the type shown in Fig. 2.1-22 can be formed durng the early stages of construction and used to convert field density and water content to the density and water content of the fine fraction. The steps to be followed for fill control are:

1. Determine the in-place density and water content of the fill.
2. Determine the proportion of both fine and coarse fractions by weight of a field sample taken directly adjacent to the location of the in-place-density test.
3. Determine the bulk specific gravity and adsorption of the coarse particles. (Note: These values need not be determined for every field sample because for a given borrow area the values of specific gravity and adsorption are relatively constant for coarse particles.)
4. Using the above equations, determine the dry density and water content of the fine fraction.
5. Perform a standard compaction test by using the appropriate compaction mold, and compute maximum dry density and optimum water content.
6. Compare dry density and water content of the fine fraction with maximum dry density and optimum water content.

Special Compaction Problems

It is impossible to compact any fill properly if it is frozen. Therefore, compaction of fills should be discontinued when the temperature is below freezing long enough to create ice in the fill or in the borrow material. Before construction begins after a deep freeze, the fill should be excavated with scrapers to a depth of about 6 in (152.4 mm) below the line of frost action.

Impervious and semi-impervious fill material should never be placed and compacted during rains unless the borrow material is so dry that a light sprinkle merely increases the water content to a value near the optimum. On embankments being compacted by sheepsfoot rollers, the fill surface may be sealed by using pneumatic-tired rollers before an expected rain. After the rain, the surface should be scarified with disks or

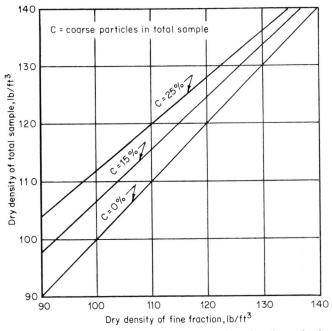

FIG. 2.1-22   Typical chart relating coarse fraction of total sample, dry density of total sample, and dry density of fine fraction (for coarse particles with specific gravity of 2.60 and having a water adsorption of zero). (1 lb/ft^3 = 16 kg/m^3.)

harrows and recompacted with the sheepsfoot rollers to create a good bond for the next lift.

Where it is necessary to compact fill in areas too confined to permit normal rolling with heavy equipment, hand compaction must be used. There are many types of hand-operated power tampers as well as those mounted on small tractors. Hand-operated power tampers work on a piston principle that thrusts the rammer into the air 30 to 40 times a minute. The action results in combined impact and vibration so that this type of compactor is very effective in compacting pervious fill. Hand-operated rammers can compact impervious fill to the proper density if their static weight is at least 100 lb (45.36 kg), the loose-lift thickness of the material is about 4 in (101.6 mm), and the rammer face overlaps the previously compacted surface to give full coverage.

EMBANKMENT SLOPE PROTECTION

At water-impounding embankments such as dams and dikes, unprotected earth slopes can be damaged rather rapidly by wave erosion, ice floes, and other debris in the reservoir. Even runoff from heavy rains can create significant gullying in earth slopes. Eventually, serious erosion can lead to an unstable slope and failure of the embankment.

Upstream Slope Protection. A few upstream slopes have been protected by a paving of soil-cement, concrete, asphalt, and even grass, especially at projects where rock is scarce and the cost of its importation prohibitive. However, the most commonly used protection is to face the slope with a layer of specially graded rock called *riprap*. The thickness of the riprap required and the gradation and size of the rock are dependent on the height of the waves acting on the slope, the pitch of the slope, and the specific gravity of the rock. The U.S. Army Corps of Engineers has used the following equations to determine the thickness, median rock size, and approximate gradation of riprap:

$$T = 20\sqrt[3]{\frac{W_A}{62.4\,G}}$$

where T = riprap thickness, in (1 in = 25.4 mm), measured normal to slope

      W_A = weight of median-size rock, lb (1 lb = 0.4536 kg)

      G = specific gravity of rock

$$W_A = \frac{(62.4)(G)(H)^2}{(1.82)(G-1)^3\,(cot\,\alpha)}$$

where H = wave height, ft (1 ft = 0.3048 m)

      α = slope of embankment

The maximum-size rock in the riprap W_{max} is equal to 4 W_A. The minimum-size rock in the riprap W_{min} is equal to $W_A/8$.

In Fig. 2.1-23 is shown the relation between the weight of rock and its size. As the embankment slope to be protected becomes steeper and the waves approaching the slope become higher, the weight of the median-size rock in the riprap increases as shown in Fig. 2.1-24.

To minimize the movement of embankment material through the voids in the riprap, a layer of sandy gravel (termed the *bedding layer*) should be placed on the slope under the riprap. Before placing the bedding layer, the embankment slope should be graded smoothly and uniformly and then compacted by several passes of a crawler tractor. The bedding layer is spread upward on the slope from stockpiles that are

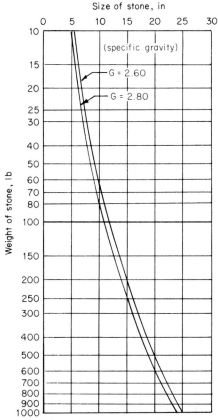

FIG. 2.1-23 Relationship between size and weight of stone (a shape midway between a cube and a sphere is assumed). (1 in = 25.4 mm; 1 lb = 0.4536 kg.)

placed along the base of the embankment. The riprap should be placed on the slope by using a *skip*, a special bucket from which rock can be placed with little segregation of particle sizes. A good riprap layer is one consisting of a well-graded rock mixture placed in a close-knit mass containing no large voids and no nests or pockets of small rocks.

The inspector must control rock gradation during placement to ensure that the riprap conforms to specifications. For about every 15,000 yd^3 (11,470 m^3) of riprap placed, a gradation test is performed. This is done by passing a sufficient quantity of a representative sample through bar screens (in effect, giant sieves) and weighing the rock retained on each screen.

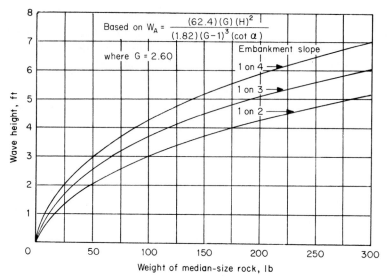

FIG. 2.1-24 Relation between wave height and weight of median-size rock required for upstream slope protection. (1 ft = 0.3048 m; 1 lb = 0.4536 kg.)

The quality of rock used for riprap must be such that it does not degrade into smaller sizes when exposed to cycles of wetting and drying or freezing and thawing. The inspector should determine which rock types are acceptable and be alert to discover and reject substandard material. A staff geotechnical engineer should observe riprap placement in the early stage of placement to determine whether or not rock quality and placement methods are satisfactory.

Downstream Slope Protection. The downstream slopes of dams, dikes, and levees and all slopes of highway fills must be protected against erosion from rainwater. It is usually necessary, especially on slopes of sand and silty sand, to provide a layer of topsoil or sod to establish a protective grass cover. The type of grass or other vegetative cover and the irrigation procedures are usually planned by agronomists.

CONSTRUCTION CONTROL RECORDS AND REPORTS

Inspectors are required to keep accurate records and prepare concise, meaningful reports during construction. These records and reports become invaluable in the analysis and correction of any difficulty that may require design changes during construction or treatment of postconstruction problems. In cases of claims or future disagreements concerning the projects, the records and reports of the inspector may become legal documents; their chief value lies in their clarity, legibility, and completeness. These records should be kept in a safe place, such as a locked filing cabinet, until they are transmitted to the proper authorities.

Good practice requires that the chief inspector or the inspector's representative submit to the project engineer a daily report or a weekly summary that includes the following:

1. Name of contractor and contract number
2. Location of work being performed
3. Description of operations
4. Date and weather conditions
5. Types of construction equipment and procedures used
6. Amount of work performed
7. Number and types of control tests used and by whom the tests were performed
8. Any violations of specifications
9. Causes and extent of construction delays
10. Any special instructions given to the contractor
11. Resulting actions taken by the contractor

Before construction begins, a set of report forms should be submitted to the project engineer for approval to ensure that the engineer will receive all the information required from the inspection team. All construction control reports should be signed by the chief inspector.

An important supplement to the written records and reports is a series of photographs showing each phase of construction. Each photograph should include some well-known object or measuring device to give a sense of scale; on the back of the photograph should be written the following:

1. Date and location of the subject matter (including the station number, offset, and elevation where applicable)
2. Brief description of the subject matter
3. Contract number
4. Identity of the photographer

SELECTED REFERENCES

Construction Control for Earth and Rock-Fill Dams, Engineer Manual 1110-2-1911, U.S. Army Corps of Engineers, 1972.

Earth and Rock-Fill Dams: General Design and Construction Considerations, Engineer Manual 1110-2-2300, U.S. Army Corps of Engineers, 1971.

Earth Manual, U.S. Department of the Interior, 1968.

Hirschfeld, R. C., and S. J. Poulos: *Embankment-Dam Engineering,* John Wiley & Sons, Inc., New York, 1973.

Johnston, M. M.: "Laboratory Comparison Tests Using Compacted Fine-Grained Soils," *Proceedings of the Seventh International Conference on Soil Mechanics and Foundation Engineering,* 1969.

————: *Laboratory Studies of Maximum and Minimum Dry Densities of Cohesionless Soils,* ASTM Special Technical Publication 523, 1973.

Laboratory Soils Testing, Engineer Manual 1110-2-1906, U.S. Army Corps of Engineers, 1970.

Schroeder, W. L.: *Soils in Construction,* 2d ed., John Wiley & Sons, Inc., New York, 1983.

Sherard, J. L., et al.: *Earth and Earth-Rock Dams,* John Wiley & Sons, Inc., New York, 1967.

PART 2

Part 2 includes the glossary and detailed information on soil-test procedures and equipment, a unified soil-classification system, and soil-identification procedures along with an inspector's checklist. This part of the chapter will be especially useful to those with little formal training in geotechnical engineering and those who need a brief refresher in that field.

GLOSSARY

Alluvium   Material deposited by streams in channels, floodplains, and deltas.

Aquifer   Geologic formation that transmits water in sufficient quantity to supply wells or springs.

Bank gravel   Gravel in natural deposits, often intermixed with sand or clay.

Bar screen   Screen having square openings to grade gravels and cobbles.

Boulder   Any detached rock fragment with a diameter larger than 10 in (254 mm).

Brooming   Process of sweeping wet grout into rock fissures to seal the rock surface.

Colluvium   Earth and rock material that has been moved and deposited by gravity.

Compaction   Process employing special equipment to decrease the void space between soil particles by rearranging the grains.

Correlation   Degree of relative correspondence, as between sets of data.

Fat clay   Clay that has a high plasticity and is difficult to compact.

Grout   Slurrylike mixture of sand, cement, bentonite, lime, and water.

Grout curtain   Type of seepage cutoff constructed by drilling a series of borings into a fissured rock foundation and injecting a lean concrete grout mix to attempt to seal the fissures.

Hardpan   Soil horizon that has become rocklike owing to the accumulation of cementing minerals such as calcium carbonates in the soil.

Inorganic soil   Soil composed of matter that is not animal or vegetable in origin.

Kneading   Action of compaction equipment such as sheepsfoot rollers to rearrange soil particles and increase densification of the soil mass.

Lean clay   Clay of low to medium plasticity and cohesion, generally due to the presence of silt or sand.

Loam   Surface soil, usually a silty sand or a sandy silt, sometimes containing organic matter.

Organic material   Any material containing animal or vegetable matter, usually in a decomposed state. Soils containing organic matter tend to be dark gray or black and will produce an odor, especially when heated.

Residual material   Material that is the product of weathering and is still located at the place where it originated.

Soil-cement   Mixture of sand or silty sand and a small percentage of portland cement that is sometimes used to face the upstream slope of a dam.

Solutioning   Dissolving of portions of calcareous formations producing vugs and voids in the formations.

Till   That part of glacial drift deposited directly by ice and consisting of a heterogeneous mixture of clay, sand, gravel, cobbles, and boulders.

Weathering   Chemical and mechanical processes acting at or near the earth's surface to bring about disintegration, decomposition, or comminution of rock.

SOIL-TEST PROCEDURES AND EQUIPMENT

Checklist of Soil-Testing Equipment

1. General
   a. Oven
   b. Balances
   c. Sample storage cans
   d. Canvas bags
   e. Glass jars
   f. Glass graduates
   g. Mechanical mixing bowl
   h. Drying and mixing pans
   i. Sample splitter
   j. Hand scoops
   k. Spoons
   l. Wrenches and screwdrivers
   m. Mallets and hammers

   n. Square and pointed shovels
   o. Distilled water
   p. Marking pencils
   q. Sample tags and labels
   r. Asbestos gloves
   s. Standard test forms
   t. Clipboard
   u. Laboratory tongs
   v. Glass graduates

2. Water-content test
   a. Weighing containers

3. Sieve analysis
   a. Set of sieves
   b. Sieve shaker

c. Mortar and pestle

4. Atterberg-limits test

   a. Liquid-limit device

   b. Grooving tool

   c. Spatula

   d. Porcelain mixing dish

   e. Porcelain evaporating dish

   f. Infrared lamp

   g. Ground-glass plate

5. Compaction test

   a. Compaction mold

   b. Compaction rammer

   c. Curing containers

   d. Straightedge

   e. Trowel and knives

   f. Concrete base

6. Minimum-density test

   a. Measuring cylinder

   b. Pouring container

   c. Straightedge

7. Maximum-density test

   a. Measuring container

   b. Pouring container

   c. Vibratory table

   d. Height-change dial

   e. Calibration bar

   f. Surcharge assembly

   g. Hoist

8. In-place-density test

   a. Sand cone and cylinder

   b. Cone-bearing plate

   c. Calibration sand

   d. Digging tools

   e. Paint brush

   f. Balance windshield

Water-Content Determination

1. *Definition of Water Content.* The water content of a soil is the ratio, expressed as a percentage, of the weight of water in a given soil mass to the weight of the solid particles in the mass.

2. *Equipment.* (see Figs. 2.1-25 and 2.1-26)

   a. Oven. The oven shall be of the type having the temperature automatically controlled to $110 \pm 5°$ C.

   b. Balances. The balances shall be sensitive to 0.01 g for samples weighing less than 50 g, sensitive to 0.1 g for samples weighing from 50 to 500 g, and sensitive to 1.0 g for samples weighing over 500 g.

   c. Weighing Containers (Tares). The containers in which to weigh the samples shall be rustproof cylinders of lightweight metal (such as aluminum) provided with tight-fitting lids and having sufficient capacity to contain the wet sample loosely.

3. *Size of Test Sample.* For routine water-content determinations, the test sample shall have a wet weight of no less than 100 g if the maximum particle size passes the No. 4 sieve openings, a wet weight of no less

FIG. 2.1-25   Speedy device for determining
water content.

FIG. 2.1-26   Forced-draft controlled-temperature oven for determining
water content.

than 250 g if the maximum particle size is 0.5 in (12.7 mm), a wet
weight of no less than 500 g if the maximum particle size is 1.0 in (25.4
mm), and a wet weight of no less than 1000 g if the maximum particle
size is 2.0 in (50.8 mm).

4. *Procedure.*   Weigh a dried, cool container and its lid to the nearest 0.01
g. Place a representative sample in the container, place the lid under
the container, and weigh the wet sample and container with the lid
included. Record this weight, the weight of the empty container and

lid, and the container number on the data sheet. Oven-dry the soil in the container to constant mass at $110 \pm 5°C$ (drying time for sands and gravels is 1 to 2 hours; for silts, from 4 to 12 hours; and for clays, from 16 to 24 hours). When in doubt as to the proper time, reweigh the sample after several successive drying periods until a constant mass is obtained. After the sample is dry, remove it from the oven, cap the container with the lid, and allow the container to cool. Weigh the sample, container, and lid, and record this weight.

5. *Computations.* The empty-container and lid weight is termed the *tare.*

Water content w (percent)

$$= \frac{(\text{weight of wet soil plus tare}) - (\text{weight of dry soil plus tare})}{(\text{weight of dry soil plus tare}) - (\text{tare})} \times 100$$

6. *Possible Errors.* Any of the following can produce erroneous results:

a. Sample was too small or was not representative of field sample.

b. Sample lost water before the wet weight was obtained.

c. Sample gained water before the dry weight was obtained.

d. Sample was not completely oven-dried.

e. Oven was at an incorrect temperature.

f. Sample was weighed while the container was hot.

g. Balance was not calibrated.

Particle-Size Analysis

1. *Definition.* Particle-size analysis is a process in which the proportion of each grain size present in a given material is determined by using a set of special sieves (see Fig. 2.1-27). Sieves are constructed of wire screens having square openings of standard sizes. The distribution of particle sizes larger then 0.074 mm (sizes retained on the No. 200 sieve) is determined by sieving. The distribution of particle sizes smaller than 0.074 mm is determined by a sedimentation process using a hydrometer; this process is not covered in the following procedure.

2. *Equipment*

a. *Oven.* The oven shall be of the type having the temperature automatically controlled to $110 \pm 5°C$.

b. *Balances.* The balances shall be sensitive to 0.01 g for weighing material passing a No. 10 (2.0-mm) sieve and sensitive to 0.1 percent of the mass of the sample to be weighed for material containing No. 10 sieve-size particles.

Fɪɢ. **2.1-27**   A set of U.S. Standard sieves for determining grain-size distribution.

    c. Sieves.   The set of sieves shall be of square-mesh woven cloth, conforming to the requirements of ASTM Specification E 11. Table 2.1-3 lists sieve sizes in current use. The set of sieves shall be provided with a close-fitting cover and bottom pan.

    d. Sieve Shaker.   The mechanical sieve shaker shall be of the Tyler (Ro-Tap) or Syntron type or the equivalent. When manual shaking is used, the operation shall be conducted by lateral and vertical motion of the set of sieves.

    e. Sample Splitters.   The sample splitter (or *riffle*) may be of any commercial type.

    f. Mortar and Pestle.   The mortar and rubber-covered pestle may be of any commercial type.

3. *Sample Preparation.*   The proper sample weights for sieving shall depend on the maximum size of particle; Table 2.1-4 lists the approximate minimum mass of sample to be used. Air-dry the field sample at room temperature, break up all aggregations in the material by using the mortar and pestle without crushing the discrete particles, and select a representative sample of the amount required by dividing the material by means of the sample splitter.

    If the material contains plastic fines coating the coarser particles, slake the sample in water to separate the particles (slake the sample from 2 to 24 hours depending on the amount and plasticity of the fines). Wash the entire sample through a No. 4 sieve, and retain both the fraction passing and the fraction retained on this sieve.

TABLE 2.1-3   Partial Sieve Series, U.S. Bureau of Standards

Mesh	Opening in	Opening mm	Mesh	Opening in	Opening mm	Mesh	Opening in	Opening mm	Mesh	Opening in	Opening mm
...	3	76.2	...	1	25.4	4	0.187	4.76	40	0.0165	0.425
...	2	50.8	...	0.75	19.1	10	0.079	2.00	100	0.0059	0.149
...	1.5	38.1	...	0.375	9.5	20	0.033	0.85	200	0.0029	0.074

TABLE 2.1-4*

Maximum particle size, in	Mass of sample, g	Maximum particle size, in	Mass of sample, g
3	6000	0.500	1000
2	4000	0.250	500
1	2000	0.187	200

*1 in = 25.4 mm.

4. *Procedure*

   a. *Material Finer Than No. 4 Sieve Sizes.*   Oven-dry the sample at 110 ± 5°C, and allow it to cool. Weigh out 200 g to the nearest 0.1 g, and record the dry weight of the sample. Transfer the sample to a No. 200 sieve in increments to avoid overloading the sieve. Wash the sample thoroughly through the sieve, discarding the particles passing the sieve. Oven-dry the material retained on the sieve, and allow it to cool. Weigh this portion of the total sample to the nearst 0.1 g, and record the value.

   Select a set of sieves (No. 4, 10, 20, 40, 100, and 200 sieves can be used to develop a grain-size-distribution curve for most soils). Arrange the nest of sieves according to size, with decreasing openings from top to bottom; attach the pan. Place the sample on the top sieve of the nest, and place the cover plate. Lock the nest of sieves in the mechanical shaker, and activate the shaker for 10 minutes. Remove the sieves from the shaker.

   Transfer the contents of the top sieve to a heavy piece of paper (such as a manila folder) by carefully inverting the sieve over the paper. Gently brush the bottom of the sieve with a dry paintbrush to free particles trapped in the sieve openings. Transfer the sample to a tared container on the balance, and weigh the material to the nearest 0.1 g. Record this weight on the data sheet.

   Repeat this procedure for each sieve and for the material recovered in the bottom pan. The sum of the weights retained on each sieve and in the pan should equal the weight of the sample before sieving within 1 percent. The percentage of material by weight retained on the various sieves is computed as follows:

$$\text{Percent retained} = \frac{\text{weight in grams retained on a sieve}}{\text{total weight in grams of oven-dry sample}} \times 100$$

The cumulative percentage retained on any sieve equals the sum of percentages retained on all coarser sieves. The percentage finer than any sieve size equals 100 percent minus the cumulative percentage retained.

Example: Dry weight of sample before it is passed through a No. 200 sieve = 200 g. Dry weight of sample retained on a No. 200 sieve = 150 g. The 150 g is then sieved with the results shown in Table 2.1-5.

TABLE 2.1-5   Sieve-Analysis Results

Sieve no.	Sieve opening, mm	Weight of soil retained, g	% retained	Cumulative % retained	% finer
4	4.76	0	0	0	100
10	2.00	30	15.0	15.0	85.0
20	0.85	25	12.5	27.5	72.5
40	0.425	31	15.5	43.0	57.0
100	0.149	40	20.0	63.0	37.0
200	0.074	24	12.0	75.0	25.0

The results of a sieve analysis may be presented as a graphical plot of the data with values of percent finer by weight on the arithmetic scale (ordinate) and values of grain size in millimeters on the logarithmic scale as shown in Fig. 2.1-10.

b. Material Containing Particles Larger than No. 4 Sieve Sizes. Process the material as described in Par. 3. Weigh out the appropriate minimum mass of sample to be used in accordance with the maximum particle size in the total sample. Record the oven-dry weight to the nearest gram. Select a set of sieves with the top sieve having openings slightly larger than the maximum particle size, and nest the set on top of the No. 4 sieve [a typical set of sieves would be 3-, 2-, 1-, ¾-, and ⅜-in (76.2-, 50.8-, 25.4-, 19.05-, and 9.525-mm) sieves and the No. 4 sieve]. Attach the pan to the bottom of the stack. Place a sufficient quantity of the sample in the top sieve so that it is not overloaded, and clamp on the cover. Agitate the set of sieves for several minutes by hand to permit the smaller particles to pass through the upper few sieves (this prevents overloading the sieves). Add the remainder of the sample to the top sieve. Clamp on the cover, and repeat the manual shaking of the sieves.

Place the nest of sieves in a heavy-duty shaker such as the Gilson or Ty-Lab type. Activate the shaker for 10 minutes. Weigh the contents of each sieve as described in Par. 3 (weigh the specimens to the nearest 0.1 g if the mass on an individual sieve is less 500 g and to the nearest 1 g if the mass is greater than 500 g).

For that fraction of the total sample passing the No. 4 sieve, perform a sieve analysis as described in Par. 4a. The percentage by weight retained on the various sieves is computed as follows:

$$\text{Percent retained} = \frac{\text{weight in grams retained on a sieve}}{\text{total weight in grams of oven-dry sample}} \times 100$$

The percentage of material by weight retained on the various sieves is computed for the fraction of the total sample passing the No. 4 sieve as follows:

$$\text{Percent retained} = \frac{\text{weight in grams retained on a sieve}}{\text{weight in grams of oven-dry sample passing No. 4 sieve}} \times \frac{\text{percent passing}}{\text{No. 4 sieve}}$$

5. *Possible Errors.*   Any of the following can produce erroneous results:

a. Total sample size was too small compared with the maximum particle size.

b. Aggregations were not broken into individual particles.

c. Fine particles coating larger ones were not released by slaking.

d. Sieves were not shaken long enough to pass all particles.

e. Portion of sample was lost during processing, sieving, or weighing.

f. Sieve screens were torn or punctured.

g. Nest of sieves was overloaded during the shaking process.

Determination of Atterberg Limits

1. *Definitions.*   The Atterberg limits are water contents which define the limits of consistency for a given soil. The liquid limit defines the upper limit of the plastic range of a given soil; the plastic limit defines the lower limit of the plastic range. The numerical difference between liquid and plastic limits is termed the *plasticity index* of the soil.

2. *Liquid-Limit Test*

a. *Equipment.*   (see Fig. 2.1-28)

(1) *Liquid-Limit Device.*   This device shall conform to the requirements of ASTM Designation D 423-66 (reapproved 1972).

FIG. 2.1-28   Liquid-limit apparatus.

(2) *Grooving Tools.*   The tool shall conform to the dimensions as shown in Fig. 2.1-29 and be of stainless steel.

(3) *Spatula.*   The blade of the spatula shall be 4 to 5 in (101.6 to 127 mm) long and have a width of ½ to ¾ in (12.7 to 19.05 mm).

(4) *Oven.*   The oven shall be of the type having the temperature automatically controlled to 110 ± 5°C.

(5) *Balance.*   The balance shall be sensitive to 0.01 g.

(6) *Sieve.*   The sieve shall be U.S. Standard No. 40.

(7) *Containers.*   The weighing containers shall be rustproof cylinders of lightweight metal (such as aluminum) provided with tight-fitting lids. They shall have a diameter between 1.5 and 2 in (38.1 and 50.8 mm) and a height between ½ and ¾ in (12.7 and 19.05 mm).

(8) *Mixing Dish.*   The dish shall be of porcelain.

(9) *Evaporating Dish.*   The dish shall be of porcelain and have a diameter between 6 and 8 in (152.4 and 203.2 mm).

b. *Procedure.*   The liquid-limit test shall be performed on material finer than the No. 40 sieve sizes. If the field sample contains no particles that would be retained on the No. 40 sieve, weigh out 200 g wet weight of a sample that has not dried below its field water content. Add distilled water to the sample a little at a time until the material is judged to be at a water content slightly higher than its liquid limit. Place the soil-water mixture in an airtight container, and permit it to temper for at least 12 hours.

If the material contains particles retained on the No. 40 sieve, weigh out a sufficient quantity to ensure that approximately 200 g wet weight of minus No. 4 particle sizes will remain after process-

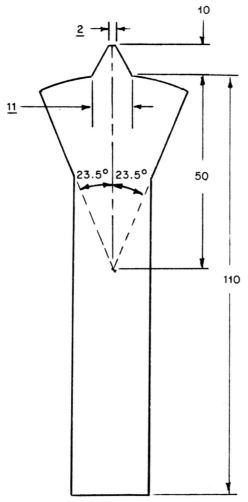

Fig. 2.1-29 Outline of Casagrande grooving tool, shown to full scale. All dimensions are given in millimeters. Underlined dimensions must be exact.

ing. Place the sample to be processed in the evaporating dish, and add enough distilled water to cover the material. Allow the sample to slake for at least 1 hour. Using the fingers, rub any fine-grained (colloidal) material from the surfaces of the larger particles. Stir the mixture gently to put the fines in suspension, and, taking care not to lose any material, pour the water and suspended fines into another evaporating dish. Use care not to pour off any coarse particles. Add clean water to the dish containing the coarse particles, and repeat the decanting process until the overlying water is clear enough so that the coarse particles can be seen on the bottom of the dish.

The excess water must be removed from the slurry of minus No. 40 sieve material until the water content of the sample is slightly higher than the estimated liquid limit. Remove the excess water by any of the following means:

(1) Evaporation, in an oven at a temperature of 110 ± 5°C or under infrared lamps, stirring the sample frequently to prevent formation of dry crusts.

(2) Filtration, using a Buchner funnel [a porcelain funnel-shaped bowl having a perforated plate located above the funnel spout; filter paper is placed on the perforated plate and the soil slurry spread on the filter paper to a depth of about ¼ in (6.35 mm)]. Filtration in such a funnel is accelerated by applying a vacuum to the funnel spout.

(3) Absorption, by spreading the soil slurry to a depth of about ¼ in in a dry plaster-of-paris dish, with two layers of filter paper to separate the soil from contact with the plaster of paris.

Before the sample is placed in the liquid-limit device, the apparatus shall be checked and calibrated. Inspect the device to see that it is in working order and check the following points:

(1) If a groove is worn on the inside of the cup to the extent that it can be felt with the fingers, the cup shall be replaced.

(2) If a worn circle ⅛ in (3.175 mm) or greater in diameter has developed at the point of contact between the base of the cup and the block on which it falls, the cup shall be replaced.

(3) The screws connecting the cup to the cam follower shall be tightened.

(4) Using the handle of the grooving tool as a gauge, adjust the height to which the cup is lifted so that the point on the bottom of the cup that comes in contact with the base of the device is exactly 0.3937 in (1 cm) above the base before the cup is released for free fall. If the adjustment is correct, a slight click will be heard when the cam strikes the cam follower. If the cup is raised off the gauge or no sound is heard, make further adjustments. The cam shall be machined so that the last ⅛ in (3.175 mm) of movement along the cam before the cup drops causes no change in elevation of the cup.

Inspect the grooving tool to determine that the dimensions controlling the groove are as shown in Fig. 2.1-29.

Mix the sample thoroughly with a spatula, and place 50

to 70 g of the material in the cup. Squeeze down and spread the material with a few strokes of the spatula, taking care to prevent the entrapment of air bubbles within the mass. Level the specimen to a depth of approximately 1 cm at the point of maximum thickness, near center of the cup.

Using the grooving tool, divide the soil in the cup so that a clean, sharp groove of the proper dimensions will be formed. Make the groove with as few strokes as possible, always keeping the beveled edge of the tool forward or downward away from the cam follower. During the grooving process, keep the grooving tool perpendicular to the cup at the point of contact.

Using the crank, lift and drop the cup at the rate of approximately two revolutions per second, and count the number of drops until the two halves of the soil pat come in contact at the bottom of the groove along a distance of ½ in (12.7 mm). Record the number of drops required to close the groove along a distance of ½ in.

Remove a slice of soil (about 10 g wet weight) from the portion of the pat which flowed together at the groove, and place in a preweighed container. Determine the water content of this specimen (all weighings shall be to the nearest 0.01 g). Transfer the soil remaining in the cup to the mixing dish, and wash and dry the cup and grooving tool.

Repeat the liquid-limit test for at least two additional trials, using portions of the sample for which the liquid limit has been adjusted by drying. Drying may be accomplished by continued mixing with a spatula while holding the dish under an electric fan. The object of this procedure is to prepare the soil specimen so as to form a consistency such that the number of drops to close the groove will be above and below 25 blows. The soil consistency should be such that the number of drops of the cup shall exceed 15 and be no greater than 35.

Material remaining in the mixing dish shall be preserved in an airtight container for liquid-limit check tests, if necessary, and for the plastic-limit test.

c. *Preparation of the Flow Curve and Determination of the Liquid Limit.* The liquid limit is defined as the water content, expressed as a percentage of the weight of the oven-dry soil, at which the two halves of a soil pat separated by a groove of standard dimensions will close along a distance of ½ in (12.7 mm) under the impact of 25 drops in a standard liquid-limit device.

The value of the liquid limit is determined by plotting a *flow curve* representing the relationship between water content and corresponding number of drops of the liquid-limit cup. The water content is plotted as ordinates on the arithmetic scale and the number of drops as abscissas on the logarithmic scale. The liquid limit is found by drawing the closest-fitting straight line through these plotted points and finding the point of intersection of this flow curve and the 25-drop ordinate, as shown in Fig. 2.1-30.

   d. *One-Point Liquid-Limit Test.* The slope of the flow line is termed the *flow index.* Experience has shown that the flow index is essentially constant for soils which are of similar geologic origin. On this basis, the value of the liquid limit may be determined from the results of a single test by using the following equation:

$$\text{Liquid limit} = w_N \left(\frac{N}{25} \right)^{\tan\beta}$$

where w_N = water content at N drops of the liquid-limit cup
        $\tan \beta$ = slope of the flow line

For many soils, the value of the $\tan \beta$ has been found to be equal to 0.12.

   The equipment and procedure to be used for the one-point method are identical to those used for the standard liquid-limit test except that the number of drops to close the groove in the soil pat shall be determined twice. After the first determination of the number of drops, remove the remaining soil from the cup, remix it thoroughly but quickly, and form a new groove. The number of drops to close the groove on the second determination should be within one drop of the first determination. The

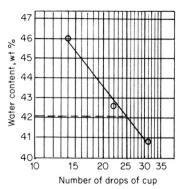

FIG. 2.1-30   Liquid-limit flow curve.

value of the water content of the slice taken from the closed groove shall be determined as in the standard liquid-limit test.

    e. Possible Errors.   Any of the following can produce erroneous results:

      (1) Field sample was not representative.

      (2) Material was air- or oven-dried before testing. (The liquid limit of soils containing organic colloids and of some soils containing inorganic colloids is lower than the standard value when they are tested after they have been dried below their natural water content.)

      (3) Coarse-grained particles were not slaked to remove the fines.

      (4) Liquid-limit device was maladjusted or had worn parts.

      (5) Dynamic resiliency of the base of the liquid-limit device was incorrect. [Resiliency shall be checked by dropping a $5/16$ steel ball from a height of 10 in (254 mm) above the top of base; resiliency is satisfactory if the ball rebounds between 7 and 9 in (177.8 and 228.6 mm).]

      (6) Groove in soil pat was not shaped to the proper dimensions.

      (7) Balance for determining water content was too insensitive.

      (8) Specimen for water-content determinations was not taken from the zone of groove closure.

3. *Plastic-Limit Test*

    a. Equipment

      (1) Surface for rolling the sample shall be a fine-ground *glass plate* or a smooth tabletop on which has been placed a piece of unglazed paper (such as that used for mimeographing).

      (2) *Containers* as used for the liquid-limit test.

      (3) *Balance* as used for the liquid-limit test.

      (4) *Oven* as used for the liquid-limit test.

      (5) *Mixing dish* of porcelain.

    b. Procedure.   From material processed exactly as that used for the liquid-limit test, take a sample of about 50 g wet weight and air-dry until the mass becomes plastic enough to be easily shaped into a ball without sticking to the fingers excessively when the sample is squeezed. From this mass, take a sample of about 8 g and form it into an ellipsoidal-shaped mass. Using the palm of the hand, roll the mass on the glass plate or on unglazed paper lying on a smooth horizontal surface. Apply just sufficient pressure to roll the mass into a thread that is $1/8$ in (3.175 mm) in diameter. When the thread reaches this diameter without crumbling, fold the thread and knead it back into an ellipsoidal-shaped mass again. Repeat the rolling process; continue this kneading, shaping, and rolling process until the sample has dried to the point where the rolled thread breaks into numerous pieces about 1/8 to 3/16 in (3.175 to 4.762 mm) long with a diameter of 1/8 in. Use a rod of 1/8-in diameter as a guide to check thread diameter. Some soils fall apart in many small aggregations of particles; others form an outside tubular layer that starts splitting at both ends.

Place all pieces of the crumbled threads into a preweighed container, and weigh the sample to the nearest 0.01 g. Determine the water content of the crumbled threads. *The plastic limit is this water content.*

c. Possible Errors. Any of the following can produce erroneous results:

(1) Incorrect final thread diameter and lengths.

(2) Uneven rolling surface.

(3) Rolling thread with fingers, causing uneven pressure.

(4) Use of paper on which to roll thread which causes accumulation of lint in sample.

(5) Insufficient kneading of sample before rerolling.

Standard Compaction Test

1. *Definition.* The standard compaction test is a procedure for determining the maximum dry density and optimum water content of a given soil. *Standard compactive effort* is defined as the compactive effort required to compact soil in a given size with a 5.5-lb (2.5-kg) rammer dropped from a height of 12 in (304.8 mm).

2. *Equipment* (see Fig. 2.1-31)

   a. Compaction Molds. Compaction molds shall be of metal and cylindrical in shape and have a detachable collar approximately 2.5 in (63.5 mm) high. The mold-and-collar assembly shall be so constructed that the unit can be fastened firmly to a detachable baseplate. For compacting samples composed of material passing a No. 4 sieve, the mold shall have an inside diameter of 4.0 ± 0.02 in (101.6 ± 0.51 mm), an outside diameter of approximately 4.5 in (114.3 mm), and a height of 4.584 ± 0.005 in (116.43 ± 0.127 mm) to give a capacity of 1/30 ± 0.0003 ft³ (0.0009 ± 0.0000085 m³). For compacting samples composed of material passing a 3/4-in (19.05-mm) sieve, the mold shall have an inside diameter of 6.0 ± 0.026 in

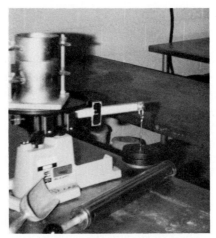

Fig. 2.1-31 Compaction-test apparatus.

(152.4 ± 0.66 mm), an outside diameter of approximately 6.5 in (165.1 mm), and a height of 4.584 ± 0.005 in (116.43 ± 0.127 mm) to give a capacity of 1/13.333 ± 0.0008 ft^3 (0.00212 ± 0.0000226 m^3).

b. Rammer.   The hand rammer shall be of metal and be of the sliding-weight, fixed-head type, having a 2 ± 0.005-in- (50.8 ± 0.127-mm-) diameter circular face and a free-falling weight of 5.5 ± 0.02 lb (2.5 ± 0.009 kg). The rammer shall be equipped with a guide for controlling the height of fall of the sliding weight to 12.0 ± 0.06 in (304.8 ± 1.524 mm).

c. Balances.   A balance of at least 25-lb (11.34-kg) capacity sensitive to 0.01 lb (0.0045 kg) and a balance of 1000-g capacity sensitive to 0.1 g.

d. Oven.   The oven shall be of the type having the temperature automatically controlled to 110 ± 5°C.

e. Weighing Containers.   Containers shall be as in the water-content test.

f. Curing Containers.   Containers shall be corrosion-resistant gallon cans (1 gal = 0.00378 m^3) or plastic buckets with airtight covers.

g. Straightedge.   The straightedge shall be of steel, 12 in (304.8 mm) long, and have one beveled edge.

h. Mixing Tools.   Equipment for mixing samples shall be mixing pans of appropriate capacity, spoon, trowel, and spatula or a suitable mechanical device for mixing the sample of soil with water.

2. *Procedure*

a. *Sample Preparation.* For material to be tested by using the 4-in-(101.6-mm-) diameter mold, a representative field sample of at least 30 lb (13.6 kg) is required. If the sample is very wet when received from the field, dry it until it becomes friable under a trowel. Drying may be effected in air or by use of drying apparatus such that the temperature of the sample does not exceed 60°C (140°F). Break up the aggregations, but do not reduce the size of the individual particles. Screen the sample through the No. 4 sieve, and discard the coarse material retained on this sieve if the dry weight of the coarse material is less than 10 percent by dry weight of the total sample. If greater than 10 percent by dry weight of coarse particles is in the total sample, do not compact the sample in the 4-in diameter mold. Take a representative sample from the material passing the No. 4 sieve, and determine its water content.

From the processed sample, weigh a quantity of air-dry soil equivalent to at least 6 lb (2.7 kg) of oven-dry soil (this is done by estimating the water content of the air-dry material). Thoroughly mix the sample with sufficient water to produce a water content 4 to 6 percentage points below the estimated optimum water content. At this water content soil will ball noticeably if plastic. Store the sample for 12 to 16 hours to permit it to absorb the water if the material is plastic (most nonplastic soils do not require this curing period and may be compacted immediately). Prepare four additional batches in the same manner, adding water to the air-dry material to produce a sample having a water content about 2 percentage points below the optimum water content, a sample having a water content at the optimum water content, another at 2 percentage points wetter than the optimum, and the last at 4 percentage points wetter than the optimum. Store these samples in airtight containers before compacting.

b. *Compaction.* Weigh the compaction mold to the nearest 0.01 lb (0.0045 kg), and record the weight. Attach the mold, with collar, to the baseplate, and place the mold on a flat, rigid foundation, such as provided by a cylinder or cube of concrete weighing not less than 200 lb (90.7 kg).

Add to the mold a quantity of the prepared soil sufficient to give a compacted depth of about 1.5 in (38.1 mm; the before-compaction depth will vary depending on the soil type and water content). Compact the layer by using 25 uniformly distributed blows of the rammer, allowing the rammer to fall freely and vertically from a height of 12 in (304.8 mm). Repeat the procedure for the second and third layer to give a total compacted sample height no greater than 5 in (127 mm). Carefully remove the extension collar without shearing off the soil to a depth below the top of the mold. Using the straightedge, trim the compacted soil even with the top of the mold. Detach the mold from the baseplate, and weigh the mold and compacted soil to the nearest 0.01 lb (0.0045 kg). Record this weight.

Extrude or carve the sample from the mold and determine the water content of a 500-g specimen taken from the center of the sample.

c. Computations.   The basic formulas are given. Table 2.1-6 gives an illustrative set of computations.

$$\frac{\text{Dry weight of}}{\text{compacted specimen}} = \frac{\text{wet weight of compacted specimen}}{1 + \dfrac{\text{water content}}{100}}$$

The wet weight of the compacted specimen is equal to the wet weight plus the mold weight minus the weight of the mold.

$$\text{Dry density (lb/ft}^2) = \frac{\text{dry weight of compacted specimen (lb)}}{\text{volume of compaction mold (ft}^3)}$$

When the field sample contains particles up to $\frac{3}{4}$ in (19.05 mm), the standard compaction test shall be performed by using the 6-in- (152.4-mm-) inside-diameter mold. Sample preparation shall be the same as that for material passing the No. 4 sieve except that the representative sample shall weigh approximately 12 lb (5.4 kg). Compaction shall be the same as for the minus No. 4 sieve material except that the sample shall be compacted in five equal layers with

TABLE 2.1-6   Illustrative Set of Computations for Standard Compaction Test*

Test no.	Wet weight of compacted soil, lb	Water content %	Dry weight of compacted soil, lb	Volume of mold, ft³	Dry density of compacted soil, lb/ft³
1	3.66	15.9	3.26	0.0333	98.2
2	3.82	18.1	3.33	0.0333	100.1
3	4.06	20.2	3.36	0.0333	102.0
4	4.05	22.0	3.31	0.0333	99.1
5	3.67	24.3	3.20	0.0333	96.0

*1 lb = 0.4356 kg; 1 ft³ = 0.02832 m³; 1 lb/ft³ = 16.02 kg/m³.

each layer being compacted by 56 uniform blows from the rammer. The after-compaction water content of each sample shall be
determined by using a specimen weighing no less than 1000 g.

d. *Presentation of Results.*   The test results shall be presented in the
form of a compaction curve; the dry densities are plotted as ordinates and the corresponding water contents as abscissas. The water
content corresponding to the peak of the curve is the optimum
water content, and the dry density corresponding to the optimum
water content is the maximum dry density for the given soil.

4. *Possible Errors.*   Any of the following can produce erroneous results:

a. Improper sample preparation (neglecting to break up aggregations and not allowing sufficient time for added water to temper the
soil).

b. Reusing previously compacted material from other tests.

c. Improper foundation on which to compact sample.

d. Improper techniques in using the rammer.

e. Using incorrect mold volume and weight.

f. Allowing too much compacted material to extend above the mold
top.

g. Specimen for water-content determination too small.

Determination of Minimum Density of Cohesionless Particles

1. *Definition.*   The minimum dry density of a cohesionless material such
as sand is the loosest state that the material can attain in the static or
in-place condition. The laboratory procedure used to simulate this
loose state is called the *minimum-density test.*

2. *Equipment*

a. *Measuring Cylinders.*   The cylinders or molds in which to test the
samples shall be of metal (preferably of cast-aluminum alloy for
lightness) and have the dimensions shown in Table 2.1-7. The
volume of each container shall be determined to the nearest 0.01
ft^3 (0.00028 m^3) by dividing the weight of water at 21°C required
to fill the cylinder by the unit weight of water at that temperature.

b. *Pouring Container.*   The pouring container shall be a metal cylinder approximately 6 in (152.4 mm) in diameter and 12 in (304.8
mm) high fitted with two detachable funnels, one having a spout
diameter of ½ in (12.7 mm) and the other having a spout diameter
of 1 in (25.4 mm).

TABLE 2.1-7 Cylinder or Mold Dimensions*

Volume, ft^3	Inside dimensions		Thickness of sides and bottom, in
	Diameter, in	Height, in	
0.1	6.000	6.112	3/8
0.5	11.000	9.092	3/8

*1 ft^3 = 0.02832 m^3; 1 in = 25.4 mm.

c. *Weighing Device.* The weighing scale shall be of the platform type and have a capacity of 100 lb (45.36 kg) and a sensitivity of 0.1 lb (0.0045 kg).

d. *Sample Splitter.* The splitter shall be as in the grain-size-distribution test.

e. *Straightedge.* The straightedge shall be of steel, 12 in (304.8 mm) long, and have one beveled edge.

3. *Sample Preparation.* Air-dry a representative sample and pass it through a sample splitter. The sample shall then be oven-dried and allowed to cool in an airtight container. For material passing the No. 4 sieve, approximately 15 lb (6.8 kg) of material is required for the test; for material containing particle sizes up to ⅜ in (9.525 mm), approximately 130 lb (58.9 kg) of material is required.

4. *Procedure.* Determine the weight of the test mold to the nearest 0.1 lb (0.0045 kg) and the volume to the nearest 0.001 ft^3 (0.00028m^3), and record these values. Fill the pouring container with the test sample and attach the funnel [use the ½-in (12.7-mm) spout for minus No. 4 material and the 1-in (25.4 mm spout for minus ⅜-in (9.525-mm) material]. Pour the sample into the measuring mold with a steady flow of material from the spout, moving the spout in a spiral path from the edge to the center of the mold. Raise the spout during the pouring process to maintain a free fall of 1 in (25.4 mm) between the spout and the top of the sample in the mold. Continue pouring the material until it rises approximately ¼ in (6.35 mm) above the top of the mold over the entire surface. Using the straightedge, carefully strike off the excess material until the soil surface is level with the top of the mold. At no time during the pouring and trimming process shall the mold or its contents be jarred or vibrated.

Weigh the mold and sample, and record the value. Repeat the test using the same sample. If the weight of the samples in both tests agrees within 1 percent, the test is complete. If not, perform addtional tests.

5. *Computations*

$$\text{Minimum dry density} \atop (\text{lb/ft}^3) = \frac{(\text{weight of specimen} + \text{mold}) - (\text{mold weight})}{\text{volume of mold}}$$

where weights are in pounds and volume is in cubic feet (1 lb = 0.4536 kg; 1 ft^3 = 0.0283 m^3).

6. *Possible Errors.* Any of the following can produce erroneous results:

  a. Neglecting to maintain a free fall of 1 in (25.4 mm) during pouring.

  b. Neglecting to pour material using a spiral pattern.

  c. Jarring or vibrating the sample at any time before final weighing.

Determination of Maximum Density of Cohesionless Particles

1. *Definition.* The maximum dry density of a cohesionless material such as sand is the densest state that the material can attain without crushing the particles. The laboratory procedure used to simulate this dense state is called the *maximum-density test*.

2. *Equipment*

  a. *Measuring Cylinders.* The cylinders or molds in which to test the samples shall be as for the minimum-density test.

  b. *Pouring Container.* The pouring container shall be as for the minimum-density test.

  c. *Weighing Device.* The weighing scale shall be as for the minimum-density test.

  d. *Sample Splitter.* The splitter shall be as in the grain-size-distribution test.

  e. *Vibratory Table.* The vibratory table shall be of the seminoiseless type with a 30-in by 30-in (762- by 762-mm) deck, have a net weight of at least 100 lb (45.36 kg), and be capable of delivering a frequency of 3600 vibrations per minute. The vibrator amplitudes shall vary from 0 to 0.015 in (0.381 mm) under a 250-lb (113.4-kg) load, and the table shall have an electrical system suitable for use with 230-V alternating current.

  f. *Height-Change-Measuring Device.* The mold shall be fitted with a dial holder and a collar: the dial indicator shall have 0.001-in (0.0254-mm) gradations and a 2-in (50.8 mm) range.

  g. *Calibration Bar.* The metal bar shall be 3 in by 12 in (76.2 mm by 304.8 mm) and have a thickness of ⅛ in (3.175 mm).

h. *Straightedge.* The straightedge shall be as for the minimum-density test.

i. *Surcharge Assembly.* The assembly shall consist of a surcharge weight capable of delivering to the top of the sample a pressure of 2 psi (13.79 kPa) and a baseplate with a hoisting handle. The surcharge guide sleeve shall have a clamping device.

j. *Hoist.* The surcharge hoist shall have a capacity of 300 lb (136 kg).

3. *Sample Preparation.* The test sample shall be prepared in the identical manner used for the minimum-density test.

4. *Procedure.* Determine the weight of the test mold to the nearest 0.1 lb (0.045 kg) and the volume to the nearest 0.001 ft^3 (0.000028 m^3), and record these values. Measure the thickness of the calibration bar and the surcharge baseplate. Seat the calibration bar across the top of the test mold. Insert the dial-indicator holder into the brackets so that the dial-indicator stem rests on the calibration bar, and obtain a dial reading. Then transfer the dial holder to the opposite side of the mold, set it in the brackets, and obtain a second dial reading with the dial stem resting on the calibration bar. The initial dial reading before compaction is computed by adding the average of these two readings to the thickness of the calibration bar and subtracting the surcharge baseplate thickness.

Using the same procedure as for the minimum-density test, fill the mold with the test specimen and attach the mold to the vibratory-table deck. Clamp the guide sleeve to the mold with the inside surface of the sleeve aligned with the inside surface of the mold. Lower the surcharge baseplate onto the sample surface, and remove the hoisting handle. Using the hoist, lower the surcharge weight onto the surcharge baseplate.

Set the vibratory-table amplitude to a rheostat reading that will deliver an amplitude of 0.015 in (0.381 mm). Vibrate the mold for 8 minutes. Remove the surcharge weight and guide sleeve, and obtain dial readings on opposite sides of the surcharge baseplate. Weigh the mold and sample to the nearest 0.01 lb (0.0045 kg). Subtract the mold weight from this value to obtain the dry weight of the sample.

5. *Computations.* The change in height of the sample due to vibration is equal to the difference in dial readings before and after vibration. The change in volume of the sample due to vibration is equal to the change in height times the area of the sample.

$$\text{Maximum dry density (lb/ft}^3\text{)} = \frac{\text{dry weight of sample}}{(\text{initial volume of sample}) - (\text{change in volume})}$$

where weight is in pounds and volume is in cubic feet (1 lb = 0.4536 kg; 1 ft^3 = 0.0283m^3).

6. *Possible Errors.*   Any of the following can produce erroneous results:

   a. Incorrect determination of change in sample height due to vibration.

   b. Misalignment of guide sleeve, causing binding of the surcharge.

Determination of In-Place Density of Soil: Sand-Displacement Method

1. *Definition.*   The sand-displacement method for determining in-place density consists of digging a sample of the material to be tested, determining the volume of the hole from which the sample was removed, and determining the dry weight of the sample.

2. *Equipment* (see Figs. 2.1-32 and 2.1-33)

   a. *Sand-Density Cone and Cylinder.*   The assembly shall consist of a glass or Plexiglass cylinder mounted on a detachable double cone. The surfaces of each cone shall have a slope of 45° and be joined at their apexes by a nondisplacement valve having an inside diameter of ¾ in (19.05 mm).

   b. *Cone-Bearing Plate.*   The bearing plate on which to seat the cone shall be of noncorrosive metal, 10 in by 10 in by ⅜ in (254 mm by

FIG. 2.1-32   Excavating a hole in fill during the determination of in-place unit weight by using the sand-cone method.

FIG. 2.1-33 Determining in-place unit weight by using the sand-cone method.

254 mm by 9.525 mm), and be provided with a recessed hole having the same inside diameter as the cone.

c. *Calibration Sand.* The sand used to determine the volume of the hole shall be composed of clean, hard well-rounded quartz particles that will pass a No. 20 sieve and be retained on a No. 40 sieve.

d. *Field Sample Containers.* The sample container shall be corrosion-resistant, have a capacity of 1 gal (0.045 m^3), and be provided with an airtight lid.

e. *Digging Tools.* The tools for excavating the sample shall include knives, spatulas, large spoons, chisels, and screwdrivers.

f. *Paintbrush.* The brush shall be 2 to 3 in (50.8 to 76.2 mm) wide.

g. *Balances.* The field balance shall have a capacity of 20,000 g and a sensitivity of 1 g. The balance for determining water content shall have a capacity of 500 g and a sensitivity of 0.1 g.

h. *Oven.* The oven shall be of the type having the temperature automatically controlled to 110 ± 5°C.

3. *Sand Calibration.* Determine the loose density of the special sand before beginning the in-place-density test by pouring the oven-dry sand into the double cone attached to the cylinder until the cylinder and one cone are filled above the cutoff valve. During the pouring process, maintain the sand level in the upper cone and take extreme care not to jar or vibrate the cone or cylinder until these are full of sand

and the valve closed. When the valve is closed, pour off the excess sand. Weigh the cone, cylinder, and sand to the nearest gram. Detach the double cone from the cylinder, and remove the sand.

Again attach the cone tightly to the cylinder, and open the valve. Pour water having a temperature of 20°C into the apparatus until the cylinder, bottom cone, and valve are filled (permit water to rise a few inches into the upper cone), and close the cutoff valve. Pour off the excess water, dry the cone with a cloth, and weigh the water-filled apparatus to the nearest gram. To obtain the weight of the water required to fill the cylinder, one cone, and the valve, subtract the weight of the empty cylinder and cones from the weight of the apparatus filled to the valve with water. The weight of water in grams is equal to the volume of water in cubic centimeters.

The following are illustrative computations for obtaining sand density:

a. Weight of apparatus filled with sand   12,854 g

b. Weight of apparatus empty   4,294 g

c. Weight of sand to fill apparatus   8,560 g (18.87 lb)

d. Weight of water to fill apparatus   5,731 g

e. Volume of water to fill apparatus   5,731 cm^3 (0.2023 ft^3)

f. Loose density of sand $\dfrac{18.87 \text{ lb}}{0.2023 \text{ ft}^3} = 93.3$ lb/ft^3 (1494.5 kg/m^3)

4. *Surface Calibration.* During the field density test, the cylinder and double cone are placed on the bearing or baseplate, which rests on level ground. The volume of the space between the surface of the cone and the ground surface must be determined. To do this, fill the cylinder and cone to the valve with the calibrated sand and close the valve. Place the baseplate on a sheet of glass, and insert the cone of the apparatus into the recessed hole of the baseplate. Open the valve, and allow the sand to fill the cone and the space between the baseplate and the surface of the glass. Close the valve, and weigh the apparatus and the sand remaining in it to the nearest gram. The weight of sand required to fill the cone and baseplate is equal to the weight of the sand-filled apparatus minus the weight of the apparatus and sand remaining after pouring. Record this surface-calibration weight for use later in the in-place-density test.

5. *Procedure.* The surface of the material to be tested shall be carefully excavated to a depth of several inches to remove irregularities caused by compaction equipment. The surface shall be so leveled that when the baseplate is seated on it no voids will exist between the surface and

the bottom of the plate. Once the baseplate has been seated firmly and horizontally, it shall not be moved until completion of the test. The recessed hole in the baseplate shall be as listed in Table 2.1-8.

Weigh the sample container and lid to the nearest gram (protect the balance from wind vibration by using a windshield surrounding three sides of it). Using digging tools such as spoons, spatulas, and knives, carefully dig out a sample within the limits of the hole in the baseplate. The upper perimeter of the hole shall be about ⅛ in (3.175 mm) inside the baseplate hole; the depth of the hole shall be no less than its diameter. Place all material removed from the hole into the sample container. All loose particles shall be removed from the hole, and the sidewalls and bottom shall be kept as free as possible of pockets and obtrusions. When all material has been removed from the hole, cap the lid tightly on the sample container and weigh the wet sample and container to the nearest gram.

Select a sand-cone device in accordance with Table 2.1-8. Fill the cylinder and cone to the valve, close the valve, remove the excess sand, and weigh the apparatus filled with sand to the nearest gram. Place the cone of the apparatus into the baseplate hole, and observe that there are no vibrations in the area due to construction equipment. Carefully open the valve completely, and allow sand to fill the hole and the cone. Without jarring or shaking the apparatus, close the valve and weigh the apparatus and sand remaining in it to the nearest gram. Determine the water content of the field sample.

6. *Computations.* The wet density of the sample in place is equal to the wet weight of the material removed from the hole divided by the volume of the hole. The dry density in place is computed as follows:

$$\text{In-place dry density} = \frac{\text{in-place wet density}}{1 + \dfrac{\text{water content}}{100}}$$

TABLE 2.1-8   Sand-Cone Dimensions*

Maximum particle size in test hole, in	Diameter of cone and baseplate hole, in	Diameter of cylinder, in	Height of cylinder, in
³⁄₁₆	7	7	10
¾	11	11	10
1.5	12	12	11

*1 in = 25.4 mm.

The following computations illustrate the method for determining the in-place dry density:

a. *Determination of Volume of Hole from Which Sample Is Taken*

Weight of cone and cylinder filled with sand	10,973 g
Weight of cone, cylinder, and sand after pour	7,163 g
Weight of sand after pour	3,810 g
Weight of sand to fill cone and baseplate	1,881 g
Weight of sand to fill hole	1,929 g (4.25 lb)

$$\text{Volume of hole} = \frac{\text{Weight of sand to fill hole}}{\text{calibrated density of sand}} = \frac{4.25 \text{ lb}}{93.2 \text{ lb/ft}^3} = 0.046 \text{ ft}^3$$

1 lb = 0.4536 kg; 1 lb/ft^3 = 16.02 kg/m^3; 1 ft^3 = 0.0283 m^3.

b. *Determination of In-Place Dry Density and Water Content*

Wet weight of sample plus tare (weighing container)	3080 g
Dry weight of sample plus tare	2916 g
Weight of tare	273 g
Weight of water	164 g
Dry weight of sample	2643 g (5.83 lb)
Water content	6.2%
Dry density	128.1 lb/ft^3

In these computations it has been assumed that the entire field sample is used to determine the water content; this procedure is necessary when the sample contains particles larger then ³⁄₁₆ in (9.525 mm).

7. *Possible Errors.*   Any of the following can produce erroneous results:

   a. Wrong type and gradation of calibration sand.

   b. Incorrect calibration of sand.

   c. Infrequent calibration of sand. Several calibrations are made to determine sand density for each 100-lb (45.36-kg) bag of sand used.

   d. Calibrated sand not dry during field test.

   e. Sand-cone apparatus jarred or vibrated as sand is poured into hole during field test.

   f. Loss of portion of sample during transfer from hole to container.

   g. Ground near hole disturbed during test. A platform, such as a wooden plank, should be used to reduce pressure from the weight of the technician.

   h. Sample permitted to dry partially before water content has been determined.

i. Loose material left in hole.

j. Volume of hole too small.

k. Baseplate not seated on ground surface properly.

UNIFIED SOIL-CLASSIFICATION SYSTEM

1. *General.*   Soils exist in an almost infinite variety and must be classified in a systematic manner to provide a general concept of their engineering characteristics for design and construction purposes. During construction, soil classification is a key means of evaluating and controlling the quality of embankment materials and of helping to ensure that the materials are placed in specified zones.

2. *The Classification System.*   The most widely used classification system is the unified classification system, a modification of the airfield classification system developed by Dr. A. Casagrande. The unified soil-classification system is based on those characteristics of the soil which indicate how it will behave as a construction material. Soils can be classified if the following is known: (*a*) the percentage by weight of gravel, sand, and fines (silt and clay); (*b*) the shape of the grain-size-distribution curve; and (*c*) the plasticity of the fine-grained material, that is, the liquid and plastic limits.

In the united system, the material is given a name and a letter symbol. The letter symbol consists of two letters, written as capitals, of which the first letter designates the primary name of the material and the second letter denotes a further description of the same material. For example, the symbol SC denotes *clayey sand*, a soil that is composed predominantly of sand with a lesser percentage of clay particles.

All soils are divided into three major groups: coarse-grained, fine-grained, and highly organic.

a. *Coarse-Grained Soils.*   These soils include gravels, sands, and all mixtures of materials predominantly of gravels and sands regardless of other components. The letter G denotes gravel, and the letter S denotes sand. Gravel is material that ranges between 3 in (76.2 mm) in diameter and the No. 4 sieve size. Sand is material that ranges between the No. 4 sieve size and the No. 200 sieve size. In a mixture of sand and gravel, the primary name denotes the predominant fraction, and the minor fraction is used as an adjective (for example, sandy gravel).

Both gravelly and sandy materials are each subdivided into four groups: well-graded (W), poorly graded (P), dirty with plastic fines

(C), and dirty with nonplastic silty fines (M). These *fines* are particles that pass the No. 200 sieve. To distinguish between well-graded and poorly graded material, the coefficient of uniformity, C_U, is computed from data taken from the grain-size-distribution curve. If C_U is greater than 4, gravels are well graded and given the symbol GW (for *well-graded gravel*). If C_U is greater than 6, sands are well graded (that is, SW).

The symbol C is used as a modifier for those sands and gravels containing plastic fines with plasticity indices greater than 7 and plotting above the A line on a plasticity chart (a chart relating liquid limit and plasticity index). The fines must constitute more than 12 percent by weight of the total sample.

The symbol M is used as a modifier for those sands and gravels containing nonplastic fines (silty fines with plasticity indices less than 4 or plotting below the A line, when these fines constitute more than 12 percent by weight of the total sample).

Following these rules, a gravelly material may be designated GW, GP, GM, or GC; sandy soils may be designated SW, SP, SM, or SC.

b. *Fine-Grained Soils.* These soils are divided into three groups: inorganic silts (M), inorganic clays (C), and organic silts or clays (O). The groups are further divided into soils having liquid limits lower than 50 percent (symbol L) and those having liquid limits higher than 50 percent (symbol H). Thus, soils composed of inorganic silts having liquid limits below 50 percent have the symbol ML. Soils composed of inorganic silts having liquid limits above 50 percent have the symbol MH. All soils in the M group plot below the A line on the plasticity chart.

The soils in the CL group include lean clays and sandy clays; those in the CH group include fat clays, gumbo clays, and most volcanic clays. All soils in the C group plot above the A line on the plasticity chart.

The organic soils (symbol O) are distinguished from the inorganic soils (symbols M and C) by their characteristic odor and dark color.

c. *Highly Organic Material.* The third major group in the classification system is designated by the symbol Pt, an abbreviation for peat, because this is a typical material in the group. Highly organic soils are characterized by decayed or partially decayed particles of leaves, sticks, grass, and other vegetable matter which impart to the mass a fibrous texture, a dark-brown or black color, and a distinct organic odor, particularly in the presence of heat.

d. *Classification System Flowchart and Plasticity Chart.* While the classification system is relatively complex, all soils can be placed in a specific category and assigned an identifying symbol as shown on the flowchart (Fig. 2.1-34), used in conjunction with the plasticity chart (Fig. 2.1-35).

SOIL IDENTIFICATION PROCEDURES

In addition to the unified soil-classification system, which requires laboratory test data to be implemented, field identification methods have been developed for determining certain soil characteristics.

1. *Dilatancy Test.* Silts may be distinguished from clays by a simple test termed the *dilatancy test.* From a sample weighing about 25 g (a quantity that will fit in the palm of the hand) remove all particles larger than about $1/32$ in (0.794 mm). Add water (or dry) until the sample has the consistency of soft putty. Place the soil pat in the open palm of one hand and shake the hand horizontally, striking it vigorously against the other hand about 6 or 8 times. If water appears on the surface of the soil pat and the pat changes to a livery consistency and becomes glossy, the soil is a silt. For silty soils, when the hand containing the pat is partially closed, the water and glossy appearance disappear, the pat stiffens, and, finally, it cracks or crumbles. Plastic clays will react very slowly to the appearance of water on the surface of the pat during the shaking test; for highly plastic clays, water will not appear at all on the surface of the pat.

2. *Toughness Test.* This test is a measure of soil consistency near its plastic limit. Prepare a sample as for the dilatancy test. Using a smooth surface, such as a clipboard, roll the specimen by hand into a thread about $1/8$ in (3.175 mm) in diameter. Fold the thread, and reroll it. Keep repeating this process. During this manipulation the water content is reduced gradually; the sample stiffens, finally loses its plasticity, and crumbles when it reaches its plastic limit. After the thread crumbles, lump the pieces together and apply a slight kneading action with the fingers until the lump crumbles again.

The tougher the thread near its plastic limit and the stiffer the lump when it finally crumbles, the more potent is the colloidal-clay fraction in the soil. Weakness of the thread at its plastic limit and quick loss of coherence of the soil lump below the plastic limit indicate a clay of low plasticity. Highly organic clays have a very weak and spongy feel at the plastic limit. Nonplastic soils cannot be rolled into a thread of $1/8$-in (3.175-mm) diameter at any water content.

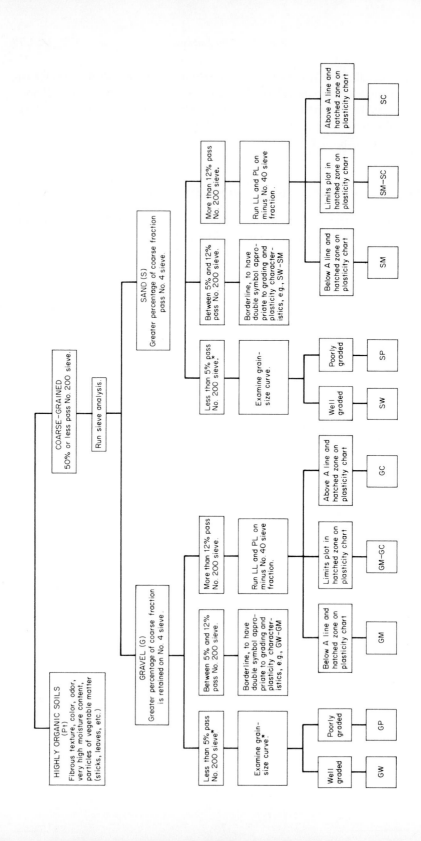

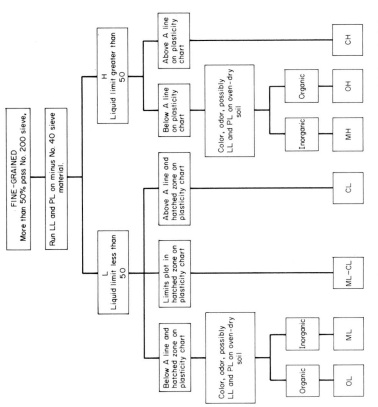

FIG. 2.1-34 Unified soil-classification system. If fines interfere with free-draining properties, use double symbol such as GW-GM, etc.

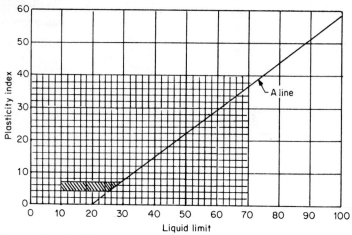

Fig. 2.1-35   Plasticity chart.

3. *Other Classification Aids.*   When sands and gravels contain soil particles finer than the No. 200 sieve sizes, they are termed *dirty*. Such sands and gravels will leave a dirt stain on a wet palm.

If a sample is molded into a ½-in (12.7-mm) cube and oven-dried, its crushing strength may be used as a measure of its plasticity. If the oven-dry cube is very easily crushed with the fingers, it is nonplastic or has very little plasticity; if the cube is difficult to crush with the fingers, the soil has a medium plasticity (its plasticity index ranges between 10 and 25). A dried cube of highly plastic soil cannot be crushed with the fingers.

If a 25-g sample is shaken thoroughly in a 200-cm^3 graduated cylinder, sand particles will settle to the bottom of the cylinder within seconds; silt particles will settle within minutes; and colloidal particles of clay will stay in suspension in the water for hours or days.

INSPECTOR'S CHECKLIST

  1. Training

    a. Attend formal courses.

    b. Study test procedures.

    c. Study plans and specifications.

  2. Field laboratory

    a. Set up location.

b. Power (ac or dc), lighting, water supply, sufficient space, shelves, benches, and cabinets.

c. Mobile laboratory (truck or van).

d. Testing equipment (spare parts, calibration).

3. Embankment foundation and abutments

   a. Clearing, grubbing, and stripping.

   b. Care of water.

   c. Spoil or debris area.

   d. Proof rolling.

   e. Inspection trench.

4. Rock foundation and abutments

   a. Remove loose rock.

   b. Remove semidetached rock.

   c. Height of vertical faces.

   d. Dental treatment.

   e. Inspection by geotechnical staff.

5. Cutoffs

   a. Check dimensions.

   b. Stability of side slopes.

   c. Dewatering.

   d. Surface erosion.

   e. Material at base of trench.

6. Excavaton

   a. Type of equipment.

   b. Haul roads.

   c. Hauling equipment.

7. Borrow area

   a. Evaluation and comparison with design data.

   b. Depth to rock and water table.

   c. Dry wet borrow areas; treat dry borrow areas.

   d. Clearing, stripping, and grubbing.

8. Compaction equipment

   a. Type and adequacy.

      (1) Sheepsfoot pressure.

   (2) Tire pressure.
   b. Quantity.
9. Compaction control
   a. Test frequency and location (control charts).
   b. Review test types required.
   c. Test report forms and worksheets.
   d. Review plans and specifications.
      (1) Material classification, gradation, degree of compaction, and limits of placement water content.
      (2) Number of passes, loose-lift thickness, and speed of compaction equipment.
      (3) Observe roller action.
      (4) Reworking and retesting of failed areas.
      (5) Contamination of pervious-fill zones.
      (6) Removal of boulders in earth-rock fill.
      (7) Compaction after freezing temperatures.
      (8) Hand tamping in confined areas.
      (9) Sealing surface against rain.
10. Riprap
   a. Gradation and quality.
   b. Placement methods.
   c. Proper thickness.
   d. Embankment slope treatment (proper compaction).
   e. Bedding layer.
   f. Nests of fines.
   g. Frequency of tests.
11. Control records
   a. Frequency and type (confer with project engineer).
   b. Photographic records.
12. General
   a. Conferences with design staff and geotechnical engineers.
   b. Understanding with contractor.
   c. Handling changed conditions.
   d. Size and authority of inspection staff.

Foundations

Robert E. White, P.E.
Consultant
Larchmont, New York

Formerly

President
Spencer, White & Prentis, Inc.
Manager, Underpinning and Shoring of the White House

As with all phases of construction, the primary purpose of field inspection of foundations is to assure that the fieldwork puts into their proper places the various elements foreseen by the design engineer in the plans and specifications. However, with foundations one is dealing also with natural materials formed by geological processes, which are quite heterogeneous compared with construction materials. The geological conditions at the site will be disclosed before work commences only by borings, which pass through a tiny fraction of the soil mass that is to be dealt with later in actual construction. Furthermore, recovery, identification, and classification of soil samples are subject to interpretation and human error.

Take groundwater as an example. An eminent engineer once said that the problems of coping with soils are those of coping with water. But water levels are subject to fluctuation owing to floods, droughts, rainfall, leaky water mains and sewers, pumping from nearby wells, and perhaps other construction jobs. And water can make some soils act in a radically different manner from how they act in a dry state.

Therefore, the risk of the unexpected is always present in foundation construction, and the field inspector must always be on the lookout for changed conditions which might call for revisions of design and specifications and contract procedures, including time schedules and being a partner, as it were, of the design engineer. The inspector must bring these changed conditions, as soon as possible, to the attention of the design engineer in a direct, positive way, not merely by a copy of a routine daily report. The author recalls an instance in which a hand-auger boring was taken to a depth of 5 to 10 ft (1.5 to 3 m) below the bottom of each spread footing for an office building. In a number of cases, the auger passed through a layer of peat (the building was built on soil that was still compressible). The inspector observed this and dutifully reported it on the standard form used for reporting on each footing. But the report was received along with a welter of other job reports, and its significance was overlooked until cracks appeared in the superstructure months later. Expensive underpinning was then required.

SPREAD FOOTINGS AND MATS

These are by far the commonest type of foundation for all kinds of structures. They are also the simplest and the oldest. They support superstructure loads by spreading these loads over a relatively large area of suitable ground. When the loads are heavy, as with tall buildings, or are closely spaced, individual footings may run together or overlap; in these cases, a single heavy slab, called a *mat* or *raft*, supports the multitude of columns and transmits their loads to the load-bearing soil or rock at the underside of the slab. Sometimes, this is called in lay language, a "floating" foundation. Nowadays, the spread footing (or mat) is almost always made of reinforced concrete.

Check the Excavation. First among the inspector's duties, then, is to see that the excavation properly exposes the soil upon which the footings are to rest. This is not difficult when one is dealing with sandy, well-drained soils, but it may be an altogether different matter when the bearing soil is clayey with a high moisture content or even a dry clay if it is being dug in rainy weather.

The inspector must see to it that all clay that has been made spongy or softer than in its natural state is removed. This is necessary because such disturbed soil has a diminished capacity to bear superimposed loads without settlement. Causes of this kind of disturbances are workers trampling the area when they are excavating it; bulldozers or trucks running over foundation-bearing soils; and rainwater or other water coming to the area which aggravates the condition and which, if possible, should be diverted. Water is usually diverted by some combination of ditches, sumps, and pumps. In sandy or other "drainable" soils, the groundwater, if present above subgrade, is lowered to below subgrade by means of deep wells, well-point systems, or special predrainage sumps.

If earth at the foundation level is inadvertently (or purposefully for some reason) excavated below subgrade, it is usually difficult to replace with compacted earth. In the usual case, specifications call for the over-excavated earth to be replaced with lean concrete (concrete of low cement content), and the inspector must be alert to see that this is done.

Check Placement of Reinforced Concrete. The next major step in the building of a spread footing or mat is placement of the reinforced concrete. This phase of the process begins with the placing of reinforcing bars. As this operation is largely carried out by hand, the worker must again walk over the soil and perhaps disturb it and diminish its bearing capacity to the point where it not only cannot carry the design loads from the superstructure but also cannot carry the "chairs" holding the reinforcing rods at the proper design distance [usually 2 to 4 in (50.8 to 101.6 mm)] above the underside of the concrete of the spread footing or mat. In this case, the common procedure is to call for the installation of a *mud mat.*

Mud Mats. A mud mat is a thin slab of lean, unreinforced concrete [4 to 6 in (101.6 to 152.4 mm) thick] that is poured over the area of the bearing soil after it has been exposed. The mud mat provides a relatively dry, clean area for walking, supporting the reinforcing chairs and bars, and resting formwork if required.

Gravel and Drains.   In some cases, the spread footing, or mat, rests on a pervious soil and water keeps seeping into the excavation. If there is an appreciable amount of seepage, some of the cement may be washed out of the concrete, which is thereby weakened. To prevent this washing-out process, it is advisable to place a layer of gravel directly beneath the subgrade of the spread footing. In this gravel layer drainage pipes are placed and arranged so as to lead into a sump from which the water may be pumped and harmlessly disposed of. Since a drainage pipe is 3 to 4 in (76.2 to 101.6 mm) in diameter as a minimum, the gravel layer must be 6 or 8 in (152.4 or 203.2 mm) thick, that is, somewhat thicker than the drainage pipe. Satisfactory drainage pipes are made of various materials: perforated fiber, farm tiles (which are laid with open joints), clay, and porous concrete (a concrete with all or most of the fine aggregate omitted).

Some clays, especially in the southwestern United States, are subject to swelling. In such cases, it is best not to delay placing the concrete in the footing because the swelling increases as the clay is exposed to the atmosphere.

Another problem soil is loess, a fine, sandy windblown deposit found over wide areas of the south and southwest of the United States. Loess, if wetted, has a strong tendency to collapse and lose its bearing capacity, so precautions must be taken against wetting.

Formwork.   It is customary to build forms for the sides of spread footings and mats. Forms are also required for the interior construction joints of mats. To provide room for forms, the earth must be excavated more widely than the size of concrete footings. After stripping, or removing the form, the space between the side of the footing and the unexcavated soil must be backfilled and the backfill compacted. This procedure may be an unnecessary expense if the soil is cohesive and can stand up without sloughing, collapsing, sliding, or raveling. So it is permissible in this case to shape the earth banks to the exact size of the footing and eliminate the time and expense of overexcavation, formwork, and compacted backfill.

OPEN CAISSONS, PIERS, AND WALLS ON ROCK

Many foundations rest on rock, which is thought to be the best bearing material, although rock can vary widely in strength and resistance to weathering. Some rocks disintegrate rapidly on exposure to air, while other rocks (e.g., limestone) can be, or have been, dissolved by groundwater, resulting in large voids whose extent and location are usually quite unpredictable. Sometimes boulders (e.g., glacial erratics) or "floaters," which may be undecomposed bedrock, can be mistaken for sound bedrock when they might be many feet above the bedrock surface.

A geologist may be helpful in pointing out these threats to the strength of the foundation, but the commonly accepted method is to drill a hole in the center of each pier that is expected to bear on rock. The cheapest and quickest way is to drill the hole by a pneumatic percussion drill (jackhammer). The nature of the rock is deduced from the action of the drill.

A more expensive, time-consuming way, but one which yields the most reliable information as well as samples, is to take core borings. (Generally a diamond drill is used in the harder rock formations.)

Quite often faults and soft seams are encountered at the bedrock surface. It is considered good practice to remove the soft materials in these faults and seams, although this may prove impractical if the seams are narrow or extend to considerable depths. In such cases, the pier excavation may have to be widened to get the required bearing area on sound rock. Sometimes, additional piers may have to be provided to support girders, which in turn support columns. Thus, the faults and seams in the bedrock are bridged over.

Another problem which often arises when bedrock is reached is that its surface slopes. The traditional way of coping with this condition is to level the surface over the whole area of the pier or in steps.

Some engineers, however, believe this to be an unnecessary expense unless the rock surface is very steep, say, with a slope greater than 1 horizontal to 2 vertical. In lieu of stepping, steel reinforcing bars may be grouted into holes drilled in the bedrock, thus becoming dowels which can develop considerable resistance value in shear.

The disintegration of rock (generally slaty or shaly) on exposure to air is usually due to the rock's losing moisture. The cure, of course, is to cover the rock with concrete as soon as possible. If this process takes too long, a sealing spray (commonly bituminous) will inhibit the loss of moisture from this sort of rock.

If piers or walls are to be carried to rock, this rock is generally specified to be "sound," and all decomposed, disintegrated, or loose rock above the sound rock must be removed. This may be an expensive procedure, as the unsound rock may be quite tough to remove, especially when compared with the cost of removing an earth overburden. Yet the unsound rock must be removed at the unit-price bid for earth excavation. Hence many arguments arise in connection with payment for piers founded on rock. A common criterion for ascertaining when sound rock is reached is for the inspector to drop a steel bar onto the surface of the rock; if it "rings," the rock is regarded as sound. Otherwise, more rock must be removed. This procedure can work well in certain types of rock in thick beds. In thin-bedded rocks (for example, rocks with closely spaced bedding planes, often containing thin seams of clay), one could to go great depths before a ringing sound is heard, if it ever is. In cases like this the inspector is caught in the middle and can only hope that the contractor and engineer will soon work out the problem between them.

CAISSONS: PNEUMATIC (COMPRESSED AIR)

This type of construction has become so expensive in the last few decades that one hardly ever encounters it. However, except for the work of excavating and concreting, the principles are the same as for piers and open (free-air) caissons. The special conditions attached to pneumatic-caisson work—hours worked versus pressure, duplication of power sources, jobsite medical laboratories, etc.—are spelled out by state law in the United States.

In pouring concrete in pneumatic caissons, it is necessary to maintain air pressure within the working chamber to keep groundwater from flowing into the concrete and washing out the cement. When the level of the concrete reaches that of the surrounding groundwater, compressed air is no longer needed and the remainder of the concrete can be placed in free air.

CAISSONS: DRILLED (AUGERED)

Since the 1950s the use of machine-drilled caissons has grown very rapidly and they have largely supplanted older types of foundation-pier construction, i.e., pneumatic and hand-dug open caissons. Alternative terms for caissons are *piers* and *shafts,* while drilling is often called *augering.*

The essential feature of the use of the drilled shaft (besides its low labor costs and economical use of concrete for load carrying) is the rapid rate at which a circular hole is excavated in earth. The rapid rate of advancing the depth of the hole takes advantage of the time element, which is called the *stand-up* time of the earth, or the time between the first drilling and the point at which the sides of the hole begin to ravel or collapse. The circular cross section of the drilled hole is conducive to the earth's "arching," which helps keep the earth stable around the hole.

In competent ground all one has to do is to set the drill at a proper location and plumbness and drill down to the desired bearing stratum. When this depth is reached, as shown by a sample of soil taken from the auger or by other means, a ready-mix-concrete truck is backed up to the hole and the wet concrete is chuted into the excavation.

Care must be taken in this operation to avoid certain unpleasant contingencies:

1. The sides of hole may slough or cave if earth is not fully cohesive (i.e., if it is sandy or gravelly as opposed to clayey), especially if water is present. In this event a steel casing (or shell or cylinder) may have to be put into place, as a sort of bracing, as soon as the unstable soil is drilled through and before the lower part of the hole is drilled. This lining process may have to be repeated one or more times depending upon conditions. This process is called *telescoping* the casing, each section of the casing being 2 or 3 in (50.8 or 76.2 mm) smaller in diameter than the section above it. The outside diameter of the casing is generally about 2 or 3 in smaller than the drilled hole.

2. If water seeps into the hole, it must be removed before concrete is poured even though it may be lying at a depth of less than, say, 3 in (76.2 mm) in the bottom of the hole. Concrete poured directly into water will segregate, forming a material that is not really concrete at all. What happens is that when the concrete hits the water, the solid ingredients of the concrete—sand, gravel, and cement—settle into the water at different rates (gravel on the bottom, then sand, then a soft, pastelike cement on top). The water rises to the top of this segregated material, where it is ready to cause the next batch of concrete dropped into the caisson to segregate, and so the segregation progresses upward. The remedy for the presence of more than a little water in the hole is to fill the hole with water to groundwater level and pour the concrete by the *tremie* method (see subsection "Slurry-Wall Methods").

3. In cases of competent ground when a casing need not be used, a conventional concrete hopper with a hole in the middle should be employed to center the flow of wet concrete so that it does not strike the sides of the hole, gouging out pieces of the sides and burying them in the concrete. If the caissons are of very small diameter, care must be taken not to pour concrete so rapidly as to trap air beneath it. One way to avoid this is to allow only a small hole, say, 6 in (152.4 mm) in diameter, in the concrete hopper.

4. If a casing is used, it is usually extracted after the concrete is poured rather than allowed to remain in place. The reason for this precaution is that the caisson material is expensive. A crane pulls the casing upward and slides it past concrete on the inside and earth on the outside. If the concrete is a harsh, dry, stiff mix, if the casing is rough or encrusted with old concrete, dirt, rust, or other material, or if the cylinder is dented, there is a danger that the concrete may be pulled upward with the casing. In this event, a void will be created in the

concrete shaft, with partial to complete impairment of the shaft's load-carrying capacity.

Most specifications will call for the casing to be buried at all times at least 3 ft (0.9 m) below the surface of the wet concrete as it is being poured. The purpose is to prevent earth from squeezing in, thus reducing the diameter of the concrete pier. Such a reduction is often called *necking*. To keep the bottom of the casing at the proper elevation, the inspector must keep careful measurements and records.

5. Frequently, caissons are strengthened by cages of vertical reinforcing steel tied to spirals or hoops of horizontal bars. These cages are generally of a diameter only a few inches less than the diameter of the caisson. If the reinforcing cage and the casing are not centered very accurately, the two may rub against each other as the casing is withdrawn and the cage of rebars may be pulled upward or distorted. Again, the concrete in the shaft may be pulled apart.

6. If there are delays in pouring the concrete in the shaft or if the weather is very hot so that the cement in the concrete takes its initial set rapidly, the concrete may be pulled apart by the casing, rendering the caisson worthless.

7. If there is a suspicion that all might not be all right with the caisson concrete, the inspector frequently orders the examination of cores recovered by diamond-core drilling. (It is customary for the owner to pay for this examination if no defects are found, but the contractor pays if defects are discovered.) Suspicions were aroused when the first columns of the superstructure of the 100-story John Hancock Building in Chicago were placed on caissons and the caissons wobbled. Extensive core drilling, costing hundreds of thousands of dollars, showed voids, mud pockets, and other defects which cost millions of dollars to repair and caused many months' delay.

Recently, there has been developed a method of testing caisson concrete (and slurry-wall concrete as well) which works on the principle of nuclear radiation. Several 2-in steel pipes are placed vertically in the caisson, and as soon as the concrete has been poured, a gamma-ray probe is lowered into the pipes. The probe sends back to the surface information which relates to the soundness of the concrete in the vicinity of the pipe. The steel of the 2-in pipe can be counted toward the reinforcing. On the basis that an ounce of prevention is worth a pound of cure, the gamma-ray test should find increasing use in foundation work.

The remedies for these troubles are perhaps obvious:

- Use clean, smooth casings free from dents or encrusted concrete.

- Use high-slump concrete [greater than 6 in (152.4 mm)].
- Pour continuously and rapidly. Keep the concrete "live."
- In dubious ground, call for the casings to remain in place; do not try to salvage them.

There are times when workers must descend into the caissons to perform a variety of tasks. Such tasks might be:

- To drill a test hole into the bearing stratum or test by other means
- To clean up loose material lying on the bottom, loose material that the drilling bucket could not pick up (a small amount may be allowed to remain)
- To remove boulders or other obstructions
- To set pumps for the removal of seepage

Because there is always some danger of soil collapse even in the most competent-appearing soil, under no circumstances should anyone be permitted to enter a hole without the protection of a steel casing, which should reach to within not less than 3 ft (0.9 m) of the bottom. It is a universal legal requirement that workers be provided with a safe place to work.

Another safety precaution to be taken before workers are allowed to enter holes drilled into organic or chemically contaminated soils (in other words, ground that may contain noxious or explosive gases) is the use of safety lamps or other gas-detection instruments. And then, of course, there are the usual safety measures to be taken; to mention a few: hard hats, ventilation, curbing around holes to keep tools or rocks from falling into the holes, and the like.

SHEETING AND SHORING

The term *sheeting and shoring* refers to systems, usually temporary, which are intended to allow excavations to be made in soils at angles steeper than their natural angles of repose. Usually the sheeting is vertical, and the excavations are made in constricted locations such as built-up areas of cities. *Sheeting* refers to materials that are in contact with the earth, the principal materials being wooden planks, H beams, and interlocking steel-sheet piling. The sheeting in turn is held by *shoring,* which generally consists of horizontal members called *wales* plus struts called *braces* (placed within the excavation) against the wales and/or tension members called *tiebacks* (placed in the soil away from the excavation). Braces can be horizontal or inclined, in which case they are often called *rakers.* Tiebacks can be in earth, in which case they are at a slight angle downward from the horizontal, or they can terminate in holes drilled into rock, in which case they are most often installed at a 45° angle. Steel and wood are the materials most commonly used for wales and braces, while tiebacks are of very-high-strength-steel tendons in the form of stranded wire (or cables) or round rods. These are held in the ground at their lower ends by *grout* (a pumpable mixture of cement and water), which, upon setting, bonds to the soil and/or rock; at the upper ends, the tendons are gripped by devices (known as *hardware*) developed primarily for the prestressed-concrete industry.

With sheeting made of wooden planks for shallow excavations, say, 10 to 20 ft (3 to 6 m) deep, the planks frequently are vertical and are driven from the surface by light (even hand-held) equipment because that is about all the wood can stand without splitting or buckling. For deeper excavations, the wooden planks are placed horizontally, one beneath the other, working from the ground surface down as the excavation proceeds in a downward direction. (The horizontal planks are also termed *lagging* or *louver boards*.) This horizontal sheeting is held by the flanges of H piles (*soldier beams,* or *soldiers*), which are driven about 6 to 10 ft (1.8 to 3 m) on centers before any substantial excavation is made. In turn, the soldiers and lagging are shored by wales and braces to provide them with the lateral support supplied by the earth until it is excavated.

With either method—soldier beams and horizontal lagging or steel-sheet piling—with internal bracing or with external tiebacks, for economy and speed the maximum amount of earth is dug out before shoring is put in. This means that in wide excavations sloping berms are left against the sheeting. These slopes are determined by the engineer and should be closely adhered to. The contractor is sometimes tempted to excavate more deeply than the allowable slopes because the less that excavation is encumbered by bracing, the cheaper will be its unit cost.

Each tier of bracing should be quite complete before the next stage of excavation is made. This practice will minimize inward deflection of the sheeting as lateral earth loads are mobilized by the excavation.

In the usual cases in which steel wales and steel braces and/or tiebacks are employed, a proper design will call for a number of web stiffeners, brackets, bearing plates, and similar accessories which are needed to prevent the main members from buckling, bowing, crumpling, twisting, etc., at connections when under load. Under pressure of getting the job done, the contractor is often tempted to proceed with the excavation before all welding in any given area is complete. A similar attitude may affect the wedging up or hydraulic jacking of struts and rakers and the jacking of prestress loads into tiebacks. The inspector must be alert to prevent this kind of corner cutting, which often leads to avoidable inward movements of sheeting and bracing systems and sometimes to failure and even collapse.

When the excavation, including the sheeting and bracing system, is complete, the building of the permanent substructure can begin; upon its completion or completion in stages, the removal of the bracing system can begin. At this completion stage the contractor is again tempted to remove bracing prematurely because the bracing (although not tiebacks) is a definite hindrance to the installation of the permanent structure. However, the sheeting must still be supported at all times by temporary or permanent means, and premature removal of bracing has led to excessive movements and sometimes to collapse.

Mention has been made of movements of the sheeting and bracing system. These movements are, of course, in an inward and downward direction and, if large, can lead to damage of pavements, nearby buildings, and underground utilities. Some specifications call for the protection system to be undertaken with no movement, and this can lead to conflicts on the job because to a greater or lesser degree, depending on the firmness of the soil and the depth of the excavation, some inward movement is inevitable. Most of the movement takes place during the excavation process, and some takes place while the lagging, wales, and braces are being installed. Then the system remains at rest until excavation starts for the next lower tier of bracing, when the movements begin again. Movements are cumulative until the bottom is reached.

It is difficult to predict the magnitude of these movements. Based on past observations, some authorities put the total minimum inward movement (that is, with a well-designed system and good workmanship) in relatively soft soil at about 0.5 percent of the depth of the excavation. This would be 3 in (76.2 mm) for a 50-ft- (15.24-m-) deep cut. This ratio is a very general guide, and many circumstances will influence the figures. Among these factors might be the type of soil; the configuration of the excavation; whether inclined braces or horizontal struts are used (there is less movement with the latter); the speed of work (the quicker a hole is dug and filled up the better); the use of bracing across corners (a corner of more than 90° leads to greater movements); the type of dewatering system (some pumping of fines at the start may be inevitable but, if prolonged, can lead to excessive loss of ground and damage due to settlement outside the sheeting system); and whether tiebacks are used (there is generally less movement with a tieback system, which is attributed to more effective prestressing of the ground than with the internal bracing system).

As has been stated, lagging is also termed *louver boards*. This name is due to the fact that the planks, which are supported by the flanges of the H beams (soldier beam or soldier piles), are usually placed with spaces between their edges. These spaces, or louvers, which are from 1 to 2 in

(25.4 to 50.8 mm) high, are designed not to save timber but to achieve two purposes:

1. *Drainage.* The function of a horizontal-lagging and soldier-beam system, in contrast to interlocking vertical sheeting, is not only to hold back earth but to allow groundwater to percolate through. This has the advantage of reducing the lateral pressure against the protection system.

2. In order to place the boards behind the soldier-beam flanges, which is a hand-trimming job, more material than the precise volume of the board must be removed. The space between the board and the earth must then be packed (or backfilled) with earth (sand is best) to prevent the original in-place earth from moving in against the board, thus causing lost ground with consequent settlement. Access for the packing is gained through the louvers.

Often, sand will flow through the louvers, either because it is carried by the flow of groundwater or because it is very dry, cohesionless sand (sometimes called *sugar sand*). The louvers will be useful for packing a filter material into place. Salt hay has proved to be an excellent filter material for many years; more recently nonwoven plastic fabrics have come on the market. These materials will allow water to drain through the louvers, but will retain the sand.

The inspector should insist on conscientious packing behind the horizontal lagging. This packing may be necessary at any stage of the work.

Many excavations penetrate earth and reach down into rock so that the sheeting system rests on rock only a few feet from a vertical rock face. If the rock is seamy or highly jointed, there is a tendency for a wedge of rock to break off or to slide, carrying the overlying sheeting (and some earth behind the sheeting) with it. With a raker-braced cut, this tendency is diminished by the upwardly directed component of the compression load in the raker. With a tieback system the tendency to break off is aggravated by the downward thrust of the soldier beams or the sheet piling. To make a rock excavation safely, certain precautions may have to be taken:

- Remove the rock in shallow benches and in short horizontal sections. As these small faces of rock are exposed, anchor them back with grouted or mechanical (expansion-shield-type) rock bolts, which may be round bars or standard wire. Epoxy grouts are popular because they gain full strength in hours rather than in days, as can be the case with portland-cement grouts.

- Set the soldier beams in holes predrilled to several feet below subgrade. Concrete the soldier beams in the holes.

- Leave a berm of rock temporarily at the vertical rock face, and install short, steep rakers from the soldier beams to subgrade.
- Spread the concentrated loads from the tips of the soldiers to the rock on either side of the soldiers.
- If rock tends to ravel or spall off, retain it with wire mesh, perhaps combined with shotcrete (gunite).

SLURRY-WALL METHODS

There are times when neither vertical steel-sheet piling nor a soldier-beam system can cope with difficult ground conditions, the main difficulties being obstructions to the driving of the sheeting or beams and the presence of groundwater which may be difficult or undesirable to lower. Also, there may be unavoidably large ground movements associated with these systems in highly plastic soils such as Chicago blue clay. In such cases a rapidly growing method, called the *slurry-wall method*, has won wide acceptance. To install a slurry wall, a trench is excavated, usually by means of a clamshell bucket, although hydraulic dredging is also used; then the trench is filled with concrete, which is usually reinforced. As the trench is being dug, it is kept filled with slurry. This slurry is a mixture of water with about 5 or 10 percent of a volcanic clay called *bentonite*, which has the property of being able to absorb many times its own weight of water. The slurry, because of its density and also because of certain physicochemical effects, forms a thin "cake" on the sides of the trench, which keeps the trench from collapsing even though the trench may be many feet deep [over 200 ft (61 m) in some cases]. The inspector should remember that the level of the slurry in the trench must at all times be kept higher than the surface of the groundwater. Failure to take this precaution leads to collapse of the trench walls.

Most specifications will call for certain controls to be exercised over the principal properties of the slurry: density, viscosity, and sand content. Simple instruments required for measuring these properties should be available on the jobsite at all times (although it must be admitted that an experienced superintendent develops an excellent feel for a proper slurry). For density, a simple scale with a cup at one end and a sliding weight on a calibrated bar at the other end is used. For viscosity, a standard funnel called a Marsh cone is used with an ordinary stopwatch; a standard volume of slurry is allowed to drain through the orifice of the funnel, and the time it takes to drain is measured by the stopwatch. Thus, viscosity is expressed in seconds. Sand content is measured in a sort of calibrated test tube; a sample of the slurry is poured into this vessel, and the depth of sand that settles out after a predetermined period is measured.

After a section of wall (called a *panel*) is excavated to subgrade, the reinforcing bars are placed. The bars are preassembled in the form of *cages*; almost always these cages are assembled on their sides at the jobsite. When ready for placement in the trench, they are upended by a crane and lowered into position. Since this handling induces stresses in the cages, they must be well constructed, that is, firmly tied and/or welded at the intersections of the horizontal and vertical bars. The cages should be equipped with precast-concrete spacers to keep the bars from leaning against the earth sides of the trench and being exposed later on. However, before a cage is placed in the trench, the slurry must be processed so that it is relatively free from sand because the digging operation tends to place sand (more present in certain types of ground than in others) temporarily into suspension in the slurry. The sand is in danger of settling out at any stage of the wall installation. If the reinforcing cage has not yet been placed, the settled sand might prevent the cage from being lowered to the plan elevation. Later, during concreting, the sand might settle out to form a *holiday* in the wall. Tests especially for sand content and to a lesser degree for density and viscosity will show when the slurry is in proper condition for rebar and concrete placement. The more rigid control over slurry is not so important during excavation.

In slurry-wall construction, concrete is always placed by the tremie method. This involves using a steel pipe, commonly 8 to 12 in (203.2 to 304.8 mm) in diameter, which is placed vertically down to the bottom of the pour and extends to above the top of the pour, where a large hopper is attached. It is important that the bottom of the tremie pipe remain at all times below the surface of the concrete as it is being poured; this in turn demands that careful measurements be made and records be kept so that the bottom of the tremie pipe is not raised too high. If the bottom of the tremie pipe is allowed to be lifted above the surface of the concrete, the concrete ingredients will immediately separate, rendering the concrete worthless.

At the very start of the tremie pour, a plug is placed in the tremie pipe to keep the concrete from mixing with the slurry. A number of types of plugs are favored by different contractors. A simple plug is an inflated rubber volley ball. Loose-fitting and hence easily pushed down through the pipe, the ball nevertheless keeps the concrete separate from the slurry and floats up to the surface of the slurry, where it can be retrieved.

The concrete itself must be very fluid and workable so that it does not hang up in the tremie pipe. A good specification for tremie concrete would require a minimum slump of, say, 7 in (177.8 mm) rather than a maximum slump. It must be borne in mind that the concrete must not only slide easily through the tremie pipe but also split the already-placed tremie concrete. The more rapid the rate of pouring, the better, not only for the benefit of costs and schedule but also for the quality of the wall. With rapid rates of pour, the tremie pipe hardly need be raised to any considerable height. To achieve high and continuous rates of pour, there must be close cooperation between the placing crew and the concrete plant. In recent years, the development of concrete pumps has made them suitable for smaller tremie pours, as for caissons dug and tremie concreted under wet, runny soil conditions.

MONITORING FOR MOVEMENTS

In almost any excavation project, including piling, caisson, and underpinning jobs, those in charge of the work must know at all times the effects on surrounding structures and areas. If significant movements are observed to be taking place, steps can be taken to

- Stop the work
- Speed the work up
- Revise designs
- Revise procedures
- Install emergency shoring

To these ends, before any work starts, settlement marks should be placed on all structures that might be influenced by the work. Adjoining or nearby buildings should be surveyed in detail to record all existing cracks and other structural defects. Preferably, this examination should be made jointly by the representative of the owner of the building and the contractor (or the contractor's insurance company) so that there will be agreement on the original conditions at the start of the work.

As the work progresses, readings on the settlement marks can be taken at intervals whose duration may vary with the character of construction activity at any given state of the project. In an emergency readings may be taken hourly; at other times they may be taken monthly. Upon installation of vertical sheeting or soldier piles, marks should be put on the faces of the sheeting or piles to monitor lateral movements. Extreme precision should not be sought. It slows the progress of surveying and becomes expensive, and this circumstance becomes a deterrent to the taking of readings when they should be taken. Accuracy to within $\frac{1}{4}$ in (6.35 mm) should be sufficient; movements of this magnitude are not very significant because they may be caused by temperature effects or instrumental error.

Marks for settlement and lateral movements should be placed so that they are easy to read because these readings should not be skimped. When readings are taken, they should be promptly plotted so that their significance can be promptly grasped. The writer knows of several calamities which were in the making but went undetected while warnings of trouble lay uncovered in a mass of numbers in a surveyor's notebook. Marks should also be planned so that they are accessible at all stages of the work and not be obliterated or damaged by construction equipment or operations.

Visual inspection is also important, and inspectors should patrol the area outside the sheeting daily, looking especially for cracks in the pavement or earth surfaces parallel to the sheeting. These cracks should be sealed with tar to keep water pressures from building up against the wedge of earth that tends to move against the sheeting. The protection system should be constantly observed for signs of distress; bowing of the sheeting boards, bowing of braces, bending of wales, and buckling at connections are some of the symptoms of incipient trouble.

Sheeting and bracing systems are designed to resist not only lateral earth pressures but also surcharge loads from three main sources: (1) cranes, concrete and dump trucks, and similar construction equipment working around the edge of the excavation; (2) street traffic; and (3) stockpiles of materials stored behind the sheeting. Such materials might be structural steel, masonry, or earth that has been excavated and stored for later use as backfill. Unless close watch and control are maintained, design loads may be substantially exceeded, thus raising the danger of failure. And indeed, this is not an uncommon cause of trouble.

Loads may also be thrown against sheeting and bracing from footings of nearby building foundations. In such cases, unless the buildings are very light and unimportant, it is best that maintenance of the buildings not be left to indirect means, such as sheeting and bracing, no matter how rigid, but that the vertical loads from the footings be carried by downward extensions of the footings to depths below the influence of the new excavation. In other words, it is best that the buildings be underpinned.

In summary, since no building or other structure is any better than its foundation, the inspector must not compromise any aspect of the precautions, but insist on complete adherence to plans and specifications to assure design integrity.

UNDERPINNING

Underpinning is putting a new foundation under an existing structure. It may also involve shoring the structure. There are two main types of underpinning: pit and pile. Both require that a small excavation be made (almost always by hand) underneath the existing foundation, be it a wall or a separate footing. This undermining of a section of foundation wall, usually about 4 ft (1.2 m) long, causes a shift of load from the undermined section to the adjacent sections of wall, which in turn throws lateral earth pressure against the sides of the pit. To resist this pressure, horizontal planks called *pit boards* are carefully placed to line the walls of the pit. Naturally, some excavation must be made larger than the neat dimensions of the pit, so as soon as a tier of pit boards is in place, provision must be made to fill with earth the space between the sides of the pit and the pit boards. In exceptionally good ground, i.e., firm, cohesive soil, more than one set of pit boards may be installed at a time, and in the case of unusually dry clays, the pit excavation may even be dug down to the final depth. In any case, the quicker the hole is dug and filled with concrete, the less the loss of ground and consequently minimum settlement of the structure being underpinned. As a very rough rule of thumb, in soils of low cohesion settlement of ¼ to ⅜ in (6.35 to 9.525 mm) may be expected when the workmanship is good.

To fill properly with earth the space between the earth sides of the pit and the pit boards, the boards should be placed so that there are horizontal spaces (louvers) between each tier of boards. The earth backfill is pushed through the louvers, which are usually about ½ in (38.1 mm) in height. It is desirable to tamp the backfill behind the boards; this is done with the fingers and the handle of a shovel. Another function of the louver is to allow the concrete to run through and fill any voids that still remain. Needless to say, the concrete should be very workable with a high slump.

The concrete is placed to within 2 or 3 in (50.8 or 76.2 mm) of the underside of the footing. The next day, *dry pack*, a moist, crumbly mix of sand and portland cement, is rammed into the space between the footing and the now-set underpinning concrete. The next pit is now ready to be excavated; usually it is not adjacent to the pit that has just been dry-packed but at some convenient distance. Thus the underpinning piers are scheduled in leapfrog fashion.

Pit underpinning as discussed above is applicable to dry or predrained soils; if water is present so as to cause loss of ground, the most common alternative is jacked piling, using the pretest method of testing a pile's load-bearing capacity and transferring the load from the test jacks to the pile by steel wedges. The pile itself is a steel pipe with a diameter usually from 12 to 16 in (304.8 to 406.4 mm). As the pile is jacked down in sections of about 4 ft (1.2 m), the earth inside the pipe or even below the bottom of the pipe is excavated to decrease the resistance to jacking down. In excavating the pile, boiling due to excessive head of groundwater may occur in some fine-grained soils. This might lead to a damaging loss of ground and consequently to damage in the structure above. The inspector should see to it that a full head of water is maintained within the pipe to counteract groundwater pressure. If the pipe cannot be jacked to a seal on an impervious stratum, it may have to be filled with concrete by the tremie process.

Before any underpinning is started, a set of level marks should be placed at various points of the buildings that are to be underpinned or may be affected by the excavation to be made. These marks, laid out by means of a level, will monitor any settlement that may take place. Convenient marks are made from sections of carpenter's rule. A few marks may also be established to monitor lateral movements; these are made by sighting with a transit. Good record keeping, including plotting of movements, will be of great help in comprehending what is going on. Sometimes when a pile is being jacked beneath a light structure, the jack may tend to raise the structure, which can cause the superstructure to crack. The inspector must be aware of this possibility and exercise control.

When an underpinning pit is large in comparison with the footing above, there is a danger that the footing will be excessively undermined, thereby overloading adjacent soil with consequent damaging settlement. In such cases, resort must be made to shoring to provide preliminary support. This shoring is usually made of wood or steel, but sometimes concrete is used. Whatever the material, the inspector should be guided by the rules and principles for those types of work. The inspector should be aware of the need for pretesting, or predeflecting, the structural elements of the shoring system, especially the members (beams) which take bending. This pretesting is most often carried out by means of wedges and hydraulic jacks. Here again, it must be emphasized that careful surveying and record keeping are called for.

Some safety aspects should be pointed out. All personnel should wear hard hats, especially when down in the pits; wooden curbs should be provided at the top edges of pit excavations to prevent tools and boulders from falling on the workers in the pits; ladders must be strong and secure; and pits should be well ventilated as a precaution against toxic gases.

DRILLED-IN CAISSONS

Drilled-in caissons (DIC) are a type of pile designed to transmit heavy loads to bedrock. They consist of heavy steel pipe, usually about ½ in (12.7 mm) thick and with a diameter of 24 to 42 in (609.6 to 1066.8 mm), driven to rock by pile hammers. If obstructions such as boulders or hardpan are encountered in the overburden, they are drilled out ahead of the heavy steel pipe (the *shell*) so as to decrease resistance to driving and to avoid damage to the shell, which is always reinforced with a tough alloy-steel cutting edge. After the cutting edge has been seated on the rock, drilling is carried out to a depth called for by the designer, from 3 or 4 ft (0.9 or 1.2 m) up to 10 or 15 ft (3 or 4.6 m). The drilled hole in the rock is called the *socket*; the heavier the load to be supported, the deeper the socket for any given diameter. The socket having been completed, it and the shell are ready to receive the core beam, which is usually a rolled structural-shape H beam weighing from a few pounds per linear foot to perhaps a 1000 lb/ft (148,800 kg/m); again, the heavier the load to be carried, the more weight per foot of steel in the core beam. Completion of the socket means that all loose dirt and chips of rock from the drilling operation (which is almost always *churn drilling)* have been cleaned out of the caisson.

The core beam is then lowered into the hole so that it extends from the bottom of the socket to or above the cutoff elevation of the shell. The space between the core beam and the wall of the socket and between the core beam and the inner surface of the shell is then filled with high-strength concrete to complete the installation of the DIC.

Because a DIC has a high load-bearing capacity, ordinarily a single DIC is used to carry the superimposed load from the column above. The DIC therefore must be installed with greater precision than the usual pile type, for which an eccentricity of one of a number of piles in a footing is not a serious matter. Special precautions are taken to ensure close tolerances in location and plumbness.

A partly buried square *template* of, say, 12- by 12-in (304.8- by 304.8-mm) timbers securely bolted together to form a hollow square a little larger than the outside diameter of the cutting edge is used to keep the shell from drifting off center. To achieve verticality, two transits should be used at the beginning of the driving to line up the shell, the transits being placed so that their lines of sight are approximately perpendicular to each other. Driving should be carried out with the hammer held rigidly in a lead. If an obstruction is encountered, drilling within the pile should be carried out at once because forcing the shell by hard driving may cause the shell to be out of plumb and/or out of round. Overdriving the cutting edge on bedrock may also damage the bottom of the shell. There is often a temptation to overdrive in order to achieve a seal between the cutting edge and the rock; this seal is deemed desirable for pumping the caisson out so that a visual inspection can be made and the concrete placed in the dry. However, more likely than not, because of the irregular surface of the rock and the fact that most rock contains fissures through which groundwater may seep, it is more prudent to plan on concreting the caisson by using tremie (underwater) methods for the following reason. If there is an upward flow of water into the caisson during the concrete placement (even though the water rises only a few inches a minute), this flow will wash out the cement from the concrete mix, rendering it weak and useless. It is best, in the long run, to place the concrete with the caisson filled with clean water.

The next operation after driving the shell, seating it on rock and drilling the socket, is to make sure that all loose dirt, clay, and silt are removed from within the caisson. This is usually effected by various kinds of bailers, especially those of the suction (piston) type, airlifts, and reverse-circulation pumping, in which a pump whose suction extends to the bottom of the caisson is used so that loose material can be sucked off the bottom.

After the caisson has been made reasonably clean, it is ready to receive the core beam. When a caisson is deep and heavily loaded, this item is often so heavy that it cannot be handled by a single crane but is lowered in two or more sections which have milled ends butted against each other. This is the same procedure practiced in the preparation of columns for multistory steel-frame buildings. Tolerances for milled ends, which are set by steel mills, do not require absolutely full contact at all points in the compression splice. The same tolerances are carried over into DIC work.

Centering devices are welded onto the core beam to assure that the core is located in the center of the caisson. These devices are merely light rods placed at intervals at right angles to the core beam. They are merely tacked in place so that they may be easily broken off in case of need.

Final cleaning of the caisson may have to be carried out before concreting begins. This is especially true of caissons which must be installed through soils with clayey overburdens or which have sockets in rock that produces a slurry when drilled. If the caisson is left undisturbed for any period of time, the clay particles may settle out and later form undesirable inclusions underneath or in the concrete that weaken it. By means of water jets the clay sediment may be thrown up into suspension, followed immediately by placement of the concrete. A better way is to remove the clay sediment by reverse circulation (suction), followed immediately by the pumping in of grout through the same pipeline. With a T connection and two valves, one on the pump suction line and the other on the grout line, a quick switchover can be made.

Needless to say, at all times careful soundings and measurements should be made of the elevation of the cutting edge, the bottom of the socket, and the depth of any sediment.

In some cases, underwater inspection by special television cameras may be desirable, although this is a costly and time-consuming process requiring large amounts of clear water to be slushed through the entire depth of the caisson for the camera to register a distinct enough image.

Tremie concrete (concrete placed underwater) may be placed by gravity methods or by a concrete pump. In gravity placement a bottom-opening bucket may be used, or else a hopper connected to a tremie pipe, say, 8 in (203.2 mm) or more in diameter, may be favored. The tremie bucket has the disadvantage that it can be accidentally opened before the bottom of the bucket is completely submerged in the previously placed batch of concrete. In this case, the concrete is ruined by segregation of the various ingredients: cement, sand, and gravel. The hopper-and-pipe method is good, but in deep caissons it has the disadvantage that considerable friction may develop in the tremie pipe, causing a stoppage in the downward flow of the concrete. To overcome the stoppage, the whole pipe and hopper may be picked up to start the flow again, but there is always the danger of raising the pipe too much, with result that the seal is lost, with consequent segregation. On the whole, the preferred method is to use the concrete pump. Placement should start with a batch of rich, fluid grout followed by high-slump [8- to 10-in (203.2- to 254-mm)] concrete with gravel aggregate, as opposed to crushed-rock aggregate, if possible; the rounded gravel flows better. In placing tremie concrete, the best results are obtained with a high rate of flow of concrete and few interruptions.

If the inspector suspects the quality of the concrete already placed, the only recourse is to get diamond-drill core borings of the in situ concrete. If the concrete is found to be defective, removal would prove to be very costly and time-consuming, but it has been done in isolated cases. Another remedy has been to drill a number of holes around the core beam and grout in reinforcing bars.

Engineering Control of Pile Installation*

Frank M. Fuller, P.E.
Consultant
Osterville, Massachusetts

<u>Formerly</u>

Assistant Vice President
Raymond International Builders, Inc.

The engineering control of pile installation can be effected only by competent on-site inspection. The primary purpose of inspection is to assure that the pile foundation has been installed according to the plans and specifications and good construction practice.

Under certain conditions the inspection or engineering control of pile installation should be very comprehensive and cover all aspects from pile material to final installation including equipment and pile load testing. Conditions requiring complete engineering control include installation of piles with very high design loads, use of marginal or unique piling systems, existence of difficult soil or installation conditions, unusual requirements such as installing extremely long piles, or use of unusual installation methods. The magnitude and complexity of the project may make complete inspection imperative. For each of these conditions the experience of the pile contractor could be an important element in establishing the degree of engineering control required. The extent of overall inspection may be dictated by the owner through the engineer or by a regulatory authority.

Qualifications of Inspector.   Of prime importance to the meaningful inspection of pile installation are the qualifications of the inspector. The required qualifications are in direct proportion to the inspector's duties, responsibilities, and authority and to the complexity of the project. The designation *inspector* implies a knowledge of what is to be inspected. For routine minor inspection, such as observing and recording the pile-driving log, the pile inspector needs to know very little about pile driving. For comprehensive inspection, however, the inspector must have the following qualifications:

1. Familiarity with basic and special pile types
2. Understanding of fundamentals of deep-foundation design
3. Comprehension of the basic principles of soil mechanics
4. Acquaintance with the fundamentals of soil exploration and sampling
5. Experience in equipment, methods, and techniques of pile installation
6. Awareness of the limitations of pile-installation equipment
7. General knowledge of the advantages, disadvantages, and limitations of various piling systems
8. Recognition of installation problems inherent in various piling systems
9. Familiarity with the plans, specifications, and contract documents governing the pile foundation for the project being inspected

10. Understanding of the obligations of the pile contractor for that project

Duties and Responsibilities of Inspector. The duties and responsibilities of a pile inspector can be very broad or quite narrow, depending upon the requirements of the owner, the engineer of record, or a regulatory authority. These duties and responsibilities should be clearly set forth and understood by all. The inspector should basically observe and report and should not assume, or be placed in, the position of directing the work. The inspector's primary responsibility is acting on the owner's or engineer's behalf to see that the piles are installed to satisfy the intent of the plans and specifications. Secondary duties and responsibilities often involve the recording of data describing the work as performed.

Authority of Inspector. In addition to responsibilities and duties, the inspector should if possible have some degree of authority. Decisions that can be made at the job level can often eliminate substantial delays and improve relationships with the contractor. Obviously there will be decisions that must be referred to the engineer of record, but these should be kept to a minimum. The inspector who has the necessary experience and training and knows the objectives of the plans and specifications can make meaningful judgments and decisions.

Records and Reports. (See Figs. 2.3-1, 2.3-2, and 2.3-3.) The inspector must keep clear, complete, and legible records. All original (field) notes and records must be retained even though the information may be transcribed for reporting purposes. In addition to inspection records and forms, it is recommended that the inspector keep a daily diary for recording the events of each construction day as they may relate to pile installation. All certificates of inspection, laboratory reports, or other documents received by the inspector must be retained and submitted with appropriate reports.

Pile Types. Piles are columnlike structural elements driven or otherwise embedded in the ground primarily to transfer superimposed loads down through soils of insufficient bearing capacity to soils of adequate bearing capacity. Piles are generally constructed of timber, steel, concrete, or a combination of these materials.

Timber piles, usually whole trees with branches and bark removed, are driven with the small end down. They are either untreated or treated with a preservative to help resist the attacks of decay, insects, and marine borers.

Steel piles are of either H section or pipe. Other shapes have been used but are not common. Steel piles are sometimes coated to protect them

PILE DRIVING LOGS

JOB NO. _____   DATE _____

PROJECT _____
LOCATION: _____   OWNER: _____
PILE TYPE: _____   HAMMER: _____   CAPBLOCK: _____

STRUCTURE _____ DRAWING NO. _____

DEPTH – ft.	PILE NO. _____ C.O. EL. _____ TIP EL. _____ LENGTH _____ft. DRILLED _____ft.		DEPTH – ft.	PILE NO. _____ C.O. EL. _____ TIP EL. _____ LENGTH _____ft. DRILLED _____ft.		DEPTH – ft.	PILE NO. _____ C.O. EL. _____ TIP EL. _____ LENGTH _____ft. DRILLED _____ft.		DEPTH – ft.	PILE NO. _____ C.O. EL. _____ TIP EL. _____ LENGTH _____ft. DRILLED _____ft.	
1	51		1	51		1	51		1	51	
2	52		2	52		2	52		2	52	
3	53		3	53		3	53		3	53	
4	54		4	54		4	54		4	54	
5	55		5	55		5	55		5	55	
6	56		6	56		6	56		6	56	
7	57		7	57		7	57		7	57	
8	58		8	58		8	58		8	58	
9	59		9	59		9	59		9	59	
10	60		10	60		10	60		10	60	
11	61		11	61		11	61		11	61	
12	62		12	62		12	62		12	62	
13	63		13	63		13	63		13	63	
14	64		14	64		14	64		14	64	
15	65		15	65		15	65		15	65	
16	66		16	66		16	66		16	66	
17	67		17	67		17	67		17	67	
18	68		18	68		18	68		18	68	
19	69		19	69		19	69		19	69	
20	70		20	70		20	70		20	70	
21	71		21	71		21	71		21	71	
22	72		22	72		22	72		22	72	
23	73		23	73		23	73		23	73	
24	74		24	74		24	74		24	74	
25	75		25	75		25	75		25	75	
26	76		26	76		26	76		26	76	
27	77		27	77		27	77		27	77	
28	78		28	78		28	78		28	78	
29	79		29	79		29	79		20	79	
30	80		30	80		30	80		30	80	
31	81		31	81		31	81		31	81	
32	82		32	82		32	82		32	82	
33	83		33	83		33	83		33	83	
34	84		34	84		34	84		34	84	
35	85		35	85		35	85		35	85	
36	86		36	86		36	86		36	86	
37	87		37	87		37	87		37	87	
38	88		38	88		38	88		38	88	
39	89		39	89		39	89		39	89	
40	90		40	90		40	90		40	90	
41	91		41	91		41	91		41	91	
42	92		42	92		42	92		42	92	
43	93		43	93		43	93		43	93	
44	94		44	94		44	94		44	94	
45	95		45	95		45	95		45	95	
46	96		46	96		46	96		46	96	
47	97		47	97		47	97		47	97	
48	98		48	98		48	98		48	98	
49	99		49	99		49	99		49	99	
50	100		50	100		50	100		50	100	

INSPECTOR

FIG. 2.3-1 Sample driving-log form. *(Raymond International Builders Inc.)*

2.3.10

from various types of corrosion. Pipe piles can be driven with the end either open or closed.

Concrete piles are of two basic types, precast and cast-in-place. Precast piles include both conventionally reinforced and prestressed concrete. Cast-in-place concrete piles are either cased or uncased; the cased piles are either mandrel-driven or driven without a mandrel. The various types of concrete piles are shown in Fig. 2.3-4.

See also subsection "Special-Type Piles."

Subsoil Information. Pile foundations should not be designed or installed without adequate subsoil information. This is obtained by conventional test borings from which soil and rock samples are recovered for analyses and tests. To be meaningful, the depth to which test borings are taken must be below the depth to which piles may be installed. Various types of soil tests can also be made in the borehole to determine soil properties. The inspector should have access to the subsoil information and be familiar with existing subsurface conditions which may affect pile installation.

It should be noted that test-boring data show only conditions existing at the location of the boring and that conditions could vary widely between boreholes. A general knowledge of the geological history of the area is helpful in being able to anticipate possible variations in subsoil conditions.

Underground Structures. It is not the responsibility of the inspector to determine the existence, location, and condition of underground structures including pipe lines. However, the inspector should be advised of such, should be alert to potential damage during pile installation, and should call the contractor's attention to any dangerous situation which seems to be developing.

ITEMS OF INSPECTION

The following subsections list items of inspection that will provide an understanding of the duties of a pile inspector involved in the comprehensive engineering control of pile installation. Some items are discussed to furnish guidance for meaningful inspection and decisions.

PILE MATERIAL

Inspection of pile material involves various items to ensure that material meets the requirements of the specifications and conforms with material

LOAD TEST REPORT

DATE _____

PROJECT_____ JOB NO. _____

LOCATION _____

TEST NO. _____ PILE DESIGNATION _____ TYPE TEST_____

PILE TYPE _____ DESCRIPTION _____ LENGTH (Tip to G.S.)_____

DESIGN LOAD_____TEST LOAD_____ BUTT DEFLECTIONS: GROSS _____ NET_____

Dates: Driven_____ Concreted _____ Tested _____

*Hammer Type and Size _____ Total Blows _____ Final Set _____Blows/in.

Pre-excavation: Depth _____ Description _____
_____
_____

Special Test Procedures and Instrumentation:_____
_____
_____
_____
_____

*Borings by _____ Job No. _____ Nearest Boring: No. _____Distance _____
Owner_____ General Contractor_____
Str. Engr. _____ Foundation Engr. _____

REMARKS: _____ _____
_____
_____
_____
_____
_____
_____
_____
_____
_____
_____
_____
_____
_____

Load test report is certified to be correct:

Signature: _____   For: _____

Signature: _____   For _____

*Attach Comparative Soil Boring and Pile Driving Logs.

FIG. 2.3-2   Sample load-test-report form. *(Raymond International Builders Inc.)*

2.3.12

LOAD TEST REPORT   **TABULATION OF DATA**

* TEST NO._____ PILE NO._____ JOB NO._____

DATE	HOUR	TEST LOAD		GAUGE READINGS			SECONDARY READINGS	BUTT DEFLECTIONS	
		INCREMENT	TOTAL	NO. 1	NO. 2	AVG.		INCREMENT	TOTAL

*Attach supplementary sheets as necessary for additional data; tell tale readings; other instrumentation data. Explain all delays, resetting of gauges etc.

FIG. 2.3-2   *(Continued)*

FIG. 2.3-3 Recording a driving log. *(Raymond International Builders Inc.)*

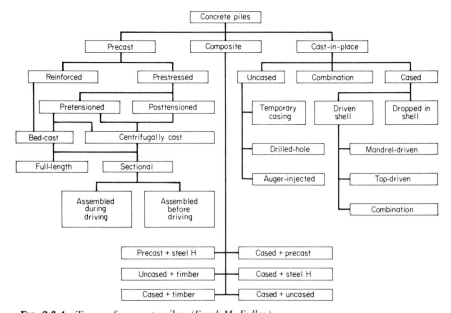

FIG. 2.3-4 Types of concrete piles. *(Frank M. Fuller.)*

2.3.14

on which the design was based. The basic pile materials are timber, concrete, and steel, and each has its unique inspection requirements.

Timber Piles

Species.   The species will often be specified because not all timber has the same strength and other properties. In some cases the subspecies may also be specified. The species should be noted on inspection reports received from the point of origin of each pile shipment.

Conditioning and Preservative Treatment.   Adequate inspection certificates should accompany each shipment of piles treated with a preservative. Certificates should show the type of conditioning used, such as air-dried, kiln-dried, steam, Bolton, or heating in the preservative and the type and retention of the preservative. These should be as specified. The type of conditioning as well as the temperature and duration of the conditioning process could seriously affect the strength of the timber. It should be noted that American Wood-Preservers' Association (AWPA) specifications prohibit steam conditioning of certain species such as Pacific coast Douglas fir and oak. For all piles, the temperature and duration of the conditioning process are limited by AWPA specifications.

Peeled or Unpeeled.   Sometimes specifications will permit unpeeled piles, but in general, and especially for all treated piles, piles will be clean-peeled, which requires the removal of all outer bark and at least 80 percent of the inner bark. Unpeeled piles require no bark removal, and rough-peeled piles require complete removal of the outer bark only.

Lengths.   Timber piles will be shipped to the jobsite according to approved ordered lengths. Standard brands on each pile should indicate the pile length. Piles shorter than those ordered are not acceptable, but piles specified according to American Society for Testing and Materials (ASTM) D 25, Standard Specifications for Round Timber Piles, may be from 1 to 2 ft (0.3 to 0.6 m) longer, depending upon the ordered length. Payment for timber piles is frequently based upon the full furnished lengths, and thus delivered lengths must agree with ordered lengths. Ordered lengths may be somewhat longer than the anticipated driven lengths to allow for extra lengths which may be required owing to subsoil conditions that vary from those indicated by test borings.

Dimensions.   Frequently the minimum diameter at the pile tip or butt, or both, may be specified. However, the dimensions of the delivered piles may not be as specified because the producer may furnish piles in accordance with the 1973 version of ASTM D 25. For all practical purposes, ASTM D 25 is developed by the timber industry and reflects current practice as set by that industry. Therefore, according to industry standards, timber piles are no longer designated Class A, B, or C as in ASTM D 25-58, and specific requirements relating to each of these classes of pile are no longer in effect. The requirements for timber piles were substantially liberalized by the issuance of ASTM D 25-73. Allowable tip and butt diameters were reduced from those specified in ASTM D 25-58. According to ASTM D 25-73, timber piles are classified as either friction piles or end-bearing piles. For friction piles, a minimum butt circumference is specified, and the minimum tip circumference results from the ordered length of the piles. For end-bearing piles, a minimum tip circumference is specified, and the minimum butt circumference results from the pile length. The pile inspector should understand that, regardless of current ASTM specifications, the engineer is at liberty to specify any wanted dimensions or other properties for timber piles and the owner is entitled to receive piles as specified, regardless of industry standards.

Taper and Straightness.   Timber piles should have a continuous taper from tip to butt, and the piles should be sufficiently straight so that a line from the center of the butt to the center of the tip lies entirely within the body of each pile. Short crooks or reverse bends could cause problems during driving, and piles with these defects should be carefully checked to see that they comply with specifications on straightness.

Knots.   The pile inspector should be aware of the differences in allowable knots between ASTM D 25-58 and D 25-73. Basically the 1973 version substantially liberalized the number and sizes of allowable knots. It would be well to check the intent of the design specifications because D 25-73 permits 2 or more times the sum of knot diameters in a given length of pile as compared with D 25-58 and permits cluster knots, which were prohibited by the earlier version. Knots generally are located along the upper portions of the tree and thus toward the pile tip. Knots at the pile tip could be quite critical and result in pile damage during driving.

Checks, Shakes, and Splits.   The extent of checks, shakes, and splits is limited by ASTM D 25. However, they are permitted by D 25 to some degree, and for timber piles that are not required to conform to ASTM D 25 severe limitation on these types of defects should be imposed or the defects prohibited. Such initial defects in a pile may be made more severe during driving and, in the case of treated timber piles, could render the preservative treatment ineffective.

Soundness.   There should be no evidence of decay or insect attack. The inspection certificate obtained from the point of origin or the treatment plant should cover this point, but the inspector should spot-check.

Special Fittings.   Specifications may require that pile tips be fitted with steel drive shoes or that during driving pile butts be protected with steel bands. All special fittings should comply with the specifications.

Precast-Concrete Piles

Design Requirements.   Adequate plant inspection reports should accompany each pile shipment, identifying the piles and certifying that they meet the design specifications including such things as the amount of reinforcing steel, 28-day concrete strengths, and effective prestress. Piles should be marked or stamped with the date of manufacture. Inspection reports should come from an independent testing or inspection firm and not from the manufacturer.

Lengths.   Precast piles will be shipped to the jobsite according to specified or approved ordered lengths. Each pile should be of the full ordered length except when sectional-type piles are permitted. Sometimes piles will be ordered with sufficient extra length to permit stripping back the concrete and exposing the reinforcing steel for the pile-to-cap connection (see subsection under "Pile Installation"). Ordered lengths may be somewhat larger than anticipated driven lengths to allow for variations in subsoil conditions.

Dimensions.   Piles should be of the shape and size specified.

Tolerances.   Piles should be straight within specified tolerances. Butt ends should be square to the longitudinal axis and free of any major surface irregularities.

Chamfers.   All corners or edges of square piles should be chamfered. The width of the chamfer face should be limited to about 1.5 in (38.1 mm) so that the reduction in any side dimension due to chamfer is not more than about 2 in (50.8 mm).

Damage.   Check piles for detrimental cracks, spalling, slabbing, or other damage. Hairline cracks are normal but should not be too numerous.

Concrete for Cast-In-Place Piles

Design Mix. A design mix with results of tests on standard cylinders should be furnished by the contractor. Copies of these data should be made available to the inspector at the start of pile installation.

Concrete Production Facilities. Concrete may be mixed in portable mixers brought to the pile locations, but generally it will be ready-mixed. Ready-mix concrete may be (1) batched and mixed at a central plant and delivered to the pile locations in agitating or nonagitating trucks (central-mixed), (2) batched at a central plant and mixed in a truck mixer in transit to or after reaching the jobsite (truck-mixed), or (3) partially centrally mixed with mixing completed in a truck mixer en route to the job or on the jobsite (shrink-mixed). The central plant may be located on the jobsite.

The concrete batch and mixing plant should be inspected for adequacy of storage facilities for materials, accuracy and reliability of batching equipment, condition of mixing equipment, and proper operational procedures.

Storage Facilities. Cement must be kept dry whether it is stored in bulk containers or in bags. To avoid contamination, stockpiles of aggregates that have been cleaned, graded, and prepared for batching should be on a hard, clean base with the area around the stockpiles spread with a bedding material of sand, gravel, or rock. Side slopes of stockpiles should have a slope of 7 in or less per foot (583 mm or less per meter) to prevent segregation. Coarse aggregate should be separated by type and size gradation. Overlapping of stockpiles should be prevented, and suitable drainage should be provided. All reasonable precautions should be taken to keep the moisture content of aggregates as nearly uniform as possible.

Batching Equipment. Concrete is usually batched by weight. Batching scales should have a recent calibration and certificate of inspection and must be clean and free of interference by other objects. Separate weigh-batching facilities should be provided for cement. Batch-weight recording and cutoff devices must operate accurately. The bottom of batch bins must be fully sloped in all directions. Water-metering devices, whether at a central mixing plant or mounted on a truck mixer, must be accurate and equipped with indicating dials and totalizers.

Mixing Equipment. All mixing equipment, whether stationary or truck-mounted, must be in good operating condition. The interior of drums should be clean, and mixing blades should not show signs of wear in excess of 1 in (25.4 mm). Truck mixers must be equipped with a reliable revolution counter.

Operations. All materials must be accurately batched, and batching should be by weight. Admixtures, if required, must also be accurately measured. Mixing drums must be cleaned after each use to prevent an accumulation of hardened concrete on the blades. All washwater must be removed from the mixing drum prior to batching. Cement should be used on the basis of first in−first out. The free-water content of the aggregates should be included as part of the total mix water. Aggregates should be allowed sufficient time to drain, and it may be necessary to have a moisture meter in the sand batcher to monitor moisture content. Proper equipment and methods must be used for handling aggregates to avoid segregation and breakage. Segregation of coarse aggregate can be reduced by separating it into several size fractions and batching them separately. Finished screening of aggregates at the batcher is recommended to avoid problems of segregaton and contamination.

Concrete Materials.   Materials including cement, sand, coarse aggregate, and water should be inspected for compliance with specifications and accepted practice.

Cement.   Cement must be of the type specified or permitted with the approval of the engineer. Mill certificates should be furnished to show that cement conforms with the requirements of the specifications and ASTM C 150, Standard Specifications for Portland Cement. Type IV cement should not be used for pile concrete. Type III, or high-early, cement may be permitted for cast-in-place-concrete test piles to get a fast gain in strength. Type II or Type V cement may be specified for sulfate exposure.

Cement remaining in bulk storage for more than 6 months or cement stored in bags longer than 3 months should be retested before use to ensure that it meets the requirements of ASTM C 150. Cement should not be used directly from the mill if it is still hot. The cement should be allowed to cool before using to reduce the possible occurrence of false sets.

Cement should be inspected for contamination by lumps caused by moisture. Cement bags should be inspected for rips, punctures, or other defects. If cement is to be batched by bag, the weights of bags should be spot-checked and should not vary by more than 3 percent.

Sand.   Sand should be clean, sharp, and well graded and be free of silt, clay, or organic material. The specific gravity and/or fineness modulus may be specified for special mixes such as reduced-coarse-aggregate concrete.

Coarse Aggregate.   Specifications may permit gravel or crushed stone. The use of crushed-rock aggregate requires more cement and sand for comparable workability; the use of air entrainment helps. Lightweight aggregates are not recommended, and slag aggregates are not generally used. Alkali-reactive aggregates or aggregates from shales, friable sandstone, and clayey or micaceous rock or cherts should not be permitted. Aggregates should be uncoated and free of silt, clay, organic material, and chemical salts. The specific gravity of the coarse aggregate may be specified. Aggregates should be well graded with a maximum size of ¾ in (19.05 mm) and with the amounts of $-3/16$-in- undersize (-4.762-mm-undersize) aggregates held uniform and within 3 percent.

Water.   As a general rule, mix water should be potable. It should contain no impurities which would affect the quality of the concrete. It should not have a sweet, saline, or brackish taste or contain silt or suspended solids. Very hard water may contain high concentrations of sulfate. Well water from arid regions may contain harmful dissolved mineral salts. If questionable, the water can be chemically analyzed. The quality of the water can be checked by comparing the strength of concrete reached at various ages for a mix using the water of unknown quality with the results of similar age tests on a mix made with water which is known to be acceptable. Impurities in mix water may affect both the compressive strength of the concrete and its setting time.

Admixtures.   The authorized or mandatory use of admixtures will be noted on the design-mix report. Special admixtures such as retarders and fluidizers may be required for pumped concrete.

Cold-Weather Operations.   The minimum temperature of fresh concrete as mixed should be about 45°F (7.2°C) for air temperatures above 30°F (-1.1°C), 50°F (10°C) for air temperatures from 0 to 30°F (-17.2 to -1.1°C), and 55°F (12.7°C) for air temperatures below 0°F (-17.2°C). Frozen aggregate or aggregates containing lumps of ice should be thawed before being used. It may be necessary to preheat the mix water and/or the aggregate. For air temperatures between 30 and 40°F (-1.1 and 7.2°C), it is usually necessary only to heat the water to a maximum of about 140°F (60°C). For air temperatures below 30°F (-1.1°C), the water can be heated to from 140 to 212°F (60 to 100°C) and the aggregate to about 45 to 55°F (7.2 to 12.7°C). Overheating should be avoided. If both the mix water and the aggregates are preheated, it is recommended that the water be mixed with the aggregates before adding the cement to avoid a flash set. The temperature of the water-aggregate mixture should not be higher than 80°F (26.6°C) and preferably about 60°F (15.5°C).

Hot-Weather Operations.   If the temperature of the concrete during mixing is above 80°F (26.6°C), it could result in increased water demand (slump loss) or an accelerated set. The easiest way to control and reduce the concrete temperature is by using cold mix water, which can be achieved by mechanical refrigeration or by using crushed ice as a part of or all of the mix water. Mixing time should be kept to a minimum, and mixing drums as well as water tanks and pipe should be painted white.

Mixing Time. Mixing time starts when the water is added to the mix and should be adequate but not excessive. Minimum mixing times vary with the size and type of the mixer and range from 1 to 3 minutes. Maximum mixing times can range from 3 to 10 minutes. For stationary mixers, minimum mixing time can be established by tests on mixer performance. For truck-mixed concrete, complete mixing requires from 50 to 100 revolutions of the drum at mixing speed. Check the manufacturer's plate on the mixer. If, after mixing, drum speed is reduced to agitation speed or stopped, the drum should be rotated at mixing speed for from 10 to 15 revolutions just before concrete is discharged.

Elapsed Time. For normal temperatures, the total time from start of mixing to discharge should not exceed about 1½ hours and should be reduced as temperatures increase. The mix should be discharged before 300 revolutions of the drum.

Slump. Slump tests should be made periodically in accordance with ASTM C 143-78, Standard Method of Test for Slump of Portland Cement Concrete, to ensure that concrete has the specified slump for proper placement in pile casings, shells, or holes. The slump for concrete as delivered to the top of the pile casing or hole should be 5 in (127 mm) for conventional concrete or 4 in (101.6 mm) for reduced-coarse-aggregate concrete, both with a tolerance of + 2 in, − 1 in (+50.8 mm, −25.4 mm). Special-type piles may require concrete having different slumps (see subsection "Special-Type Piles"). Sometimes it is advisable to check the slump just before adding the final water at the jobsite to avoid too high a slump or a wet mix.

Slump Loss. Slump loss can be caused by overmixing, by hot weather, by pumping through long lines, or by delays in delivery and placement of concrete. Overmixing can and should be avoided. If necessary, all the mix water can be added and all mixing done upon delivery at the jobsite. This could prevent overmixing and may help in eliminating slump loss due to hot weather. If concrete is to be pumped to the pile locations, the slump should be increased without changing the water-cement ratio or concrete strength to compensate for slump loss during pumping. All preparations should be made for depositing concrete upon delivery, and delivery schedules should be arranged to eliminate delays in placing concrete.

Retempering.   The addition of water to the concrete mix to compensate for slump loss resulting from delays in delivery or placing is permissible provided the design water-cement ratio is not exceeded and the concrete has not attained its initial set. Initial set is not to be confused with a false set, when the concrete appears to stiffen but can be made workable with agitation.

Delivery Tickets.   A delivery ticket must accompany each load or batch of concrete. The delivery ticket is for the purchaser, but the inspector should be furnished a copy. It should include sufficient data to identify the producer, project, contractor (purchaser), truck mixer used, and specified concrete mix or strength. Other information which should be on the delivery ticket is the date of delivery, type and brand of cement, maximum aggregate size, weights of cement, sand, and coarse aggregate, type and amount of admixtures, quantity of water, time batched, reading of revolution counter and time when water was first added, volume of batch [cubic yards (1 yd^3 = 0.7645 m^3)] and amount of water added by the receiver. The inspector should note the times of delivery and placement and the air temperature.

Concrete Strength.   Standard cylinders for compression tests should be made periodically or as specified in accordance with ASTM C 31, Standard Method for Making and Curing Concrete Test Specimens in the Field, to ensure that concrete of required strength is being furnished. The frequency for making test cylinders will vary with the job size and other factors, but generally a test set (minimum of two cylinders) should be made for each daily pour or for every 50 yd^3 (38.2 m^3) placed. Also a test set should be made for each age at which compression tests are to be run. The inspector should ensure that cylinders are properly cast, handled, stored, sealed, packaged for shipment, and shipped so as not to invalidate test results. For strict concrete control, test specimens should be cast in cast-iron or tin-can molds. Although widely used, cardboard or paper molds are not recommended for molding test cylinders for strict concrete control. If cardboard molds are used, they should conform with ASTM C 470-79, Specifications for Molds for Forming Concrete Test Cylinders Vertically. Jobsite curing or the use of cardboard molds may contribute to low strength-test results. Grout strengths for special-type piles will be determined by standard cube tests in accordance with ASTM C 91, Specification for Masonry Cement. (See "Auger-Grout Pile" and "Cast-in-Situ Pile" in the subsection "Special-Type Piles.")

Results of Tests.   The pile inspector should be furnished with copies of the results of all concrete compression tests as called for in the specifications. It is advisable to obtain 3- and 7-day break results at the beginning of the job in order to detect trends in concrete strengths. The results of 7-day tests are also valuable in monitoring concrete-strength trends as the job progresses so that if necessary remedial measures can be taken before too much concrete is placed.

Strength Variations. Variations in concrete strength as determined by standard cylinder tests are normal. Several criteria are used to determine the acceptability of variations. For example, the concrete is considered satisfactory if the average of three consecutive tests is equal to or greater than the required 28-day strength and no test falls below the required 28-day strength by more than 500 psi (3447 kPa). Another acceptance criterion is that 80 percent of the tests show strengths greater than the design strength and that not more than 1 test in 10 is less than the required 28-day strength. A third is that the average strength from consecutive tests be greater than the required 28-day strength. If the test results show that concrete strength is below that specified, the cause of low-strength concrete should be investigated. Low strength could be caused by unsatisfactory materials, by improper batching and mixing, or by the use of excess water in the mix. Low cylinder breaks could also result from improperly preparing, curing, handling, or testing cylinder specimens.

Verification of Concrete Strengths. If the results of standard cylinder tests are low, cores can be removed from piles for testing. Core tests are considered satisfactory if the average of three cores is equal to or greater than 85 percent of the required 28-day strength and if no core strength is less than 75 percent of the specified 28-day strength. The results of tests on cores are normally lower than those on standard cylinders. It should be noted that pile concrete in a long steel shell embedded in the ground will cure at a rate slower than that for test cylinders or exposed concrete. Curing conditions are ideal, but the rate of strength gain is lower than normal. Concrete strength in completed piles can also be checked by various nondestructive methods such as penetration-resistance tests. See ASTM C 803-79, Method of Tests for Penetration Resistance of Hardened Concrete.

Steel Pipe and Tube Piles

Material Specifications. Mill certificates or laboratory test reports should be furnished to show that the pipe or tube conforms to the required material specifications covering yield strength. Pipe may be specified by grade with reference to ASTM A 252, Standard Specification for Welded and Seamless Steel Pipe Piles

Lengths.   Pipe pile material may be delivered in random or double random lengths or in ordered lengths. The lengths of tapered portions of tube piles will be determined by the type and size specified. The lengths of extension pieces for tube piles will be as ordered in 10- to 40-ft (3- to 12-m) lengths in 5-ft (1.5-m) increments. Generally payment for pipe and tube pile material is made for the quantity incorporated in the finished foundation. However, if pile material is to be paid for on the basis of approved ordered or furnished lengths, the total delivered lengths of pipe or tube piles should be checked. Extra pieces of pipe and extra lengths or pieces of tube piles may be ordered to provide for piles that may drive longer than anticipated.

Dimensions.   Diameter and wall thickness or gauge should meet the minima specified. Although a minimum wall thickness or gauge may be specified, this does not relieve the contractor from responsibility to furnish thicker walls or heavier gauges if necessary to install the piles properly without damage or to achieve required pile penetration. For tapered tube piles the type of lower pile section (designating the degree of taper) should be as specified.

Pile Fittings.   Special closure plates or points may be required by the specifications. When pipe piles are closed with a flat steel plate, the diameter of the closure plate should not be more than ¾ in (19.05 mm) larger than the outside diameter of the pipe. The specifications may permit splicing pipe piles with steel sleeves with or without welding. Splicing sleeves should conform with the specifications.

Welding.   The welding on of boot plates at the tips of pipe piles will be done on a horizontal rack in advance of pile driving, or pipe may be shipped to the job with closure plates attached. Tube piles will be furnished with closure points welded on by the manufacturer. Splice welding of pipe or tube piles may be done on a horizontal rack or "in the leaders." (See the subsection "Pile Splicing.") The qualifications of welders and all welding should conform with American Welding Society (AWS) D 1.1, Structural Welding Code.

Steel H Piles

Material Specifications.   Mill certificates or laboratory test reports showing that the material meets the specifications as to type of steel and properties including yield strength should be furnished. If the required yield strength is higher than 36 ksi (248.2 MPa), the identity of all steel must be continuously maintained from the point of manufacture to the pile location, or coupons must be taken and tested from each piece to see that it meets the specifications.

Lengths. If pile material is to be paid for on the basis of approved ordered or furnished lengths, the total delivered lengths of H piles should be checked. Piles will generally be shipped in mill lengths. Extra lengths of H piles may be ordered to provide for driving piles longer than anticipated.

Dimensions. The pile size, weight per foot, and thickness should meet the minimum requirements of the specifications. Piles should be of H section conforming with American Institute of Steel Construction (AISC) HP shapes.

Types. Specifications may permit either rolled or built-up shapes.

Pile Fittings. Specifications may require pile-tip reinforcement, which could be special steel castings or fabricated points or pile tips built up with steel plates. Splicing material or fittings may also be specified. Pile-cap plates may be required (See "Cap Plates" in the subsection "Pile Installation.") All pile fittings should conform with the specifications.

Special Coatings. The materials and method of application for special coatings should comply with the specifications. If applied off site, certificates of inspection and/or compliance should be furnished. If welding of coated piles is necessary, the special coating must be properly applied to all welded areas or to those portions of the pile where the coating has been damaged.

Welding. Pile-tip reinforcement will be welded on a horizontal rack before piles are driven. Splicing may be completed on the rack, or fittings may be welded to the bottom of pile sections which are to be added as driving progresses, and splice welding is completed in the leaders. (See "Pile Splicing" in the subsection "Pile Installation.") Pile-cap plates, if required, will be welded on after piles have been cut off to grade. The qualifications of welders and all welding should conform with the AWSD 1.1, Structural Welding Code. Note that special welding procedures may be required for high-yield-strength steel or special steels.

Pile Shells

Pile shells covered by this subsection are made of relatively light-gauge corrugated steel and driven with the aid of an internal steel mandrel. They are considered to be non-load-bearing and serve primarily as a form to protect the concrete as it sets and cures.

Dimensions. Nominal outside diameters of pile shells should be in accordance with the specifications. For tapered or step-tapered pile shells, the minimum nominal tip diameter may be specified with the butt diameter resulting from the rate of taper and pile lengths. If the minimum butt diameter is specified, the required tip diameter will be governed by the taper and pile length.

Lengths. Payment is usually made for pile lengths actually installed. If payment is to be made for furnished lengths, the inspector should verify that the delivered lengths agree with the approved ordered lengths.

    Uniform Diameter. Shells of uniform diameter will usually be shipped to the job in uniform lengths up to about 80 ft (24.4. m). Lengths of shell can be spliced together by butt welding on a horizontal rack to make up the required pile lengths.

    Tapered Shells. Tapered or step-tapered shells will generally be shipped to the job in section lengths of 4, 8, 12, or 16 ft (1.2, 2.4, 3.6, or 4.8 m). Longer section lengths also are used. Shell sections are usually assembled on a horizontal rack to make up the required pile lengths.

Shell Gauges. Sometimes minimum shell gauges may be specified, but generally the responsibility for determining and furnishing the required shell gauges is left to the contractor.

Closure Plates. Step-tapered pile shells will generally be furnished with boot plates attached. Shells of uniform diameter may have closures welded on before shipment to the job, or they may be welded on in the field. Closure plates should conform with the specifications.

Reinforcing Steel

Material Specifications. Mill certificates or laboratory test reports showing that the material meets the specifications as to type of steel and properties including yield strength should be furnished. Reinforcing-steel bundles should have identification tags attached.

Size and Length. Longitudinal reinforcement should be bundled according to size and length, which should be in accordance with the specifications. The sizes and diameters of spirals or hoops should be as specified. Longitudinal steel may be spliced to the required lengths by welding, by approved splicers, or by adequate lapping and wiring.

Bending. Hook- or L-shaped bends should conform with the plans and specifications. The diameter of all bends should not be less than 6 times the minimum bar thickness or diameter. All bending should be done with the bars cold. Bars that have been bent should not be restraightened.

Fittings. Plans or specifications may require special fittings such as spacers for centering reinforcement in the pile casing or hole.

Surface Condition. All reinforcement materials must be new and free from rust. Before actual use, reinforcement must be free from rust scale, loose mill scale, oil, grease, paint, dirt, and all other coatings which will destroy or reduce the bond between steel and concrete.

MATERIAL HANDLING AND STORAGE

Timber Piles

Unloading. Timber piles may be unloaded by controlled roll-off. Dumping should not be permitted.

Handling. Generally treated timber piles should not be handled with timber tongs, cant hooks, peaveys, or pile chains. Piles should be handled so as to avoid puncturing or breaking through their outer treated portion. AWPA standard M 4-80 permits the use of pointed tools provided that the side surfaces of the pile are not penetrated more than $\frac{1}{2}$ in (12.7 mm). This may be difficult to control. Treated timber piles should not be dragged along the ground.

Storage. Timber piles in storage for any length of time should be on adequate blocking and supported to avoid permanent bends. Piles should be stacked on treated or nondecaying material and with an air space beneath them. Storage areas should be free of debris, decayed wood, and dry vegetation (this presents a fire hazard) and should have sufficient drainage to prevent the piles from lying in water.

Precast Piles

Unloading.   Precast piles should be unloaded by lifting them in a horizontal position. Dumping or rolling off the precast piles should not be permitted.

Handling.   Precast piles should be handled with proper slings attached to predesignated pickup points or inserts. Impact loads should be avoided.

Storage.   If precast piles are stored on blocking, it should be placed at predesignated support points to avoid overstressing and cracking the piles.

Steel Pipe and Tube Piles

Unloading.   Controlled dumping or roll-off unloading of pipe or tube piles may be permitted.

Handling.   Sufficient pickup points should be used to avoid bends in pipe or tube piles. A closed-end pile should not be dragged along the ground with the open end first.

Steel H Piles

Unloading.   H piles should be unloaded by lifting them in a horizontal position. Dumping piles should be prohibited.

Handling.   H piles lifted in a horizontal position should have their webs vertical to avoid bending. Coated H piles must be carefully handled so as to avoid damage to the coating.

Storage.   H piles should be stored on adequate blocking. Nesting of piles with their flanges vertical is recommended.

Pile Shells

Unloading.   Dumping of pile shells should not be permitted, but they may be roll-off−unloaded.

Handling.   Pile shells should be handled at all times so as to avoid permanent deformations. A closed-end shell should not be dragged along the ground with the open end first.

Storage. Pile shells should be stored out of mud or standing water. If in storage for a long period of time, shells should be protected from the elements.

Cement

Storage. Bag cement must be stored off the ground on adequate racks and protected from the elements, especially moisture.

Concrete Aggregates

Handling. Aggregates should be handled so as to avoid breakage, segregation, and contamination. The required gradation must be maintained.

Storage. (See "Concrete Production Facilities: Storage Facilities" in the subsection "Pile Material.")

Reinforcement

Handling. Reinforcing steel should be handled in bundles with appropriate lifting slings located at sufficient pickup points to avoid permanent bending. Bundles should not be broken until the steel is to be used. All necessary precautions must be taken to maintain the identification of the steel after the bundles have been broken. This can be done by keeping the steel separated according to type, size, and length with a tagged piece in each stack.

Storage. Reinforcing steel should be stored off the ground on suitable racks or blocking so as to avoid permanent bends. The steel should be stored so as to prevent excessive rusting and contamination by dirt, grease, or other bond-breaking coatings.

PILE EQUIPMENT

Figure 2.3-5 illustrates the basic parts of a typical pile-driving rig. Some parts of the rig are critical to the proper installation of piles (See also Fig. 2.3-6.)

Leaders

Leaders hold the pile and hammer in proper alignment to avoid eccentric hammer blows, which could damage the pile or cause it to drive off

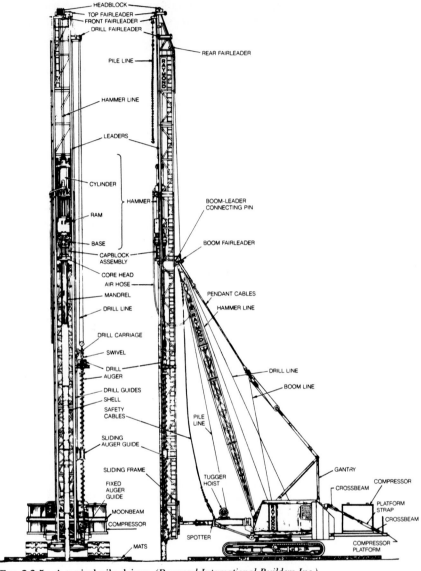

Fig. 2.3-5   A typical pile driver. *(Raymond International Builders Inc.)*

location or invalidate a dynamic-driving formula. They also serve to hold the pile in the specified alignment and provide means for supporting the pile during driving. The leaders, in combination with the boom, spotter, moonbeam, and sliding frame, also permit driving the pile on any required angle or batter. Leaders should be of sturdy construction and

FIG. 2.3-6 Pile-driving rig equipped with a pre-drilling auger installing out-batter piles. *(Raymond International Builders Inc.)*

fixed at two points, normally the boom tip and the spotter. The use of swinging leaders or spud-type leaders is generally not recommended except possibly for small jobs. Leaders should be equipped with some type of extension which would permit the hammer to travel below the bottom of the leaders during driving. Leaders also serve as a mounting for ancillary equipment such as a jet or a drill.

Preexcavation Equipment

The jet or drill should be mounted on the leaders on the same driving radius as the hammer and pile to assure proper positioning for pile alignment and location. If necessary to avoid whipping, the jet pipe or drill stem should be supported by some type of traveling guide. Drill bits or augers should be of the specified size to avoid overdrilling. Drill stems should be of adequate size to handle the necessary water pressures and volumes for effective preexcavation and removal of soil cuttings for the size of hole drilled. Drill stems, kelly bars, and jet pipes must be long enough to reach the necessary preexcavation depths. Jet pumps should be of sufficient size and capacity to provide the required volume of water at the necessary rates and pressures.

Power Source

The power source used to operate the pile-driving hammer such as a boiler or a compressor should be of adequate capacity. Boilers can be sized by horsepower, which can be based on the pounds of steam consumed per hour or the ASME rating or on the square footage of heating area. Compressors will be rated according to the standard volume of compressed air in cubic feet produced per minute (1 ft^3/minute = 0.000472 m^3/second). The hammer manufacturer's data can be used as a guide for determining the required boiler or compressor capacity. However, the actual required capacity will depend upon such things as the length and size of piping and hose connecting the hammer to the power source, the condition of the hammer (wear of piston rings, etc.), and leaks in the system. For air-operated hammers, the consumption figure normally reported is based upon adiabatic compression and the required pressure at the hammer. However, as the air is compressed, it is cooled down for practical reasons. Further heat losses occur before it reaches the hammer. As the air cools, the volume decreases and the pressure drops. Therefore, unless the air is reheated after normal compression, the output of the compressor should be from 30 to 50 percent greater than the adiabatic consumption figure normally reported.

The condition of the boiler and the quality of water used could affect the volume of steam produced and therefore the effective capacity of the boiler.

The manufacturer's data will generally specify the minimum pressure required at the hammer for operation at normal efficiency. Adequate pressure at the hammer is important for double-acting, differential, or compound hammers. It is impractical to measure the pressure at the hammer, and therefore it is customary to mount the pressure gauge at the boiler or compressor discharge. The pressure as measured at the boiler or compressor should be higher to provide for line losses. For steam, the amount of excess pressure would depend upon the length and sizes of piping and hose. With the boiler mounted on the rig and with recommended piping and hose sizes used, the normal minimum required increase in pressure is about 15 psi (10.34 kPa). For air, friction losses in the line tend to be compensated for by pressure gains due to the friction heating the air. There are no energy loss and no reduction in ability to do work resulting from friction losses.

Pile-Driving Hammers

(See Tables 2.3-1 and 2.3-2.)

Hammer Types. Typical pile-driving hammers include drop, single-acting, double-acting, differential, compound, diesel, and vibratory hammers. In addition, there are special-type hammers such as air-gun, vibratory-impact, and electrohydraulic hammers.

Drop Hammer. Drop hammers are rarely used to install foundation piles except for compacted-concrete piles as described under "Compacted-Concrete Pile" in the subsection "Special-Type Piles."

Single-Acting Hammers. Single-acting hammers are powered with compressed air or steam pressure, which is used to raise the hammer ram for each stroke. The delivered energy results from the kinetic energy developed by the gravity fall of the ram.

Double-Acting Hammer. Double-acting hammers can be powered by steam but usually are powered with compressed air, which is used both to raise the ram and to accelerate its fall. This type of hammer exhausts at both the upstroke and the downstroke, and the operating pressure on the downstroke is applied to the full top area of the piston. Double-acting hammers have light rams and high speed and are not as effective in driving piles as hammers with heavy rams.

Differential Hammer. Generally, differential hammers are powered by either steam or compressed air. However, this type of hammer has been designed and built to operate by high-pressure hydraulic fluid. The steam, air, or hydraulic fluid is used both to raise the ram and to accelerate its fall. Differential hammers exhaust during the upstroke, but those powered by hyraulics do not exhaust to the atmosphere, thus reducing noise and pollution. During the downstroke, the cylinder both above and below the piston is open to the operating fluid and thus under equal pressure. The accelerating downward force results from the operating-fluid pressure acting on the top of the piston, which is of larger area than the bottom of the piston (difference equals area of piston rod). These hammers have shorter strokes than comparable single-acting hammers and combine the advantages of the heavy ram of the single-acting hammer with the higher operating speed of the double-acting hammer.

Compound Hammer. The compound hammer is a variation of the differential hammer utilizing compressed air or steam both to raise the ram and to accelerate its fall. The hammer exhausts during the upstroke, at the top of which both exhaust and inlet valves close and no additional motive fluid is introduced into the cylinder. The cylinder spaces both above and below the piston are interconnected, permitting the motive fluid to raise the ram and also enter the top of the cylinder as it expands.

TABLE 2.3.1 Impact Pile-Hammer Specifications, 4000 to 100,000 ft·lb[a]

Rated energy, ft·lb[b]	Model or size	Make or manufacturer[c]	Type[d]	Ram or piston weight, lb	Total operating weight, lb[e]	Normal stroke, in[f]	Boiler capacity, hp	Air consumption, scfm[g]	Operating pressure at hammer, psi[h]	Required hose size, in[i]
100,000	40X	Raymond	S-A	40,000	62,000	30	250[j]	...[k]	135	4
93,220	MRBS-850	Menck	S-A	18,960	27,800	59	185	1950	142	4
91,100	K-45	Kobe	S-A-D	9,920	25,600					
90,000[l]	030	Vulcan	S-A	30,000	55,410	36	247	1833	150	3
90,000[l]	300	Conmaco	S-A	30,000	55,390	36	247	1903	150	3
87,000	D-44	Delmag	S-A-D	9,500	22,300					
84,000	M-43	Mitsubishi	S-A-D	9,460	22,660					
83,180	D-36	Delmag	S-A-D	7,940	17,700					
83,100	D36-02	Delmag	S-A-D	7,900	17,700					
81,250	8/0	Raymond	S-A	25,000	34,000	39	140[j]	...[k]	135	3
80,000	B45	BSP	D-A-D	10,000	27,500					
79,500	J-44	IHI	S-A-D	9,720	21,500					
79,000	K-42	Kobe	S-A-D	9,260	23,300					
75,000	30X	Raymond	S-A	30,000	52,000	30	200[j]	...[k]	135	3
75,000	B-500	Berminghammer	S-A-D	6,900	16,500					
70,800	K-35	Kobe	S-A-D	7,720	18,700	49	185	1590	114	3
67,825	MRBS-750	Menck	S-A	16,500	25,520					
66,100	D30-02	Delmag	S-A-D	6,600	13,150					
63,900	B35	BSP	D-A-D	7,700	12,200					
63,500	J-35	IHI	S-A-D	7,730	16,900					
62,000	M-33	Mitsubishi	S-A-D	7,260	16,940					
60,100	K-32	Kobe	S-A-D	7,050	16,500					
60,000	S-20	MKT	S-A	20,000	38,650	36	190	NA	150	3
60,000[l]	020	Vulcan	S-A	20,000	42,020	36	217	1634	120	3

60,000[l]	200	Conmaco	S-A	20,000	44,560	36	217	1634	120	3
59,500	DE-70B	MKT	S-A-D	7,000	14,600	31	100[j]	—[k]	135	3
59,500[m]	DE70B/50B	MKT	S-A-D	7,000	14,600	39	100[j]	—[k]	135	3
56,900	22X	Raymond	S-A	22,050	31,750	15.5	260	1746	142	4
56,875	5/0	Raymond	S-A	17,500	26,450	36	210	1275	120	3
54,250	D-30	Delmag	S-A-D	6,600	12,300	36	198	1275	120	3
50,700	K-25	Kobe	S-A-D	5,510	13,100	39	85[j]	—[k]	120	2.5
50,200	200C	Vulcan	Diff.	20,000	39,050	18	150[j]	—[k]	120	3
48,750[l]	016	Vulcan	S-A	16,250	33,340					
48,750[l]	160	Conmaco	S-A	16,250	33,200					
48,750	4/0	Raymond	S-A	15,000	23,800					
48,750	150C	Raymond	Diff.	15,000	32,500					
48,500	J-22	IHI	S-A-D	4,850	10,800					
48,500	D22-02	Delmag	S-A-D	4,850	11,400					
45,700	B25	BSP	D-A-D	5,510	15,200					
45,200	MRBS-500	Menck	S-A	11,000	15,200	49	80	1060	110	3
45,000	M-23	Mitsubishi	S-A-D	5,060	11,220					
43,400	N-60	VN-Vulcan	S-A-D	5,280	12,760					
43,400	DA-55-B	MKT	S-A-D	5,000	17,000					
42,500	DE-50B	MKT	S-A-D	5,000	12,000					
42,500[m]	DE70B/50B	MKT	S-A-D	5,000	12,600					
42,000[l]	014	Vulcan	S-A	14,000	27,500	36	200	1282	110	3
42,000[l]	140	Conmaco	S-A	14,000	30,750	36	179	1164	110	3
41,300	K-22	Kobe	S-A-D	4,850	11,700					
41,280	160D	Conmaco	Diff.	16,000	35,400	15.5	237	1550	160	3
40,625	3/0	Raymond	S-A	12,500	21,225	39	70[j]	—[l]	120	2.5
40,625[l]	125CX	Raymond	Diff.	15,000	32,800	15	150[j]	—[k]	120	3
40,625[l]	125	Conmaco	S-A	12,500	21,430	39	119	940	125	2.5
39,500	D-22	Delmag	S-A-D	4,850	11,200					
37,500	S-14	MKT	S-A	14,000	31,700	32	155	NA	100	3
37,375[l]	115(K)	Conmaco	S-A	11,500	20,250	39	161	1066	120	2.5
37,375[l]	115(C)	Conmaco	S-A	11,500	20,780	39	99	910	120	2.5

TABLE 2.3-1 (Continued)

Rated energy, ft·lb[b]	Model or size	Make or manufacturer[c]	Type[d]	Ram or piston weight, lb	Total operating weight, lb[e]	Normal stroke, in[f]	Boiler capacity, hp	Air consumption, scfm[g]	Operating pressure at hammer, psi[h]	Required hose size, in[i]
36,850	DA-55-B	MKT	D-A-D	5,000	17,000	15.5	211	1425	140	3
36,000	140C	Vulcan	Diff.	14,000	27,984	15.5	211	1425	140	3
36,000	140D	Conmaco	Diff.	14,000	31,200					
32,549	N-46	VN-Vulcan	S-A-D	3,960	9,845				110	2
32,500	2/0	Raymond	S-A	10,000	18,550	39	55[j]	..[k]	80	2.5
32,500	S-10	MKT	S-A	10,000	22,380	39	130	1000	105	2.5
32,500[l]	010	Vulcan	S-A	10,000	18,750	39	157	1002	100	2.5
32,500[l]	100(K)	Conmaco	S-A	10,000	18,700	39	145	1002	100	2.5
32,500[l]	100(C)	Conmaco	S-A	10,000	19,280	39	85	820		2.5
32,000	DE-40	MKT	S-A-D	4,000	9,825					
30,225	OR	Vulcan	S-A	9,300	18,050	39	140	1020	100	2.5
30,000	520	Link Belt	D-A-D	5,070	12,545					
30,000	CPD-15	Bolt	S-A-pneu.	14,200	30,000	...	...	600	250	2
27,100	D-15	Delmag	S-A-D	3,300	6,600					
26,200	B15	BSP	D-A-D	3,300	9,000					
26,000	08	Vulcan	S-A	8,000	16,750	39	127	880	83	2.5
26,000[l]	80(K)	Conmaco	S-A	8,000	16,700	39	121	880	85	2.5
26,000[l]	80(C)	Conmaco	S-A	8,000	17,280	39	75	730	85	2.5
26,000	S-8	MKT	S-A	8,000	18,300	39	120	850	80	2.5
26,000	M-14S	Mitsubishi	S-A-D	2,970	7,260					
25,200	K-13	Kobe	S-A-D	2,870	8,000					
25,000	B-225	Berming-hammer	S-A-D	2,850	6,800					
24,600	N-33	VN-Vulcan	S-A-D	3,000	7,645	16.5	180	1245	120	2.5
24,450	80C	Vulcan	Diff.	8,000	17,885					

24,450	80CH	Raymond	Diff.-hyd	8,000	17,780	16.5	...	...	5100	2.5
24,450	80C	Raymond	Diff.	8,000	17,780	16.5	80[j]	...[k]	120	2.5
24,375	0	Vulcan	S-A	7,500	16,250	39	128	841	80	2
24,374	1/0	Raymond	S-A	7,500	16,100	39	50[j]	...[k]	110	2.5
24,000	C-826	MKT	Comp.	8,000	17,750	18	120	875	125	
23,800	DE-30B	MKT	S-A-D	2,800	7,250					
23,800[m]	DE30B/20B	MKT	S-A-D	2,800	7,250					
23,800[n]	DA-35-B	MKT	S-A-D	2,800	10,000					
23,150[o]	MS300	MKT	S-A	6,614	9,800	420	50	750	115	2.5
22,500	D-12	Delmag	S-A-D	2,750	6,050					
22,400	DE-30	MKT	S-A-D	2,800	8,125					
21,000[n]	DA-35-B	MKT	D-A-D	2,800	10,000					
19,500	1-S	Raymond	S-A	6,500	12,500	36	40[j]	...[k]	104	1.5
19,500	65C	Raymond	Diff.	6,500	14,675	16	70[j]	...[k]	120	2
19,500	65CH	Raymond	Diff.-hyd	6,500	14,615	16	...	...	5000	2
19,500[p]	06 & 106	Vulcan	S-A	6,500	11,200	36	94	625	100	2
19,500[l]	65(K)	Conmaco	S-A	6,500	11,200	36	94	650	100	2
19,500[l]	65(C)	Conmaco	S-A	6,500	12,100	36	94	650	100	2
19,200	65C	Vulcan	Diff.	6,500	14,886	15.5	152	991	150	2.5
19,150	11B3	MKT	D-A	6,500	14,000	19	126	900	100	
18,200	440	Link Belt	D-A-D	4,000	10,300					
18,000	312	Link Belt	D-A-D	3,855	10,375					
17,000	DE-20B	MKT	S-A-D	2,000	6,450					
17,000[m]	DE30B/20B	MKT	S-A-D	2,000	6,450					
16,250	S-5	MKT	S-A	5,000	12,460	39	85	600	80	2
16,000	DE-20	MKT	S-A-D	2,000	5,375					
16,000	C-5	MKT	Comp.	5,000	11,880	18	80	585	100	2.5
15,100	50C	Vulcan	Diff.	5,000	11,782	15.5	125	880	120	2
15,000[p]	1 & 106	Vulcan	S-A	5,000	9,700	36	81	565	80	2
15,000	1	Raymond	S-A	5,000	11,000	36	40[j]	...[k]	80	1.5
15,000[q]	15M	Raymond	Diff.	5,000	10,300	18	60[j]	...	120	2
15,000[l]	50(K)	Conmaco	S-A	5,000	9,700	36	81	565	80	2

TABLE 2.3-1 (*Continued*)

Rated energy, ft·lb [b]	Model or size	Make or manufacturer [c]	Type [d]	Ram or piston weight, lb	Total operating weight, lb [e]	Normal stroke, in [f]	Boiler capacity, hp	Air consumption, scfm [g]	Operating pressure at hammer, psi [h]	Required hose size, in [i]
15,000 [f]	50(C)	Conmaco	S-A	5,000	10,600	36	81	565	80	2
15,000	312	Link Belt	S-A-D	3,855	10,375					
13,100	10B3	MKT	D-A	3,000	10,850	19	104	750	100	2.5
9,100	D-5	Delmag	S-A-D	1,100	2,750					
9,000	C-3	MKT	Comp.	3,000	8,500	16	60	450	100	2
9,000	S-3	MKT	S-A	3,000	9,030	36	50	400	80	1.5
8,800	DE-10	MKT	S-A-D	1,100	3,100					
8,750	9B3	MKT	D-A	1,600	7,000	17	85	600	100	2
8,300	DA-15	MKT	D-A-D	1,100	5,000					
8,100	180	Link Belt	D-A-D	1,725	4,550					
7,500	105	Link Belt	D-A-D	1,445	3,885					
7,260	30C	Vulcan	Diff.	3,000	7,036	12.5	85	488	120	1.5
7,260	2	Vulcan	S-A	3,000	6,700	29	49	336	80	1.5
6,500	105	Link Belt	S-A-D	1,445	3,885					
4,150	7	MKT	D-A	800	5,100	9.5	65	450	100	1.5
4,000	DGH-900	Vulcan	Diff.	900	5,000	10	75	580	78	1.5

[a] Diesel-hammer specifications subject to change.

[b] Energy ratings for diesel hammers are generally based on the maximum piston stroke. Actual stroke and energy would depend on driving conditions. Energy ratings for other hammers are fixed by ram weight and stroke and, in addition for double-acting, differential, and compound hammers, by piston areas and operating pressures.

[c] Berminghammer Corp. Ltd. Hamilton, Ont.; Bolt Associates, Norwalk, Conn.; BPS International Foundations Limited, Clayden, Suffolk, England; Conmaco, Kansas City, Kans.; Delmag-Pileco Inc., Houston, Texas, and the Foundation Equipment Co., Newcommerstown, Ohio; IHI—Maruka Machinery Corp. of America, Houston, Texas; Kobe—L. B. Foster Co., Schiller Park, Ill., Linkbelt Speeder Division, FMC Corp., Cedar Rapids, Iowa; Menck—Conmaco, Kansas City, Kans.; MKT Corporation, Dover, N.J.; Raymond International Inc., Houston, Texas; Vulcan Iron Works, West Palm Beach, Fla.

^{d}S-A = single acting steam-air; D-A = double-acting steam-air; S-A-D = single-acting diesel; D-A-D = double-acting diesel; diff. = differential; comp. = compound; hyd. = hydraulic; pneu. = pneumatic.

^{e}Total weights for diesel hammers are without drive caps. For other hammers, weight includes base.

^{f}Strokes for diesel hammers vary with driving conditions and other factors.

^{g}Air consumption is based on adiabatic compression. Unless the air is reheated before entering the hammer, the actual consumption will be greater. The compressor capacity should be from 30 to 50 percent higher than the air consumption indicated.

^{h}Pressure at boiler should be from 15 to 25 psi higher to provide for line losses.

^{i}Piping should be the next larger size.

^{j}Based on 10 ft^2 of heating surface per horsepower.

^{k}Required air to operate any hammer at normal efficiency depends upon many variables. The manufacturer prefers to consider each case rather than assign fixed scfm numbers.

^{l}Adjustable energy. Check on trip setting.

^{m}Interchangable pistons. Check on the piston used.

^{n}Convertible to either double-acting or single-acting mode.

^{o}Variable energy due to variable stroke. Check on the stroke setting by operator.

^{p}For Model 106 the ram weight can be either 6500 or 5000 lb. Weight is changed by adding or removing two 750-lb weights which fit inside cylinders formed in the ram. Check on the ram weight used.

^{q}Internal hammer used with special Raymond mandrel.

NOTE: 1 ft^2 = 0.929 m^2; 1 ft·lb = 135.6 J; 1 hp = 746 W; 1 in = 25.4 mm; 1 lb = 0.4536 kg; 1 psi = 6.894 kPa.

After the piston or ram reaches the top of its stroke, the continued expansion of the motive fluid acting on the differential area between the top and the bottom of the piston accelerates the piston on the downstroke.

Diesel Hammer.   Diesel hammers are self-contained power units using the explosion of diesel fuel under the ram or piston both to raise the ram for the next stroke and to exert some push on the pile. The hammer is started by raising with a line the ram or piston to the top of its stroke and releasing it, permitting it to fall by gravity inside the cylinder. During the downstroke, the ram activates a fuel pump, which injects diesel fuel into the combustion chamber at the base of the cylinder just before the ram reaches the end of its stroke. Some hammers are of the impact atomization type, whereas others have an atomized fuel-injection system. The ram compresses the air in the cylinder, and the air-fuel mixture ignites under pressure and heat. The resulting explosion raises the ram for its next stroke. As long as sufficient pile-penetration resistance is encountered, the hammer will continue to operate. If there is little or no resistance to pile penetration, the hammer will stop. The hammer can be stopped at any time by cutting off the fuel flow.

There are two basic types, single-acting and double-acting. For the single-acting type, the cylinder in which the ram operates is open at the top. For the double-acting type, the cylinder is closed at the top, and entrapped air above the ram is compressed as the ram rises. This compressed air may help to accelerate the fall of the ram but also shortens the stroke.

Vibratory Hammer.   Vibratory hammers or drivers apply a dynamic force to the pile from paired rotating weights set eccentrically from their centers of rotation and positioned so that when rotated the horizontal forces are canceled and the vertical forces are added. The oscillator containing the rotating weights must be rigidly connected to the pile to transmit the longitudinal vibrations effectively. Vibratory drivers are more effective for installing nondisplacement-type piles (or steel sheeting) in granular or cohesionless soils. The driving effectiveness of the vibratory hammer can be increased by applying a bias weight or force to the nonvibrating portion of the driver. Vibratory drivers of the low-frequency type have operating frequencies ranging from 0 to about 2000 vibrations per minute, and the oscillator is powered with an electric or a hydraulic motor. The high-frequency type operates at frequencies ranging from 0 to about 8000 vibrations per minute, which is within the resonant frequency range of most piles. The oscillators for these drivers are powered by either gasoline or diesel engines.

Hammer Energy.   Pile-driving hammers are available in various sizes, ranging from a few hundred ft·lb (1 ft·lb = 1.356 J) per blow to over

800,000 ft·lb (1084.7 kJ). Normally foundation piles are installed with hammers ranging from about 10,000 to 50,000 ft·lb (13.56 to 67.79 kJ). Hammers smaller than about 10,000 ft·lb are used principally for underpinning work or for installing sheeting; hammers larger than about 50,000 ft·lb have been developed to drive long, heavy piles for offshore and other marine structures.

The required type and size (rated energy) of the pile-driving hammer will generally be specified. For vibratory drivers the required size may be stated in terms of dynamic force available at a specified frequency. Hammers somewhat larger than specified may be used, except that the hammer energy used to drive timber piles should be limited to about 15,000 ft·lb (20.34 kJ) per blow.

The energy delivered by an impact hammer depends upon the mass of the ram and its velocity at impact. Note that hammer energy is not a function of operating speed. Under field conditions it is very difficult to measure the terminal velocity of the ram.

Special equipment has been developed actually to measure the amount of hammer energy being delivered to the top of the pile. This equipment, known as a pile dynamic analyzer, is sometimes used to monitor and control pile installation. It requires special instrumentation to be attached to the pile or to a "follower" inserted between the pile and the driving system. Based upon a wave-equation analysis but inputting the actual measured hammer energy, a direct readout of the pile-soil capacity during driving can be obtained. If such measurements are taken during retapping of the piles, the effects of soil freeze or relaxation can be taken into account. It is impractical to use such equipment on all piles, and the equipment is not found on routine jobs. However, this type of equipment can be used to check hammer performance periodically.

Drop Hammer.   The theoretical energy delivered by the drop hammer can be determined from the weight of the hammer and its fall. However, friction losses will occur, and other energy reductions could result from such things as the force necessary to overhaul the hammer line or the snubbing of the hammer just prior to impact.

Single-Acting Hammer.   The rated energy of a single-acting hammer can be checked by determining the weight of the ram from its material and volume and measuring the stroke. In addition to normal energy reduction due to mechanical losses in the hammer, the delivered energy could be affected by improper positioning of the valve trip wedges on the slide bar. Sufficient steam or air pressure must be furnished to raise the ram to the full height of its stroke, and the opening of the inlet valve must be timed so as to avoid back pressure. The energy of the single-acting hammer can be varied by several methods such as changing hammer rams, changing slide bars and the hammer stroke, adding or removing weight from the ram, or using a split trip combined with a multiple-wedge slide bar. The inspector should check to see that the hammer is set up to deliver the required rated energy.

Double-Acting Hammer. For double-acting hammers, delivered energy depends upon the ram weight and stroke plus the force developed by the operating pressure. Although the correct pressure must be maintained at the hammers, it is very impractical to try to measure this pressure. However, gauges could be mounted at the power source or somewhere in the line with sufficient excess pressure furnished to compensate for line losses. The maximum kinetic energy developed by any double-acting hammer cannot exceed the total weight of the hammer multiplied by the length of the ram stroke.

Differential Hammer. As with the double-acting hammer, the delivered energy of the differential hammer is a function of operating pressure. To assure sufficient operating pressure, gauges can be mounted at the power source. The energy delivered by the differential hammer can be varied by changing slide bars and adjusting the stroke. Valve trips and slide-bar wedges must be correctly positioned to ensure a full stroke and avoid back pressure. Differential hammers are delivering their full available energy when the hammer base rises slightly during the downstroke.

Diesel Hammer. The method used to determine the rated energy of diesel hammers varies within the industry. Many methods are based on the weight of the ram or piston and its stroke, but there is no uniformity on the lengths of strokes used in rating the hammers. Some manufacturers use the maximum stroke attainable, while others use a more conservative and realistic normal stroke. The actual stroke would depend upon the type of pile being driven and the driving resistance.

Theoretically, three basic forces result from the diesel cycle: (1) compression, (2) impact, and (3) combustion. To these might be added a fourth force resulting from the compression and subsequent expansion of the air at the top of the cylinder in a double-acting diesel hammer. During the compression cycle on the downstroke the impact of the ram is cushioned, resulting in some energy loss. This loss could be considered as being compensated for by the force gained from the explosion. Therefore, overall energy would be equal to the ram weight times its stroke. During the compression cycle on the upstroke for double-acting hammers, the ram slows down and the stroke shortens. The accelerating force resulting from the expansion of the compressed air could be considered to compensate for the shortened stroke.

The energy resulting from the explosion of the diesel fuel would depend upon the type and amount of fuel injected and the efficiency of combustion. The type and quantity of fuel used should be in accordance with the manufacturer's data. The fuel pump can be checked to see if it delivers the correct amount of fuel by disconnecting the pump and activating it for several strokes while measuring the quantity of fuel dispensed. When the driving resistance is low, when the hammer is driving on lightweight springy piles, or when the piston rings are badly worn, the full compression and explosive force cannot be achieved. Evidence of poor combustion would be a black exhaust, whereas a light-blue exhaust would indicate good combustion. Preignition which could cushion the hammer blow or prevent actual impact could occur if the wrong type of fuel is used. Fuel with too low a flash point could lead to preignition with reduced hammer performance. Preignition could also occur with impact atomization hammers owing to overheating.

Unless the rated energy is verified by tests, it is recommended that the theoretical energy delivered by the hammer be computed from the weight of the ram and its stroke. All diesel hammers should be equipped with a stroke indicator. When the energy being delivered by a diesel hammer can be controlled by a throttle adjustment, the throttle must be set to deliver the required energy. Some diesel hammers are equipped with interchangeable pistons or rams. Others are convertible to either the double-acting or the single-acting mode. The inspector should check the piston weight being used or the mode of hammer operation.

Vibratory Driver. (See Table 2.3-2.) The amount of dynamic force delivered by a vibratory driver would vary with the steady-state frequency. This frequency would depend upon the type and weight of the pile being driven, the type of soil into which the pile is being driven, and the available horsepower. A limiting factor may be the design of the oscillator itself. For electric-powered drivers the operating frequency can be adjusted by changing the sprocket ratios. The inspector should learn which sprocket ratio is being used. The available dynamic force is also a function of the eccentric moment being developed by the rotating weights, which in turn depends upon the mass of the weights and their eccentricity. For the high-frequency resonant driver, the available dynamic force would depend upon the type and size of rollers (eccentric weights) being used, which would determine not only the eccentric moment developed but also the available frequency. Check the type and size of the rollers in the oscillator.

Hammer Cushion (Capblock)

The hammer cushion, or capblock, is inserted between the striking part of the hammer and the pile or drive cap to protect the hammer from damaging impact stresses. However, the hammer cushion must be stiff enough to transmit the driving energy adequately to the pile. A commonly used capblock is a one-piece hardwood block with its grain parallel

TABLE 2.3-2 Vibratory-Pile-Driver Data

Dynamic Force, tons[a]	Eccentric moment, in·lb	Make or manufacturer[b],[c]	Model	Type	Frequency vibrations/minute[c]	HP[d]	Vibrating weight, lb[e]	Total operating, lb
204.5	10,000	ICE	10,000	Hydraulic	1,200	580	18,300	24,500
48.3–88.9–141.9[f]	6,940	PTC	2-75 VT	Electric	700–950–1200[g]	300	19,257[h]	39,200
127.8	4,000	ICE	812	Hydraulic	1,500	330	10,500	14,700
116	3,000	ICE	V-20	Hydraulic	1,650	295	9,000	10,700
111.3	4,000	MKT	4,000	Hydraulic	1,400	299	9,440	18,800
111.2	3,480	Foster	40 H	Hydraulic	1,500	302	8,700	21,500
73.6–107.0[i]	79–173[i]	Bodine	BRD-100 AB	...[g]	6,600–8,100[i]	800	2,000	22,000
48.3–72.9–102.5[f]	6,940	PTC	2-60T	Electric	700–860–1020	240	16,000	38,000
98.5	2,400	MKT	V-18	Hydraulic	1,700	248	11,100	15,400
64.0–65.0–79.2[j]	58–105–128[j]	Bodine	BRD-1000 B	...[g]	6,600––8,100[j]	800	2,000	22,000
78.3	1,800	MKT	V-16	Hydraulic	1,750	156	7,600	9,250
24.1–44.5–71.0[f]	3,470	PTC	2-75	Electric	700–950–1200[g]	150	9,740	20,300
70.1	1,442	MKT	V-14	Hydraulic	1,850	140	8,300	10,500
65.4	1,800	ICE	416	Hydraulic	1,600	175	7,175	12,200
56.0	1,152	MKT	V-10	Hydraulic	1,850	110	8,100	10,000
55.6	1,740	PTC	20 H	Hydraulic	1,500	151	9,300	12,900
24.1–36.4–51.3[f]	3,470	PTC	2-50, 2-60	Electric	700–860–1020[g]	100–120	9,400	16,500
48.4	1,740	Foster	1,700	Hydraulic	1,400	147	7,200	12,900
39.0	1,220	PTC	14 H	Hydraulic	1,500	147	7,200	6,700
38.3	1,200	Foster	1,200	Hydraulic	1,500	70	6,320	6,700
36.4	1,000	ICE	216	Hydraulic	1,600	115	2,700	4,500
29.9	1,000	MKT	V-5	Hydraulic	1,450	59	4,000	9,300
22.5–29.9[f]	1,740	PTC	2-40	Electric	955–1,100[g]	80	8,110	13,500
11.3–15.0[f]	870	PTC	2-20	Electric	955–1,100[g]	40	5,800	7,000
14.8	260	PTC	3 H	Hydraulic	2,000	25	1,540	1,590
8.0	174	PTC	2-3	Electric	1,800	6	1,540	1,500

[a] At maximum frequency shown when driving a 2000-lb pile in granular soil.

[b] L. B. Foster Company, Schiller Park, Ill.; ICE—International Construction Equipment, Matthews, N.C.; MKT Corporation, Dover, N.J.; PTC—Pileco Inc., Houston, Texas.

[c] Steady-state frequency.   [d] Horsepower at the oscillator.   [e] Without pile but with standard head.

[f] Force depends on sprocket ratio used and corresponding maximum frequency.

[g] Maximum frequency depends on sprocket ratio used.   [h] Including heavy casing head.

[i] Lower force and moment and higher frequency with steel rollers; higher force and moment and lower frequency with tungsten-alloy rollers.

[j] Lower force and moment and higher frequency with steel rollers; intermediate force and moment and lower frequency with tungsten carbide rollers; higher force and moment and lower frequency with tungsten-alloy rollers.

NOTE: 1 hp = 746 W; 1 in · lb = 0.1129 N · m; 1 lb = 0.4536 kg; 1 ton = 907.2 Mg. Specifications are subject to change.

to the pile axis and enclosed in a tight-fitting steel sleeve. This type of capblock becomes crushed and burnt during pile driving, resulting in variations in elastic properties, and requires frequent changing. Many hammer cushions in use today are of laminated construction with alternating layers of aluminum and Micarta disks or similar material. Others are made of such materials as asbestos. These capblocks are generally stiffer than the wood capblock and more efficiently transmit hammer energy to the pile. Also, these hammer cushions retain fairly constant elastic properties and are relatively long-lived.

The minimum type of capblock should be as specified. Capblocks with high elastic properties such as wood chips, pieces of wire rope, etc., are generally prohibited. The inspector should record the type and description of the hammer cushion used.

Pile Cushion

When precast-concrete piles are being driven, pile cushions will be required to protect the heads of the piles from sharp impact stresses and to distribute the hammer blows uniformly over the tops of the piles. A pile cushion is placed between the drive cap and the head of the pile. A new pile cushion should be used at the start of driving each pile. The type of wood and the thickness of the cushion should be as specified or with properties as used in a wave-equation analysis or as used in the establishment of driving criteria. The inspector should record the type and description of the pile cushion used.

Drive Cap (Drive Head, Bonnet)

Drive caps are steel castings or forgings which are attached to the hammer base and into which the head of the pile is inserted for driving. Drive caps used for timber, steel H, pipe, or tube piles should be of the correct size and provide full bearing over the entire cross section of the pile. Drive caps for precast-concrete piles should be sufficiently loose so as not to restrain the pile from its tendency to rotate during driving.

Follower

The follower is a structural member used as an extension of the pile to drive the head of the pile below the ground or water surface or below the level to which the hammer can reach. The follower may also serve to accommodate reinforcing steel or prestressing strand which may project beyond the head of a precast pile for the pile-to-cap connection.

Followers should be of steel and sufficiently rigid or stiff to assure adequate transmission of hammer energy. The bottom of the follower should be formed like, or fitted with, a drive cap suitable for the type of pile being driven. A pile cushion may be required between the pile head and the bottom end of the follower. The use of a follower may be subject to the approval of the engineer of record. If a follower is used, it should be described as to material, size, length, and weight.

PILE INSTALLATION

Site Preparation

Generally, specifications will require that excavation be carried out to at least pile-cutoff grade before piles are driven. There may be conditions such as extreme variations in pile-cutoff grades, unusual subsoil conditions, or closely spaced pile groups which make excavation to below pile cutoff impractical before piles are driven. If piles are to be driven through overburden (soils which will subsequently be removed) the inspector should be aware of the possible effects of driving piles through overburden soils on such things as pile-butt location, pile payment, the cutting off of piles, or the use of followers. There should be agreements as to the responsibilities of the parties concerned with these matters.

Excavation banks should be properly sloped or adequately sheeted and braced to take all possible surcharge loads during and after pile driving and to protect the piles from detrimental ground movements. Groundwater and surface water should be controlled to provide reasonably dry work areas.

Pile Layout

(See Fig. 2.3-7.) The pile inspector should be familiar with the pile layout including positions and sizes of pile groups, number and arrangement of piles within each group, and locations of isolated piles. In general, piles will have a uniform spacing or group arrangement. The positions of pile-location stakes should be checked; this can generally be done visually by comparing the group layout with the pile-location plan, by counting the number of stakes, and by checking on any nonuniform spacing in the field layout. Frequently pile groups are also on line and at some uniform spacing. Obvious discrepancies in alignment or spacing should be checked. Distances between pile groups can be checked to detect any major survey errors. The inspector should be aware of possible construc-

FIG. 2.3-7 Spotting pile on a location stake.
(Raymond International Builders Inc.)

tion activity which may dislodge or move pile-location stakes before piles are installed. If such construction activity occurs, the location and number of pile stakes should be checked before piles are driven.

Pile Spacing

Normal pile center-to-center spacing is about twice the average diameter or diagonal dimension. Special-type piles may require increased spacing. (See the subsection "Special-Type Piles.") The required spacing for friction piles may be greater than that for point-bearing piles. If there is any evidence of pile interference during driving such as driving a pile into a pile already driven, it may be necessary to increase pile spacing. The possibility of pile interference increases with increasing pile lengths and flexibility. The use of a stiffer pile or increasing pile spacing beforehand is recommended for very long piles.

Identification of Piles

Each pile on the job should have a unique designation which should be noted on the pile-numbered plan and used on all pile-driving logs, pile reports, and other job records.

Preexcavation

The use of preexcavation methods such as predrilling or prejetting may be permitted by the specifications or be subject to the approval of the engineer. Preexcavation may be required to assist in pile penetration of dense upper strata, to reduce pile heave, or to assist in driving piles to the required penetration. Sometimes the depth of preexcavation will be limited by the specifications, and in most cases the specifications will require driving the pile below the depth preexcavated. The inspector should observe the discharge of soil cuttings in order to estimate the volume of soil removed. Prolonged jetting or drilling without advancing the jet or drill should be prohibited. Jetting should not be permitted in soils containing large gravel, cobbles, or boulders. These could collect at the bottom of the jetted hole, making subsequent pile driving impossible.

Pile Spotting

The tip of the pile (or auger or drill bit) should be accurately spotted over the pile-location stake (Fig. 2.3-7). To avoid errors due to parallax, the positioning of the pile can be checked by measuring to two reference stakes 90° apart. Sometimes a template can be used to assure accurate positioning.

Pile Alignment

Piles are installed either vertically (plumb) or on a batter. The degree or rate of batter and the direction of batter will be indicated on the plans. Both the leaders and the pile or casing should be positioned as accurately as possible to the alignment required by the plans. For drilled piles or when piles are preexcavated, the drill stem or jet pipe must also be properly lined up. If batter piles are installed, the piles or holes must be oriented in the direction shown on the plans.

Before driving starts and after the pile point has been properly spotted, the alignment of the pile and equipment should be checked by using a mason's level (Fig. 2.3-8); for batter piles the level can be held on a simple wood template cut to the correct batter angle and held against the leaders,

FIG. 2.3-8   Checking pile alignment before driving. *(Raymond International Builders Inc.)*

pile, or drill stem. The pile or drill rig should be on a stable and level hard standing (preferably timber mats) so that alignment of the pile and equipment will be maintained. Alignment of piles should be checked periodically during driving, and such checks should be made on exposed lengths of not less than 5 ft (1.5 m).

If a pile is to be driven through soils which are to be subsequently removed (overburden soils) or through water, the initial alignment of the pile is critical. Any misalignment could result in the pile butt being off design location at cutoff; the amount of mislocation would increase with increasing depths of overburden or water.

If pile alignment below the ground surface is considered critical enough to specify an axial-alignment tolerance for the full length of the pile, only those piles for which axial alignment after installation can be determined throughout the pile length should be used. This includes pipe, tube, or shell-type piles plus those precast-concrete and steel H piles which are fitted with a full-length inspection duct down which an inclinometer could be lowered to measure axial deviations.

Any type of pile could be deflected off required axial alignment during driving. This could be caused by subsurface obstructions, sloping rock surfaces, densification of soil during driving, and certain subsoil conditions such as cavernous limestone. Under soft soil conditions, the forces of gravity could cause flexible piles driven on a batter to deflect downward as they are driven. Piles that are less stiff, for example, steel H piles, are more readily deflected off line. Also, flexible drill stems used for preexcavation or for installing drilled piles could easily be deflected off line. The chances of bending increase with increasing pile lengths or flexibility.

Excessive deviations from the specified axial alignment can sometimes be controlled by using a stiffer pile, by predrilling, or by the removal of obstructions. Under some conditions such as driving piles in cavernous limestone, there is no practical method for eliminating pile bending.

Batter Piles

If the actual driven lengths of vertical piles, batter piles, or opposing batter piles are longer than anticipated, the possible interference of piles should be investigated. It may be necessary to relocate the batter piles or change the degree or direction of batter to avoid pile interference.

Pile Length in Leaders

If payment for piles is based on the length of pile raised in the leaders, the inspector should record such length for each pile. It should be noted that additional lengths of pile may have to be added during installation. If the lengths of piles cut off are reused, the pay lengths of piles should be adjusted so that double payment is not made for pile material.

Driving Formulas

The basis for the development of most dynamic pile-driving formulas is equating the energy resulting from the hammer weight W falling a distance H to the work done in moving the pile a distance S against a resistance R $(WH = RS)$. To this basic equation have been applied various terms and factors to account for hammer efficiency, inertia losses, and losses of energy in the hammer-capblock-pile-soil system. To some have been applied a factor of safety so that the formula results in the safe or allowable load. More than 400 driving formulas have been proposed.

Driving formulas range from the relatively simple *Engineering News* formula

$$R = \frac{2WH}{S + 0.1}$$

to the complicated Hiley formula

$$R_u = \frac{e_f\, W_r\, h}{s + \tfrac{1}{2}\,(C_1 + C_2 + C_3)} \times \frac{W_r + e^2 W_p}{W_r + W_p}$$

See *Pile Foundations* by R. D. Chellis (in References) for more details on driving formulas. There is no indication that the more complicated of these empirical formulas are any more accurate than the simple ones. All can show a wide scatter when compared with load-test results. These formulas can be used for relatively light loads and in cases in which the formula has been calibrated for pile and soil conditions.

A more accurate and rational dynamic formula, which is solved by computer, is the wave equation. The wave equation can take into accurate account all the variable factors which could affect pile capacity as determined by dynamic methods. In the absence of soil freeze or relaxation, the wave equation could give an accurate measure of the static capacity of the pile based on dynamic measurements. The accuracy and reliability of a wave-equation analysis depends on how the hammer-cushion-pile-soil system was modeled, how the computer program was written, and the accuracy of the input data. Not all wave-equation programs are equally valid, and proper selection of input data is often a matter of sound engineering judgment based upon experience. It should be noted that wave-equation analysis also determines maximum compression and tension stresses in the pile material during driving.

Installation Criteria

Piles can be installed by dead weight, by dynamic impact, by drilling, by jacking, by vibratory driving, or by a combination of these methods.

Dead Weight.   For the dead-weight method and in the absence of soil freeze the ultimate capacity of the pile as installed is limited to the amount of weight applied. This is not a practical way to install piles. If used, the amount of weight applied should be recorded.

Dynamic Impact.   The specifications may require that the piles be driven to a required length or tip elevation or to a minimum penetration resistance during final driving or to a combination of such driving criteria. The required pile length and/or penetration resistance may be established by load-test results. Final driving resistance may also be established as a result of drive-test piles installed immediately adjacent to test-boring locations. The required penetration resistance may be specified or may result from a wave-equation analysis or the application of a driving formula. The introduction of fresh capblock material just prior to the measurements of final pile set should not be allowed. The applicability of a specified penetration resistance or the use of a dynamic formula will depend upon the drivability or stiffness of the pile.

The stiffer the pile, the more effective the hammer blows in obtaining pile penetration. Therefore, lightweight, springy piles may appear to have high capacity by a dynamic formula, whereas in reality much of the hammer energy is being dissipated in elastic losses. Conversely, a heavy, stiff pile may appear to have low capacity by a dynamic formula, whereas in reality the hammer blows are fully effective in achieving pile penetration and mobilizing capacity. A wave-equation solution reflects pile stiffness or drivability. If a required penetration resistance is specified, consideration should be given to the effects of pile stiffness; a heavy, stiff pile will penetrate more deeply than a lightweight, springy pile for the same penetration resistance. Also the lightweight, springy pile may not be achieving the required capacity.

Adherence to an established driving resistance permits each pile to seek its own required capacity regardless of normal variations in depth, density, and quality of the bearing strata or variations in pile length. This characteristic is not found in several of the special-type piles described in the subsection "Special-Type Piles."

Drilling.   Drilled piles will generally be installed to a required depth. The drilling operation and soil cuttings should be observed to assist in evaluating the subsoil conditions at each pile location and to correlate with those at test-pile locations. If conditions such as a hole of adequate size, absence of groundwater, and insertion of a temporary steel liner permits, the hole may be entered and the bottom inspected or tested to ensure that an adequate bearing stratum has been reached. (See "Bored Pile" in the subsection "Special-Type Piles.")

Jacking.   For piles installed by jacking, ultimate capacity is generally limited by the reaction available to resist the jacking force. If this method is used, the jacking force should be recorded.

Vibratory Driving.   If piles are to be installed with a vibratory driver, the specifications may require that the piles be driven to a required length or tip elevation. Additional subsoil information based upon closely spaced borings may be necessary to establish required pile lengths. Driving criteria may involve a minimum rate of penetration for a specified dynamic force or frequency. The specifications may require that installation criteria be verified by means of a conventional impact hammer and/or load test. The specifications may also require that the final penetration resistance of all piles be checked with an impact hammer.

Driving Log

Probably the most common duty of the pile inspector is the recording of the driving log. This involves more than just counting blows. The inspector should observe, record, and evaluate occurrences during pile installation which may affect the integrity or the bearing capacity of the pile or prevent it from meeting the specifications or which may affect existing piles or structures.

Impact Driving. The specifications may require that the number of hammer blows required for each foot of pile penetration be recorded. This is especially true for test piles. However, the general case is to record the driving log during final penetration of the pile and record the final driving resistance in blows per inch (1 in = 25.4 mm). The basic driving log can be observed by marking the pile off at even 1-ft (0.3-m) intervals and counting the number of hammer blows delivered as adjacent 1-ft marks pass a fixed reference point. If the pile is penetrating rapidly, it may be impossible to record blows per foot, and under such conditions the total number of blows for a given length of penetration may be recorded. A convenient way of observing final driving resistance in blows per inch is to put random marks on the pile and count the number of blows delivered as one of the marks passes adjacent inch marks on a rule held near the side of the pile.

For piles that are inserted in predrilled or jetted holes or for very heavy piles and soft soil conditions, the pile will run into the ground under its weight and the weight of the hammer. The depth of run should be recorded if complete driving logs are required.

Vibratory Driving. If piles are to be installed with a vibratory driver, the inspector should record, in addition to pile length and other data, the final penetration rate in feet per minute and the steady-rate frequency in vibrations per minute during final pile penetration.

Soil Freeze

Some cohesive-type soils exhibit a sharp decrease in shear strengths when being remolded and disturbed by pile driving but regain their strengths with time after pile driving stops. This is known as soil freeze or setup. During driving, penetration resistance is relatively low and dynamic formulas are not applicable. The occurrence of soil freeze can be checked by retapping piles some time after final driving. The amount of soil freeze and the rate at which it occurs can vary over a wide range. Some soils show substantial soil freeze in a matter of hours, but others may require days or even weeks to regain full strength. Under such conditions the application of dynamic-driving formulas should be on the basis of retap data.

Relaxation

Relaxation is a term applied to a decrease with time of final pile-penetration resistance. It could result from driving friction piles into dense, fine submerged sand, inorganic silt, or stiff, fissured clay or from driving point-bearing piles into a friable shale or a claystone.

Where soil conditions indicate that pile relaxation could occur, some piles should be retapped several hours after they and adjacent piles have been driven. If upon retapping it is observed that the original final driving resistance has decreased, all piles should be retapped and further such checking done until penetration resistance and/or depths of penetration are satisfactory.

Interruption of Pile Driving

Generally, specifications will require that piles be driven their full lengths without interruption. If the driving of a pile is interrupted, the cause and duration should be noted. Where soil-freeze conditions exist, any prolonged interruption in pile driving will result in an increase in pile-penetration resistance when driving is resumed. In extreme cases, it may not be possible to achieve further pile penetration. In such cases, if the pile is not long enough or has not reached the required bearing strata, it may be necessary to abandon and replace the pile. If piles are to be driven to a specified penetration resistance, driving after an interruption should continue long enough to break the soil freeze.

Abrupt Changes in Driving Resistance

Sudden increases in driving resistance, either real or apparent, could be caused by the pile's hitting underground obstructions or hard soil strata, by the introduction of fresh capblock material, by the brooming of the butts of timber piles, by the cracking or spalling of the butts of concrete piles, or by elastic yielding of steel piles. Sudden decreases in pile-driving resistance could be caused by the breaking below ground surface of timber or precast piles, by the plastic yielding of a steel pile, or by any pile's encountering unexpected soft soil strata.

Abrupt changes in pile-driving resistance should be investigated to determine the cause. If they are not investigated or if pile breakage is found to be the cause, the pile should be rejected. The investigation may indicate that some remedial measures, such as changing pile-installation equipment or methods or using a different type of pile, must be taken.

Obstructions

Obstructions may be buried timber, logs, or tree stumps, boulders, old foundations, slag or rock fill, or other objects which may prevent the pile from reaching the necessary penetration or cause the pile to bend or to drift off location or which may damage the pile. Obstructions near the ground surface will be evident by the pile's tending to drift off location at the start of driving or by the refusal of the pile to penetrate. The presence of deep obstructions may be difficult to detect and could seriously damage the pile or prevent the pile from obtaining the necessary bearing capacity. Deep obstructions may be indicated by an unexpected refusal of the pile to penetrate or by substantial differences in tip elevations for adjacent piles. Such conditions should be investigated by test borings. It may be necessary to remove or dislodge obstructions to install piles properly. Sometimes obstructions can be pushed aside, broken up, or pierced with a spud. Shallow obstructions can often be readily removed, but for deep obstructions special methods may be required to break up or bypass the obstructions or the pile may have to be relocated.

If obstructions such as boulder formations are known to exist, the inspector should observe the pile driving or installation carefully to detect any unusual occurrence which may indicate pile damage or misalignment.

The tips of steel H piles are very susceptible to overstressing and deformation. The use of some type of reinforced tip for steel H piles is recommended if obstructions exist. The tips of timber piles also can be easily damaged by obstructions. The use of steel drive shoes may help prevent tip damage, but if too much reliance is placed on the reinforced tip and the pile is driven hard, it may be damaged elsewhere. The tips of precast-concrete piles could also be damaged by obstructions, but the use of some type of tip protection is unusual. The most effective remedy for steel, timber, or concrete piles is to avoid overdriving. (See "Overdriving" below.)

Piles such as pipe, tube, or the shell type can be visually inspected for damage after the casing has been driven. If other types of piles are driven in ground which is seriously obstructed, some of the driven piles should be pulled for inspection as the work progresses. In extreme cases, consideration should be given to selecting the pile type and/or methods of installation which would resolve the problems of obstructions.

Overdriving

Overdriving of piles should be avoided. Whether or not piles are being overdriven is often a matter of judgment based upon the pile material involved, the subsoil conditions, the driving equipment used, and the installation method. Pile damage could occur when the pile material is exposed during driving to dynamic stresses which are higher than the yield or ultimate strength of the material. A proper wave-equation analysis can reveal the driving stresses to which the pile may be subjected. Pile damage could also occur by a repetition of hammer blows that results in fatigue failure. This is especially true for timber piles. Overdriving of timber piles could cause brooming at the pile tip or butt or actual breaking of the pile. If a sudden high resistance to penetration is encountered when driving timer piles, driving should cease immediately.

Steel piles could deform by plastic yielding or by rupture, or by both. Damage to precast-concrete piles could be in the form of cracks, spalling, or actual breakage.

Pile Splicing

The type of splice to be used may be specified. If the splice is to withstand prolonged driving, it should be as strong in all respects as the basic pile material. The splice must be capable of transferring all required stresses including compression, tension, or bending. Whether pile sections are spliced together on a horizontal rack or in the leaders, the individual sections must be in accurate axial alignment. Specifications may prohibit the splice's being located in the upper portion of the pile as installed.

Where soil conditions are such that soil setup or freeze can occur rapidly, the use of pile splicing during driving should be limited. Under extreme conditions it may be impossible to resume further penetration of the pile after the splice has been made. If splicing is necessary under such conditions, the splice should be a type which can be completed in the shortest length of time.

Precast Piles. There are several types of precast-pile splices or joints. These include various types of mechanical joints, welded joints, sleeve joints, and dowel joints. Some are specifically designed for installing sectional precast piles. Some of these joints cannot take bending or tension.

Pipe Piles. Pipe piles can be spliced by using either inside or outside drive sleeves with or without welding. Splices can also be made by butt welding.

Tube Piles. Tube piles may require special preparation for heavy-duty welded splices. The manufacturer's recommendations should be followed.

H Piles. H piles are spliced by either simple butt welding or by using special splice fittings or the welding on of fishplates. If special splice fittings are used, they should at least be tack-welded.

Pile Shells

Uniform Section. Shells are spliced with butt welds.

Step-Tapered Sections. Joints are generally screw-connected and made watertight by the application of a waterproofing compound or the use of an O-ring gasket. Joints can also be welded. Note that step-tapered piles may be made up of different section lengths giving different rates of taper.

Pile Heave

When driving displacement-type piles in highly incompressible soils, ground heave may occur. Under such conditions the possibility of pile heave should be checked. This can be done by taking level readings on the tops of driven piles before and after adjacent piles have been driven. However, for corrugated pile shells, such check level readings should be made on a telltale pipe resting on the closure plate at the pile point. Upward movements of the tops of such shells are not harmful when they are due to shell stretch.

When pile heave is observed, piles should be redriven to the original penetration or final resistance after pile driving has progressed beyond pile-heave range. Pile heave is more critical for point-bearing piles and may not affect the capacity of friction piles. Cast-in-place concrete should not be placed until pile driving has progressed beyond the pile-heave range.

If piles are not suitable for redriving (for example, uncased cast-in-place concrete piles) and heave occurs, the driving sequence and/or methods of installation must be modified to eliminate heave and all heaved piles should be replaced.

If ground or pile heave occurs, the effects on existing structures should be observed. Pile heave can be controlled or eliminated by proper pre-excavation methods.

Retapping

When it is necessary to redrive or retap piles to a specified penetration resistance, it should be done with the same or equivalent type and size of hammer used for initial driving. It should be noted that the first few hammer blows may not be indicative of actual driving resistance. Ground freeze may have occurred. Furthermore, the hammer may not be delivering its full stroke until it has warmed up.

Retapping or redriving of uncased cast-in-place piles should not be permitted. Redriving on cast-in-place concrete encased in a steel shell or pipe is permissible providing the proper hammer-pile-cushion system has been established by prior use or designed by a wave-equation analysis. For pile shells such as pipe or tube not originally driven with an internal mandrel, the concrete filling produces a much stiffer pile and results in more effective transmission of hammer energy. Therefore, for such piles the actual retap resistance will be less than the original final resistance for the same formula capacity. A wave-equation analysis will show the comparable final resistances for the load involved.

Variations in Pile Lengths

If possible, extreme variations in pile lengths in any one group should be avoided. The cause for extreme variations in pile-tip elevations for adjacent piles or piles within a group should be investigated. Length variations could be caused by obstructions or unusual subsoil conditions such as cavernous-limestone formations or radical glacial deposits. There may be no practical remedy for extreme variations in pile lengths. Additional piles may be required.

Length variations could also result from the gradual densification of the subsoil and shortening of the piles as driving progresses. To minimize this, pile driving for large groups should start at the center of the group and continue outward uniformly.

Pile Cutoff

Piles should be cut off perpendicularly to the longitudinal axis within 1 in (25.4 mm) of required elevation or below all damaged portions. By checking against the pile plans, the inspector can visually verify that the piles have been cut off at approximately the correct elevation. Such visual checking should detect major discrepancies in pile-cutoff elevations.

Waste Piling

Pile lengths which are cut off will be the property of the owner if pile material is paid for on the basis of furnished lengths or become the property of the contractor if piles are paid for from tip to cutoff grade. In either case, the specifications may require the contractor to dispose of waste piling.

Treatment of Timber-Pile Butts

The butts of treated timber piles should be treated with preservatives in accordance with the specifications. Generally three coats of hot creosote oil are required, followed by sealing the end surface of the pile with a heavy application of coal-tar pitch.

Cap Plates

Steel H piles which are installed to carry very high design loads and are capped with concrete may require steel cap plates to be welded to the tops of all piles for adequate load transfer by bearing between the piles and the concrete caps. Alternatively the piles may be embedded a sufficient length into the concrete cap to transfer the load through bond. Cap plates should at least be tack-welded to the piles.

Pile Buildup

Pile butts that are too low in elevation can be built up to the proper grade. This is readily accomplished for cast-in-place concrete piles by adding a section of shell or pipe before concrete is placed. For other types of piles, especially when the specifications prohibit splices along the upper portion of the pile, it may be necessary to verify with the engineer the acceptability of a pile buildup. In some cases, the bottom of the pile cap can be lowered to accommodate such a pile, the top of which is below the required cutoff grade.

Cleaning Out Piles

Open-End Pipe Piles. The specifications may require that pipe piles driven open-ended be cleaned out and filled with concrete. The length of pile to be cleaned out may vary from a few feet at the top to the full length. Subsoil conditions may dictate that open-end pipe piles be cleaned out periodically to achieve the necessary penetration. It should be noted that an open-end pipe pile which picks up an immovable plug during driving will behave as a displacement-type pile.

Soil inside such piles can be removed by drilling, by washing with a jet with or without an airlift, or with various types of grab buckets. It may be necessary to break up large boulders with some type of churn-drill chopping bit or cable tool or with a hammer grab. Care must be taken to avoid

FIG. 2.3-9   Sunlight reflected from a mirror
permits internal inspection of a driven pile
shell. *(Raymond International Builders Inc.)*

removing soil from beneath the final pile-tip elevation or from alongside
the pile.

Pile Shells and Casings.   Unless pile shells or casings or drilled holes are
kept covered until concrete can be placed, various types of debris could
fall into the casing or hole. If soil gets into pile shells or closed-end casings,
it can be removed by washing (jet) either without or in combination with
air or steam pressure. If soil enters the shell through a tear in the side, the
pile can be salvaged by cleaning out if the hole is small and plugs. It may be
necessary to keep the shell filled with water and place concrete by tremie
(see below, subsection "Tremie Placement").

    Foreign objects can often be removed with some type of grab or hook.
Pieces of wood can sometimes be speared with a pointed length of reinforcing steel or floated to the top by filling the shell with water. Water can
be removed with a bailing bucket, a steam siphon, or a small submersible
pump. If the lift is not too high, conventional pumps can be used.

Pile Alignment after Installation

The major factor in pile alignment is the alignment of the upper portion of the pile as it enters the pile cap or structure; this should be in accordance with the design and within the specified axial-alignment tolerance. The alignment tolerance may be specified in degrees or as a rate such as 1 in in 4 ft (25.4 mm in 1.2 m) or as a percentage of length. The alignment along the top portion of the pile can be checked with a mason's level over a minimum 5-ft (1.5-m) length of pile. For batter or tapered piles a template should be used to compensate for the batter or taper.

Of secondary importance is the alignment of the pile below ground surface. If the alignment tolerance relates to the full length of the pile, there should be an understanding by the parties concerned as to how the tolerance is to be applied, for example, to each incremental length of the pile or to the overall length of the pile. Alignment tolerances applied throughout the pile length are not considered practical or warranted.

Misalignment of piles below ground surfaces can take the shape of (1) the axis of the pile being straight but not on required alignment, (2) the pile being bent, or (3) a combination of these. The pile bend can be either sharp (called a dogleg) or smooth with various radii.

The approximate axial alignment of pipe, tube, or shell-type piles or drilled holes can be checked visually by using a mirror and reflected sunlight or a droplight. Alignment could also be checked by lowering a plumb bob down the pile and noting the offset for a given depth. For pipe piles, the alignment can be checked by lowering a proving "plug," the diameter and length of which are designed to prevent the plug from passing a bend in the pile having a minimum specified radius of curvature. (See Fig. 2.3-9.)

Deviation from axial alignment could be measured with some type of inclinometer lowered down the pile or through a special tube fitted to or cast into the pile. Except for research types of projects, the use of such instruments is considered impractical.

Generally, long, sweeping bends in friction or point-bearing piles are not considered detrimental. The capacity of piles with sharp bends or doglegs can be checked by an analysis involving structural and soil-mechanics principles. Except possibly for very sharp doglegs in extremely soft soil, soil resistance is generally more than sufficient to restrain the pile from buckling under its design load. If the capacity of a bent pile is in doubt, it can be checked by a proof-load test.

Pile Deformation

Piles can be deformed at the tip, along the shaft, or at the butt. Tip deformation for timber, precast-concrete, or steel H piles cannot be detected unless the piles are pulled for visual inspection. (See above, subsections "Obstructions" and "Overdriving.") Pile deformation along the pile shaft could be in the form of a reduction in the cross-sectional area, a break in the pile, or, in severe cases of overdriving, a folded bend in the pile. Except for pile shells or casings which can be visually inspected internally after being driven, such deformations cannot be observed unless the pile is pulled or excavated.

Reductions in cross-sectional area could be caused by obstructions, by soil pressures, or by driving pipe or tube piles into rock fissures or crevices. For shell, pipe, or tube piles the cross section of the pile can be checked visually during internal inspection or by lowering a *proving ball* down the pile. Generally any reduction of 10 percent or less is considered satisfactory. (For reductions in cross-sectional area for uncased cast-in-place-concrete piles, see the subsection "Special-Type Piles.")

The occurrence of detrimental deformation may be controlled or eliminated for shell, pipe, or tube piles by the use of heavier gauges or wall thicknesses, by preexcavation, by filling a section of driven pipe with concrete before adding and driving additional pipe lengths, or by inserting dummy cores in pile shells or filling them with water until such time as shells are concreted.

Placing Reinforcing Steel

The number and arrangement of longitudinal bars and the diameter of the reinforcing cage should be as specified. Longitudinal steel to resist bending should be tied with hoops or a spiral with the specified pitch or spacing and should have sufficient spacers to center the cage in the pile casing or hole. Longitudinal steel to resist uplift loads may be bundled and placed in the center of the pile. Except for short dowels, reinforcing steel for cast-in-place piles should be placed before concrete is poured. All steel must be free from dirt, rust scale, loose mill scale, oil, grease, and any other coating which would affect the steel-to-concrete bond. The concrete cover should be at least 3 in (76.2 mm) for uncased cast-in-place-concrete piles and 1½ in (38.1 mm) for cased piles.

Placing Concrete for Cast-in-Place Piles

A minimum distance between pile driving and concrete placement may be specified. Tests have indicated that vibrations from pile driving have no detrimental effect on fresh concrete, and a criterion of one open pile between the driving and concreting operations is considered satisfactory. However, for practical reasons a minimum distance of 10 ft (3 m) is often specified. Concrete should not be placed, however, until pile driving has progressed beyond the heave range and all heaved piles have been properly reseated. Also, concrete should not be placed as long as relaxation is occurring.

The shell, tube, or pipe should be inspected just prior to filling it with concrete and should be free of all foreign matter and contain not more than about 4 in (101.6 mm) of water unless tremie placing of concrete is permitted. Concrete should be placed in each pile shell, casing, or hole without interruption. If it is necessary to interrupt the concreting process long enough so that the concrete could take its initial set or harden, steel dowels should be inserted in the top of the concreted portion of the pile. When concreting is resumed, all laitance should be removed and the concrete surface should be flushed with neat fluid grout.

When discharging concrete from the mixer, the concrete flow must not be restricted by a partially opened gate. Concrete chutes must be steep enough so that the concrete flows freely and does not have to be pushed or shoveled. If a hopper or concrete bucket is being used, concrete should not be discharged directly from the mixer into the hopper or bucket but should be discharged into a funnel-type downpipe centered over the hopper or bucket. When discharged from the hopper or bucket, the concrete should be drawn off from the center.

Concrete containing a reduced amount of coarse aggregate and a compensating increased quantity of sand and cement is recommended for filling long pile shells or those driven on a batter or containing heavy reinforcement. Such concrete, if properly designed and mixed, is very workable and cohesive.

The top 6 to 10 ft (1.8 to 3 m) of the concreted pile should be rodded. Vibration of concrete is unnecessary and may promote bleeding.

Conventional Placement. The mix design of concrete and the equipment and techniques used to place the concrete must be such as to prevent separation of the coarse aggregate. Concrete should be of proper slump (see "Slump" in the subsection "Pile Material") and should be deposited in a rapid continuous pour through a steep-sided funnel centered at the top of the pile. The diameter of the discharge end of the funnel should not be larger than 10 in (254 mm). When conventional concrete is used, about a pailful of flowable grout should be poured into the pile shell before placing concrete. Pregrouting is not necessary when reduced-coarse-aggregate concrete is used.

Tremie Placement. The tremie method should be used for placing concrete through water. Concrete can be poured into the tremie tube or pumped through a tremie pipe. The bottom of the tremie should be closed with a detachable plug or hinged-flap valve before it is lowered through the water, or a movable plug can be inserted in the top of the tremie just before concrete is placed to prevent the concrete from coming in contact with water in the tremie. The tremie tube must be resting on the bottom of the casing or hole before concreting begins. It should then be raised only a few inches (1 in = 25.4 mm) to start the flow of concrete and to ensure good contact between the concrete and the bottom of the casing or hole.

As the tremie is raised during concreting, it must be kept below the surface of the concrete in the pile. Before withdrawing the tremie completely, sufficient concrete should be placed to displace all free water and watery concrete.

Bleeding.   Bleeding is evidenced by a collection of water and cement on top of the concrete after placement. It could be caused by excess water in the mix or by poorly graded aggregates. The amount of mixing water could be reduced by a water-reducing admixture. If the quality of aggregates is the problem, corrective measures should be taken to improve the gradation.

Cold Weather.   For concrete placed in pile shells, casings, or holes, cold weather is not as critical as it is for concrete placed in aboveground forms. However, suitable precautions should be taken (see "Cold-Weather Operations" in the subsection "Pile Material"). The temperature of concrete as placed should not be less than about 40°F (4.4°C). Concrete should be discharged promptly upon delivery. The tops of freshly poured cast-in-place-concrete piles should be adequately protected from freezing. This can be done by covering the pile butts with salt hay or soil or, in extreme cases, by using tarpaulins and heaters.

Hot Weather.   If the weather is extremely hot, special measures may be required to keep the concrete temperature down to acceptable limits during mixing and placing (see "Hot-Weather Operations" in the subsection "Pile Material"). The time between mixing and placing should be reduced to a minimum, and concrete must be placed promptly upon delivery. The temperature of the concrete as placed should be below 80°F (26.6°C) to avoid flash sets.

Concrete for Special-Type Piles.   See the subsection "Special-Type Piles" for other concreting requirements for special types of piles.

Piles Overlooked

Before the pile rig is moved away, the inspector should check that all piles in the immediate area have been installed.

Pile-to-Cap Connections

The plans or specifications may require that the tops of piles be anchored into the pile caps. For steel piles this can be done by welding short dowels to the pile. For cast-in-place concrete without internal reinforcement, dowels can be embedded in the concrete at the pile butt; internal reinforcement, if used, can be extended into the cap. However, if such pile-to-cap connections are required for uplift loads, reinforcing steel should extend the full length of the concrete piles.

For timber piles special fittings consisting of steel bars and/or straps can be bolted or otherwise fastened to the top of the pile. All exposed steel including bolts must be galvanized, and all holes or other cuts must be treated with several applications of hot creosote oil followed by a seal coat of coal-tar pitch.

For connections involving precast piles, the piles could be made with the longitudinal or prestressing steel projecting the required length beyond the pile butt. For such piles, a special drive cap or follower is required to accommodate the steel extension. In other cases it may be necessary to strip the concrete back from the top of the pile to expose a sufficient length of reinforcing steel or prestressing strand for the pile-to-cap connection or for attaching additional lengths of steel. The pile top has to be left a sufficient height above cutoff grade, and stripping must be done carefully to avoid damage to the pile.

To make the cap connection, the precast pile may also be cast with dowel holes at the top into which steel dowels are grouted after the pile has been driven.

Pile-Butt Locations

Final pile positions should be checked as the work progresses so that, if necessary, additional piles can be installed before the equipment is moved off or cannot reach the required locations of the additional piles. If piles are found to be installed beyond the permissible tolerance for butt location, the resulting loads on the piles should be checked, and if any have more than a 10 percent overload, additional piles may be required. The number of additional piles required in any one group may be determined by the number necessary to balance the group to maintain the design center of gravity. Added piles must be installed at the proper locations. If a pile group to be corrected is adjacent to a property line, the locations of additional piles should be checked to ensure that they do not encroach on other property.

Piles off Location

After piles have been installed and butt locations checked, piles could be pushed off location by various types of construction activity or by general ground movements. Under soft soil conditions, heavy construction equipment should not be permitted to operate immediately adjacent to piles. Excavations should not be made only along one side of piles without bracing the piles or the excavation bank. General ground movements could result from unstable slopes or from inadequately braced or tied sheeting. Heavy rains could cause ground loss or movement.

Pile shells not yet filled with concrete can sometimes be pulled back into position. If concrete has already been placed in pile shells or for uncased cast-in-place concrete piles, piles that have been pushed off location should be inspected for breaks. If the piles cannot be inspected properly or repaired satisfactorily, they should be rejected and replaced.

If timber, precast-concrete, or steel piles are pushed off location, the piles should be inspected for breaks or severe bends. It may be necessary to excavate alongside piles. If the pile can be pulled back into position, the force applied to the pile should be limited to avoid breaking the pile. This is especially true when there is a long-moment arm as in marine construction.

Unsupported Pile Lengths

If, after installation and cutoff, a portion of the pile extends above the adjacent ground surface, the unsupported lengths may have to be braced or stay-lathed until backfill operations have been completed or the piles incorporated into the structure.

Backfilling around high-cutoff piles must be done carefully and preferably by hand. Construction equipment must not be allowed to hit the pile, and the backfill should be placed in uniform lifts around the pile.

Excavating Overburden

If piles have been installed with tops below ground surface, the excavation to pile-cutoff grade must be carried out carefully so as not to damage the piles. Hand excavation is recommended.

Pile Lengths

The inspector should record the length of each pile installed as measured from tip to butt. If pile-tip and pile-butt elevations are recorded, they should be referenced to an established permanent datum which is identified.

For pipe, tube, or shell piles the lengths can be measured by lowering the weighted end of a steel tape down the pile after it has been driven and cut off to grade and before concrete is placed. Because of stretching a cloth tape should not be used.

For timber, precast-concrete, and steel H piles the installed length of pile can be determined by measuring the length driven and subtracting the cutoff length. The driven length will include all lengths added in the leaders.

For measurement of installed lengths of special-type piles see the subsection "Special-Type Piles."

Pay Quantities

The inspector may have to record or verify quantities of pay items. Payment for the pile foundation could be by lump sum, principal sum with adjustment prices, unit price, or a combination of these methods.

Usually no extra payment is made for withdrawn, rejected, or abandoned piles, for pile splicing, or for cutting off piles. Pile buildups may be included in the total pile footage installed. If pile materials are paid for on the basis of full ordered and furnished lengths, waste piling actually becomes the property of the owner. The contract documents may require that the contractor dispose of this material, and if it has any salvage value, the approximate quantities should be recorded and proper credits given to the owner.

Lump-Sum Method.   For contracts on a lump-sum basis it is necessary only to verify that all work is completed in accordance with the plans and specifications or subsequent revisions. Revisions should be covered by change orders. If additional work is performed under a work order, the satisfactory completion of such work should be verified.

Principal-Sum Method.   For the principal-sum method a stipulated payment is made for a specified total aggregate length of piling or for a specified number of piles having a stated base individual length. For final payment, the principal sum is adjusted on the basis of added or omitted piles or increases or decreases in pile lengths. The method of payment, and therefore the method for adjusting the principal sum on the basis of actual quantities of piles installed, should be understood so that the information necessary to make the computations can be properly recorded and certified.

Payment is usually made for actual pile lengths installed, measured from tip to cutoff elevation. However, when the pile-cutoff grade is below the ground or water surface existing at the time of pile driving and the pile is installed to that ground or water surface (the pile is driven through overburden), payment may be made from pile tip to ground or water surface. This does not apply to any type of uncased cast-in-place-concrete pile. For cased concrete piles, the concrete is generally placed to cutoff grade, and if full payment is made for overburden footage, a credit should be given for omitted concrete. If, after final pile cutoff, the lengths cut off are reused, double payment for these pile lengths should be avoided.

The actual installed length of each pile as well as the total number of piles installed should be recorded with added or omitted piles identified. Adjustments to the principal sum will be either plus or minus, depending upon whether they represent added or omitted work. Adjustments will be made on the basis of adjustment unit prices in the contract.

Unit-Price Method.   All piling may be paid for on the basis of unit prices; sometimes the furnishing of pile materials and the driving of piles are paid for under separate unit prices. In such cases, the furnished pile lengths as well as the installed lengths must be recorded accurately. Payment may be made for the full lengths delivered to the jobsite or for the lengths of each pile raised in the leaders. The pay quantity for installing piles will generally be that measured from pile tip to cutoff grade. The exception may be when piles are installed through overburden; payment for overburden footage may be made as described under "Principal-Sum Method." This should not apply when a follower is used to drive the pile head to cutoff grade below the ground or water surface or for uncased cast-in-place-concrete piles, especially auger-grout piles (see "Auger-Grout Piles: Forming Pile Butts" in the subsection "Special-Type Piles").

Combination Method.   Sometimes the lump-sum method is combined with either the principal-sum or the unit-price method. For example, mobilization and demobilization of the pile-installation equipment and contractor's spread may be paid for on a lump-sum basis with payment for piles either on a principal-sum or a unit-price basis.

Other Items.   Other items of work relating to pile installation are frequently paid for on a unit basis. Included are those items which may or may not be required or, if required, for which the extent or quantity of such work is not known in advance. Examples are:

Load testing, per test (for stated total load)

Reinforcing steel, per pound (1 lb = 0.4536 kg)

Preexcavation (drill or jet), per foot or per pile (1 ft = 0.3048 m)

Overburden footage, per foot

Retapping piles, per pile or per rig-hour

Use of casing (bored piles), per foot

Extra grout (auger-grout piles), per cubic yard (1 yd = 0.7646 m^3)

Some items of work, such as extra moving of the pile-driving equipment, cribbing, spudding, removal of obstructions, and delays caused by others, may be paid for on an hourly or a daily rate.

Force-Account Work. Sometimes the contractor will be authorized to perform work on a force-account basis. For such work, the contractor is usually reimbursed for all labor, material, and equipment involved with appropriate factors for tools, payroll costs, overhead, and profit. For force-account work, the inspector should verify that the work was performed together with the quantity and type of labor including supervision, the type of equipment, the quantity and type of materials, and the time involved in such work.

Pile Caps

Pile installation will generally be considered complete when piles are capped or otherwise incorporated into the structure. The proper design and construction of pile caps are necessary for the satisfactory performance of the pile foundation.

Cap Excavation. Pile-cap excavations must be of the required depth and lateral dimensions to provide for the proper embedment of pile butts and minimum edge distances. The bottom of the excavation should be level and clear of all loose material. If the soil at the bottom is very soft, a working mat should be installed. This base course could consist of about 4 in (101.6 mm) of lean concrete or about 6 in (152.4 mm) of cinders or well-graded gravel or crushed rock. The base course is not considered a part of the pile cap, and if it is installed, the excavation level should be lowered accordingly. Note that the size or shape of pile caps may be revised from that shown on the plans owing to redesigns required because of added piles or other field conditions.

Pile Butts. Pile butts must extend the required embedment length above the bottom of the excavation or form (or top of the base course). The top and sides of all pile butts must be clean and free of all dirt and other foreign matter.

Forms. Forms must be sufficiently tight to prevent leakage of mortar and constructed and braced so as to retain the wet concrete without distortion. Shapes, positions, dimensions, and edge distances to piles should be checked for conformance with the plans or subsequent revisions. Subject to the approval of the engineer or if permitted by the specifications, side forms may be of soil, provided it will stand without caving in and the sides of the bank are cut neatly to the minimum required dimensions. Proper provisions must be made for accurate positioning and support of anchor bolts.

Reinforcement. Reinforcement should be of the specified type and size. It should be positioned and spaced according to the plans and subsequent redesigns and supported on metal or plastic chairs or small concrete blocks. All steel must be clean and free from dirt, rust scale, loose mill scale, oil, grease, and any other coating which could affect the bond. Reinforcing should have a minimum concrete cover of 3 in (76.2 mm).

Concrete. All concrete must be in accordance with the specifications regarding type, strength, ingredients, and slump. (See "Pile Material: Concrete for Cast-in-Place Piles"; "Material Handling and Storage: Cement; Concrete Aggregates"; and "Pile Installation: Placing Concrete for Cast-in-Place Piles" for applicable control provisions.) For example, the maximum size of the coarse aggregate and the required slump will differ from those used for concrete for cast-in-place piles. Forms or excavations should not contain free water, and concrete should be spread and compacted with vibrators. If soil is used for the sides of the form, all precautions must be taken to prevent caving of the soil during concrete placement. Anchor bolts or other embedments as called for on the drawings should be placed in accurate positions as concrete is poured or immediately thereafter.

Curing. Until it is cured, concrete should be protected from extreme heat or cold. Precautions must be taken to prevent the concrete from a rapid loss of moisture during the curing period. Completed caps should be kept wet for at least 10 days after placement of concrete. Note that wind could have a substantial drying effect; the concrete could be protected by windbreaks or covers if necessary.

Payment. Generally, pile caps are not constructed by the pile contractor. However, if such work is included in the pile contract, the inspector should verify that all pile caps were completed according to plans and specifications or subsequent redesigns. Pile caps may be paid for on a unit basis per cubic yard, or separate unit prices may apply to such things as excavation, formwork, reinforcement, and concrete. Depending upon contract payment provisions, the inspector should keep accurate records of appropriate quantities involved. If pile caps are redesigned, the required additional quantities should be recorded separately.

SPECIAL-TYPE PILES

Special-type piles include the bored pile, the auger-grout pile, the cast-in-situ pile, the compacted-concrete pile, and the enlarged-base pile. Each of these requires special installation and inspection considerations. There are other types of special piles, but these are not commonly used.

For some of the following described special-type piles, there are no means such as a measure of penetration resistance to reveal variations in subsoil conditions during installation. Therefore, more closely spaced test borings may be required to define properly the vertical position and thickness and the adequacy of the bearing strata.

Bored Pile

This type of pile includes those uncased cast-in-place-concrete piles installed by drilling a hole to the required depth and filling the hole with concrete. There are three basic installation methods: (1) the dry method, (2) the casing method (often combined with a slurry), and (3) the slurry-displacement method.

The dry method is applicable in those soils in which the drilled hole will remain open for placement of concrete. Where soil conditions, such as soft soils of low shear strength or granular soils with no cohesion, can cause caving or sloughing of the soil, the casing method is used. A temporary casing or liner is installed through the layer of unstable soil and sealed off in a stratum of impermeable soil. If the layer of unstable soil is relatively thick, it may be necessary to use a drilling-mud slurry to maintain the hole until the casing can be set. After the casing has been set, normal drilling proceeds and the hole is cleaned out before concrete is placed. The casing is generally removed during concrete placement. If the temporary casing cannot be sealed off or if the soils are predominantly unstable, the slurry-displacement method can be used. During drilling, the hole is kept filled with a slurry which is displaced during the concreting operation. Generally these piles are uncased, but sometimes ground conditions necessitate leaving a steel casing or liner in place.

Required Lengths.   Required pile lengths may be specified for each area of similar subsoil conditions. However, additional subsoil information may be required. The inspector should be alert to any changes in the drilling operation which may indicate variations in subsoil conditions, such as changes in the rate of advance of the drill or changes in the type or consistency of the soil cuttings. Any observed changes should be investigated in case pile lengths may have to be adjusted. If the drilled hole is large enough and a temporary steel liner is inserted, the soil at the bottom of the hole can be inspected or tested for adequacy. In other cases a test boring can be made within the drilled hole and soil or rock samples recovered. Such test borings can reveal whether or not the bearing stratum is of adequate thickness as well as bearing capacity.

Unstable Soils.   If the hole is to be drilled through soft clay, soft silt, peat, or loose granular soil, it will be necessary to install a steel casing through the zones of unstable soils or to use a drilling-mud slurry to maintain the hole. If the soil is extremely soft, the steel casing should not be removed.

Groundwater Control.   If groundwater is permitted to enter the hole either through the side or from the bottom, the rate of flow may be such as to cause soil erosion, resulting in contamination of the concrete, collection of unsatisfactory bearing material in the bottom of the hole, or loss of bearing capacity of the soil at the bottom of the hole. In extreme cases, such conditions could preclude drilling the hole to the required depth. Temporary or permanent steel liners should be inserted and, if necessary, the hole filled with water or slurry to balance the hydrostatic head. If an artesian aquifer is encountered, the water pressure may be such as to prevent the drilling of the holes or the proper placement of concrete. Under such conditions the drilling of release wells may provide a solution.

Use of Slurry.   The slurry must be of sufficient density and specific gravity to offset hydrostatic and lateral soil pressures and maintain the hole. The shear-strength characteristics of the slurry as determined by its viscosity and the density of the slurry should be controlled to obtain optimum conditions for displacement of the slurry during the concreting process. Tests to determine density, viscosity, and shear strength should be carried out initially until a suitable mix has been established.

   All reasonable steps should be taken to prevent contamination of the slurry. Discarded slurry which has been pumped or displaced from a drilled hole should be removed from the site. If slurry is to be reused, its quality should be checked periodically.

Cleaning the Bottom of the Holes.   After drilling to the required depth, the bottom of the holes should be cleaned of loose materials by using a cleanout bucket. If the hole is underreamed, the underreaming tool should not be permitted to ride up while underreaming is in process.

Inspection of Bottom.   If it is necessary to enter the hole for direct inspection of the bearing material or conditions at the bottom of the hole, the hole must be a minimum of 24 in (609.6 mm) in diameter and a full-length steel casing must be inserted. All safety precautions, such as ensuring that the hole is free of noxious gas, groundwater is controlled, methods of communication are adequate, lifelines are furnished, and support personnel are in attendance at all times, must be taken.

Placing Concrete.   For the dry method and the casing method and providing the drilled hole can be dewatered, concrete may be placed by conventional methods. (See "Placing Concrete for Cast-in-Place Piles: Conventional Placement" in the subsection "Pile Installation.") Concrete must be deposited vertically in the center of the hole through a funnel hopper. The chuting of concrete directly into the hole, allowing it to hit the side of the hole, must be prohibited. For the slurry-displacement method or when concrete is to be placed through water, the tremie method should be used. (See "Placing Concrete for Cast-in-Place Piles: Tremie Placement" in the subsection "Pile Installation.") Concrete should be of sufficiently high slump to prevent arching in the steel casing. (See "Placing Concrete for Cast-in-Place Piles" for other concreting requirements.)

To prevent contamination of the concrete or an accumulation of unsatisfactory material at the bottom of holes, for all holes deeper than about 20 ft (6 m) or which extend through soils which could slough off during concrete placement, a steel liner or casing should be inserted before pouring concrete. A steel liner may also be required to seal off the flow of groundwater, which could affect the quality of the concrete.

Withdrawal of Casing.   If the steel casing or liner is to be withdrawn as concrete is placed, it is recommended that withdrawal be by the vibratory method to reduce the possibility of concrete arching in the casing. As the casing is withdrawn, observations should be made to ensure that the concrete is not being raised up with the casing and that the concrete level is always above the bottom of the casing. The height of concrete above the bottom of the casing should be sufficient to provide an unbalanced head to resist lateral soil pressures. This is to prevent the necking down of the concrete shaft or complete discontinuity in the shaft as the soil tends to squeeze in and to ensure positive displacement of all slurry.

After each use, the temporary steel casing or liner should be thoroughly cleaned of all concrete to prevent a buildup of hardened concrete, which could contribute to arching and cause the fresh concrete to be lifted with the casing.

Casing Left in Place. Steel casings or liners should be left in place through zones of extremely soft soils or to protect the concrete from groundwater movements.

Drop in Concrete Level. If the level of concrete in the pile shaft drops after completion, this may be caused by the weight of concrete pushing into soft surrounding soils. This can be prevented by leaving a steel casing in place. Before additional concrete is placed to bring the pile to the required cutoff grade, reinforcing-steel dowels should be inserted in the top of the pile and all laitance and contaminated concrete should be removed.

Installation Sequence. When piles are to be installed through soft soils and especially if permanent steel liners or casings are not used, it may be necessary to install piles in a staggered sequence to permit the concrete in completed piles to set up before adjacent piles are drilled. Otherwise, the weight of unset concrete may be sufficient to break through the wall of soft soil between the completed pile and the pile being drilled.

Installed Length. The installed lengths of all bored piles should be recorded. If possible, the elevations of the tops of piles should be recorded and referenced to a permanent fixed datum. Pile lengths can be determined by measuring with a steel tape the depth of the hole from a fixed reference and deducting the distance down to the cutoff grade.

Auger-Grout Pile

This type of pile is installed by drilling a hole with a continuous-flight hollow-stem auger and pumping grout down through the hollow stem, filling the hole as the auger is withdrawn.

Required Lengths. Required pile lengths may be specified for each area of similar subsoil conditions. However, additional subsoil data may be required. Subsurface conditions could change radically within very short distances, and the inspector should be alert to any changes in the drilling operation which may indicate different subsoil conditions, such as torque required to drill, the rate of advance of the auger, or changes in type or consistency of soil cuttings. Any observed changes should be investigated as to cause in case pile lengths may have to be adjusted.

Equipment. The auger flight should be continuous from top to bottom with no gaps or other breaks. The discharge hole at the bottom of the auger should be below the bar containing the cutting teeth. Augers over 40 ft (12.2 m) long should be laterally supported by intermediate movable guides spaced a maximum of 20 ft (6.1 m) apart. The mortar pump should be a positive-displacement piston-type pump capable of developing pressures at the auger tip during group pumping in excess of any hydrostatic pressures or lateral soil pressures at rest. A pressure gauge should be mounted in the grout line as close to the auger head as is practical. The grout pump should be equipped at the discharge end with a metering device capable of accurately measuring the volume of grout pumped.

Grout.   The grout should be of proper consistency to be pumped yet not too fluid. If the water-cement ratio is less than 4.5, the grout mix is too dry. If the grout splashes when poured into a container of grout or if, when flowing down a chute, the mix gets a glossy sheen (sand grains disappear below water and cement surface), the grout is too wet. Strengths will be determined from cube tests (see ASTM C 91). Admixtures are used to improve the pumpability of the grout and to retard its set.

Drilling.   When drilling to the required depth, the auger should be advancing continuously at a rate which would prevent removing excess soil. If the auger is advancing too slowly or rotation is continued without advancement, the removal of excess soil could have a detrimental effect on adjacent structures or piles. After reaching the required depth, rotation of the auger should stop. Auger flights full of soil assist in maintaining the hole and subsequent pumping pressures and help prevent removal of excess soil.

Pumping Grout.   At the start of pumping grout, the auger should be raised from 6 to 12 in (152.4 to 304.8 mm), and after grout pressure has built up, indicating discharge of grout, the auger should be redrilled to the original depth before forming the pile. A positive pressure must be maintained during grout pumping. To ensure a properly filled full-size hole, the pumping pressure, considering all line losses, should be greater than any hydrostatic or lateral soil pressures. However, when installing such piles in very soft soils, excessively high pumping pressures should be avoided. Such pressures could cause upward or lateral movement of unset adjacent piles. Under such conditions it is advisable to install piles in a staggered sequence. Pumping pressures are normally reduced during final withdrawal of the auger.

Withdrawing Auger. During pumping of grout to form the pile the auger should be withdrawn in a smooth, continuous motion and not in jerks or lifts. The auger may turn very slowly during withdrawal, but in no case should a counterclockwise rotation be permitted. The rate of withdrawal should be such that a positive pressure is maintained in the grout line at all times. Unless these precautions are taken, necking down or discontinuities of the grout shaft could occur, or the grout column could contain soil inclusions.

Interruptions and Pressure Drops. The formation of each pile should be a continuous, uninterrupted operation once grouting has started. If the grouting process is interrupted or grouting pressures drop below acceptable levels, the auger should be redrilled to the original tip elevation and the pile re-formed.

Volume of Grout. The volume of grout placed should be greater by about 10 percent than the theoretical volume of the hole created by the auger. The normal wobble of the auger will create a hole larger than theoretical. If a considerable excess of grout is pumped, the cause should be investigated. The excess may be due to very soft soils and excessive pumping pressures or to the grout flowing into fissures, crevices, or solution channels and cavities in lime-rock formations. Grout may also be lost in underground structures such as sewer lines. The injection of excess grout may be totally wasteful or damaging to underground or adjacent structures.

Forming Pile Butts. To form and protect the pile butt properly, a steel sleeve should be placed at the top of the pile before grouting that portion of the pile and removing the auger. The steel sleeve should extend from pile-cutoff grade or ground surface, whichever is higher, to a point not less than 1 ft (0.3048 m) below pile-cutoff grade or the ground surface, whichever is lower, and should be left in place. If a steel sleeve is not used, the ground surface adjacent to the pile should be at least 1 ft higher than pile-cutoff grade and the hole should be filled with grout to the ground surface; the pile butt is then trimmed to grade. Excess grout should be pumped to displace as much potential laitance as possible.

Placing Reinforcing Steel

Steel to Resist Bending. Reinforcing steel required to resist bending should not be placed by pushing the steel down into the unset-grout column if the embedded length of the steel is greater than about 5 ft (1.5 m). If the required embedment length is longer than about 5 ft, longitudinal steel should be the full length of the pile and placed through special ducts on the auger before the grouting operation begins. The auger must be restrained from rotating during withdrawal, and the steel must be prevented from coming up with the auger as it is withdrawn. Steel with less than 5-ft embedment should be fabricated into cages of the required diameter with suitable tie steel and carefully placed in the fluid grout. The cage should be centered and accurately aligned with the longitudinal axis of the pile.

Steel to Resist Uplift. Reinforcing required to resist uplift forces should be full-length and may be placed through the hollow auger stem before grouting starts, or it may be pushed down the center of the grout column, provided the pile is at least 16 in (406.4 mm) in diameter, the grout is still quite fluid, the steel consists of a single bar or a bundle of bars, and the steel is carefully centered, is not bent, is not permitted to bend, and can be pushed to the bottom of the grout column. If placed through the hollow stem, the steel should be prevented from coming up with the auger.

Drop in Grout Level. Completed piles which are still unset should be checked periodically during and after installation of adjacent piles to see if the grout level is maintained. If any drop in grout level occurs in a completed pile during the drilling of adjacent piles, the completed pile should be rejected and replaced. If the grout level subsides when no adjacent piles are being installed, the subsidence may be caused by the fluid grout's squeezing out into soft soils. The cause of subsidence and the extent of pile damage should be investigated by a test boring and core drilling of the pile shaft. If the grout level drops and the pile is salvageable, precautions should be taken to prevent contamination of grout at the top of the pile resulting from sloughing soils or surface water. Before additional grout or concrete is placed to bring the butts of satisfactory piles to grade, all laitance and contaminated grout should be removed and steel dowels should be used at the joint. If the grout has set, it would be preferable to increase the depth of the pile cap rather than build up the pile.

Installed Length. The installed length of each auger-grout pile can be determined by knowing the total length of the auger used and observing the depth or elevation to which the auger tip is drilled before grouting starts. It may be convenient to have the leaders marked off in 1-ft (0.3-m) increments and an index mark on the top drill guide to measure auger penetration. Depths or elevations should be referenced to a fixed datum. Pile lengths can be calculated from tip and specified butt elevations or distances to the tip and butt from a fixed reference.

Payment Quantities. Auger-grout piles should be paid for in accordance with "Pile Lengths" in the subsection "Pile Installation." If grout is placed above cutoff grade, no extra payment should be made for pile lengths above cutoff or for trimming pile tops back to cutoff grade.

The contract may provide for payment per cubic yard for the volume of grout pumped in excess of the theoretical volume of the piles. In such cases grout-metering devices must be accurate, and the inspector must keep records of the actual volume of grout pumped. Waste grout resulting from spillage or excess pumping once the pile hole has been filled should not be included in this pay item.

Cast-in-Situ Pile

This type of pile includes those uncased cast-in-place-concrete piles which are installed by driving a casing with a sacrificial closure plate or a removable internal mandrel, filling the casing with concrete or grout during or after driving and withdrawing the casing.

Required Lengths. Required pile lengths may be specified for each area of similar subsoil conditions. The required driving criteria may also include a minimum penetration resistance. Penetration resistance during driving may include frictional resistance, which could be altered during pile installation by withdrawal of the casing. In some cases the pile-driving logs may give an indication of varying subsoil conditions. If substantial variations are indicated, the cause should be investigated by means of a test boring.

Spacing. Normal pile spacing is from 4 to 5 times the diameter. This spacing may have to be increased if piles are installed in very soft soil or boulder formations unless the piles are driven in a staggered sequence.

Driving Sequence. If piles have to be driven in a staggered sequence, the concrete or grout in a completed pile should be at least 3 days old before driving the adjacent piles.

Placing Reinforcing Steel

Steel to Resist Bending. Reinforcing steel required to resist bending should be fabricated into cages of the specified diameter, and if the embedment length is longer than about 5 ft (1.5 m), it should be installed centered in the casing before concrete or grout is placed. The steel cage must be prevented from coming up as the casing is withdrawn. If the embedded length of the cage is not greater than about 5 ft, it may be pushed into the fluid-concrete or grout column. Such steel must be carefully centered in the pile and accurately aligned with the pile's longitudinal axis (see "Placing Reinforcing Steel" in the subsection "Pile Installation.")

Steel to Resist Uplift. Reinforcing required to resist uplift should be full-length. It may be placed in the center of the casing before concrete or grout is placed, or it may be pushed down the center of the concrete or grout column, provided the control provisions for placing steel in this manner are in accordance with "Placing Reinforcing Steel: Steel to Resist Uplift" above.

Placing Concrete or Grout. After the casing has been driven to the required depth, concrete may be placed in accordance with "Placing Concrete for Cast-in-Place Piles" in the subsection "Pile Installation." Concrete must be of sufficiently high slump to prevent arching in the casing as it is withdrawn. If concrete or grout is placed during the driving operation, it must be of very high slump [10 or more in (254 or more mm)]. Actually the normal slump test is not applicable. The suitable viscosity of the mix is determined by a flow-cone test. A water-reducing and -retarding admixture must be used to give at least a 4-hour retardation. Grout strengths will be determined by cube tests (see ASTM C 91).

Filling Pile Hole to Cutoff Grade. To ensure that the pile hole is filled to cutoff grade, it may be necessary to have a sufficient extra length of casing filled with concrete or grout to compensate for the concrete or grout which will fill in the space occupied by the steel casing as it is withdrawn. Alternatively, extra grout or concrete could be added during withdrawal of the casing. Also, the upper portion of the pile hole could be cased off with a steel liner to prevent soil from caving in on top of the concrete or grout column after the casing is withdrawn and to permit placing additional concrete or grout to grade. If the liner is withdrawn, the concrete or grout must be sufficiently fluid to prevent it from arching and coming up with the liner. Withdrawal by vibratory means would help prevent this.

When installing this type of pile, it is often difficult to fill the hole to precisely the required cutoff grade. In most cases excess concrete or grout will be placed, and pile butts must be trimmed back to the required elevation.

Withdrawing Casing. The driven casing should preferably be withdrawn by vibratory methods to help prevent arching of the concrete or grout in the casing. The casing should be thoroughly cleaned periodically to prevent a buildup of hardened concrete or grout which may cause arching. This should be done at each interruption in the installation schedule no matter how short.

Protection of Butt.   A short steel sleeve should be placed at the top of the pile to protect the unset concrete or grout at the butt and to ensure proper filling without contamination. This is especially necessary if the cutoff grade is below the ground surface. The sleeve should not be removed.

Pile Heave.   If ground heave occurs during driving of adjacent piles, all completed piles should be checked for evidence of pile heave. If pile heave is detected, all heaved piles should be abandoned and replaced.

Obstructions.   If subsurface obstructions including boulders are known to exist, the piles should be installed in a staggered sequence, permitting the concrete or grout to harden before driving adjacent piles. If the ground is heavily obstructed, completed piles should be carefully observed for signs of movement or damage when adjacent piles are driven. If movement or damage is evident, further investigation may be required to determine whether or not the pile is satisfactory, or the pile may have to be rejected and replaced.

Concrete or Grout Subsidence.   When installing piles in extremely soft soils, the concrete or grout level of completed piles should be checked for subsidence. If the concrete or grout level in the pile has subsided, the cause and possible damage to the pile should be investigated. This can be done by making a test boring alongside the pile, by excavation, or by coring the pile. Before additional concrete or grout is placed to bring the tops of satisfactory piles to the required grade, all laitance and contaminated concrete or grout should be removed and steel dowels should be inserted in the tops of the piles.

Lateral Support.   If, after withdrawing the casing, a space is left between the pile and the soil, the space should be filled with fluid grout or by washing in sand to reestablish the lateral support of the soil.

Installed Length.   The installed lengths of cast-in-situ piles can be determined by knowing the length of drive casing used and observing the depth or elevation to which the bottom end is driven. The casing should be marked off in 5-ft (1.5-m) increments with incremental marks numbered according to distance from the bottom. Depths or elevations should be referenced to a fixed datum. Pile lengths can be calculated from pile tip and specified butt elevations or distances to the tip and butt from a fixed reference.

Compacted-Concrete Pile

This type of pile is installed by (1) driving to the required depth a steel casing or drive tube closed at the bottom with a gravel or zero-slump-concrete plug using a drop weight operating inside the casing, (2) restraining the casing from further penetration while driving out the closure plug, (3) placing small batches of zero-slump concrete in the bottom of the casing and ramming out each batch to form an enlarged base, and (4) forming either an uncased or a cased concrete shaft to the required pile-cutoff grade. For uncased shafts, small batches of zero-slump concrete are placed in the casing and rammed out with the drop weight as the casing is withdrawn. For cased shafts, a steel shell or pipe is placed inside the drive casing and, with a small amount of zero-slump concrete at the bottom, is tapped into the enlarged base. The drive tube is then withdrawn and the shell filled with conventional concrete.

Required Lengths. The bases for compacted-concrete piles should be formed in granular materials, which should be of adequate thickness to contain the compaction resulting from forming the base and to spread the load so as not to overstress underlying soils. The elevations or depths at which pile bases are to be formed will be specified. It is necessary that the vertical location and thickness of the bearing stratum as well as the character and properties of the underlying soils be clearly defined by test borings.

Spacing. The normal spacing for compacted-concrete piles is from 4 to 6 ft (1.2 to 1.8 m). Greater spacing may be required for piles installed with uncased shafts in soft soils or boulder formations unless the piles are installed in a staggered sequence.

Driving the Casing. The bottom of the drive casing or tube should be closed with a gravel or zero-slump-concrete plug of sufficient thickness so that it will arch in the drive tube and not be driven out under the blows of the drop weight. If the plug is driven out, the tube must be withdrawn and redriven with an adequate plug. The drive tube should be driven to the depth at which the enlarged base is to be formed. The inspector should observe the driving of the casing in comparison with that of a test pile or a pile installed at a test-boring location. If a radical change is noted, the cause should be investigated by means of a test boring in case pile lengths need to be adjusted.

Concrete. All concrete should conform with specifications for cast-in-place piles, except that concrete for forming the bases and uncased shafts of compacted-concrete piles should be of zero slump. However, the concrete should contain enough water to ensure hydration of the cement.

Hammer Energy. The weight of the drop hammer must be known to calculate the fall required to deliver the specified energy. To check on the hammer fall and thus the delivered energy, a mark should be placed on the hammer line which will show above the top of the casing when the hammer is raised to its full required height. The drive casing should be at least as long as the required fall plus the length of the drop hammer. During the fall, the hammer should not be restrained by the operator, nor should the hammer line be snubbed just at impact. As the hammer falls, it must overhaul the hammer line, and therefore all sheaves, drums, etc., must turn freely and easily. The inspector must carefully observe the actions of the rig operator and the operations of the hammer to determine whether or not the hammer energy is being seriously affected.

Formation of Base. After being driven to the required depth, the drive tube should be raised not more than about 6 in (152.4 mm) and restrained from further penetration. If, in driving out the closure plug, the entire plug is expelled, creating a void below the casing or allowing soil and/or water to enter, the casing should be withdrawn and redriven with an adequate plug.

In forming the enlarged base, batches of zero-slump concrete of known volume should be placed in the bottom of the drive tube and rammed out with the drop weight, delivering a specified energy. For the design load involved, the specifications will indicate the minimum number of hammer blows of a stated energy required to drive out the last batch of concrete of a stated volume. The minimum volume of the base may also be specified.

During base forming, a sufficient height of dry concrete must be kept in the drive tube at all times to maintain a seal and exclude all water and soil. If water or soil enters the tube, the pile must be abandoned and redriven. The inspector should keep a constant record of the quantities of concrete placed in the tube, the elevation of the bottom of the tube, and the elevation of the top of the compacted concrete. The intrusion of soil can be monitored by observing the position of a mark on the hammer line relative to the top of the drive tube as each charge of concrete is placed. After each batch of concrete has been placed in the tube, the distance to which the mark rises must not exceed the additional depth of concrete in the tube. If the mark rises above the calculated increase in depth of concrete, it must be assumed that foreign matter has entered the tube and the pile should be abandoned. The entry of water will be indicated by a softening of the hammer blows.

If, in attempting to form the base for any pile, the total volume of concrete placed is more than 50 percent greater than that for a test-pile base, the cause should be investigated. A test boring may reveal a change in subsoil conditions requiring an adjustment in pile lengths. Intrusion of groundwater may soften the concrete, precluding the formation of a normal base. Possible interference with adjacent pile bases should be considered, and, if necessary, pile spacing may have to be increased.

Formation of Shaft

Uncased Shaft. The number of hammer blows and the energy required for driving out each batch of concrete in forming the shaft will be specified; the volume of each batch of zero-slump concrete will also be specified. In forming the shaft, the concrete must not be driven out below the bottom of the drive casing. The concrete level in the drive tube should be kept at a sufficient height above the bottom of the tube at all times to form an adequate seal. This can be monitored in a manner similar to that described under "Formation of Base." The casing should be withdrawn as the concrete is rammed out and not in lifts. If an adequate seal is not maintained, water and soil could enter the tube and contaminate the concrete. If the concrete is driven out below the bottom of the drive tube or if the tube is raised in lifts, water and soil may fill the void created, producing a reduction (necking) of the shaft cross section or even a complete interruption of the concrete shaft. If soil or water enters the drive tube or the concrete shaft, the pile should be rejected. If the shaft is to be formed through unstable or organic soils or extremely soft soils, a cased shaft is recommended.

Cased Shafts. The steel shell or pipe inserted in the drive tube should be adequately connected to the pile base before the drive tube is withdrawn to ensure a positive seal and a good, sound joint between base and shaft. This is usually done by placing a small batch of zero-slump concrete in the shell and tapping it into the base with the drop weight. The inner shell or pipe should be restrained from moving upward as the drive tube is withdrawn. After withdrawal of the drive tube and before filling the shell with concrete, the bottom of the shell or pipe should be inspected to determine whether or not any soil or water has entered. If soil has intruded, the pile should be rejected. If only water has entered, it should be removed before placing concrete. Concrete should be placed in the shell or pipe in accordance with "Placing Concrete for Cast-in-Place Piles" in the subsection "Pile Installation." The annular space between the cased shaft and the soil should be filled with grout or clean sand, washed down to reestablish lateral support.

Reinforcing Steel

Uncased Shaft. The reinforcing steel should be made up in cages and placed inside the drive tube after the base has been formed or just before the last batch of base concrete is compacted. If the steel cage is placed after the base has been formed, a small batch of zero-slump concrete should be placed in the tube and tapped down with the drop weight operating inside the cage to anchor the cage to the base. The formation of the shaft should be in accordance with "Formation of Shaft: Uncased Shaft," with the drop hammer operating inside the cage. Care must be exercised to ensure that the cage is not lifted when the drop weight is raised or damaged as the weight falls. If the cage consists of a number of large-diameter longitudinal bars enclosed in a spiral steel on a small pitch, it may be difficult to ram zero-slump concrete out through the steel cage without deforming the cage; the use of a more workable concrete mix or a cased shaft may be necessary. Extra caution must be exercised in forming the upper portions of the pile shaft to ensure that the drop hammer is not raised out of the cage and allowed to damage or dislodge the reinforcement as it drops.

Cased Shafts. For cased shafts, the reinforcing steel should be placed inside the steel shell or pipe before concrete is poured and in accordance with "Placing Reinforcing Steel" in the subsection "Pile Installation."

Heave. If pile heave occurs (see "Pile Heave" in the subsection "Pile Installation"), all compacted-concrete piles that have heaved must be rejected and replaced. If only ground heave ocurs, piles with uncased shafts should be rejected.

Pile Butts. When forming uncased shafts, it is difficult to form the shaft precisely to cutoff grade. The top of the pile shaft should be at or above the required elevation and trimmed back if necessary.

Base Configuration. The development of high capacity for a compacted-concrete pile depends not only on the formation of an enlarged base but also on the uniform densification or compaction of the surrounding granular soil and concentric loading of the base. The base therefore should be of relatively symmetrical shape. The configuration of bases should be checked periodically by probing. If a clubfoot or an elongated (vertical) base has been formed, the capacity of the pile should be tested.

Records. In addition to the normal records of installed lengths and payment quantities, the inspector should keep an accurate record of the volume of concrete in each pile base, the number of hammer blows and energy required to compact the last batch of concrete [generally 5 ft^3 (0.1416m^3)] in forming the base, and the elevation at which each base was formed.

Installed Length. The installed length of a compacted-concrete pile can be determined from the elevation or depth to which the bottom of the drive tube is driven with reference to a fixed datum and the cutoff elevation or depth referenced to the same datum. To facilitate taking measurements, the drive tube should be marked off in 1-ft (0.3-m) increments with each 5-ft (1.5-m) mark numbered with the distance from the bottom.

Pay Length. The pay length of a compacted-concrete pile should be that measured from the depth to which the drive tube is driven to the cutoff grade. No extra payment should be made for bases regardless of size or for trimming off pile butts.

Load Tests. The actual capacity of a compacted-concrete pile is a function of many variables such as the density, thickness, and physical properties of the granular stratum in which the base is formed, the type and bearing capacity of the underlying soils, the proper shape and formation of the base, the degree of compaction of the surrounding soils, the dynamic energy applied in forming the base, and the integrity of the pile shaft and its connection with the base. The method of installation and the final product are sensitive to the actions of the rig operator.

For these reasons the actual capacities of the piles should be checked by conducting periodic proof-load tests. This is especially important if the results of closely spaced reliable test borings are not available. Piles to be tested should be selected at random by the engineer from among those installed.

Enlarged-Base Pile

This type of pile is generally installed by driving with or without a mandrel, a steel shell, or pipe to which is attached an enlarged precast-concrete base at the tip. After driving the base to the required depth, the mandrel (if used) is removed and the shell or pipe is filled with concrete to the required cutoff grade. The enlarged base could also be attached to a steel H pile or formed with a precast-concrete pile.

The enlarged-base pile is similar in function to the compacted-concrete pile and requires many of the same controls.

General. The applicable control provisions of subsections "Pile Material," "Material Handling and Storage," and "Pile Installation" for the type of pile shaft used must be enforced. The following are special provisions for the enlarged-base pile.

Required Lengths. The required pile length or the elevation to which the enlarged base is to be driven may be specified. The development of high capacity for this type of pile requires that the base be driven into a stratum of granular soil which can be compacted by the displacement action of the base. The bearing stratum must be of adequate thickness and underlain by satisfactory soils. More closely spaced test borings may be required to define the type, thickness, and vertical position of the bearing stratum and the adequacy of the underlying soils.

If sufficient and reliable subsoil information is available to establish the required elevations of pile bases, final penetration resistance may be correlated with that of test piles.

Spacing. The center-to-center spacing of enlarged-base piles should be at least 3 times the maximum base diameter or diagonal dimension.

Base Construction. Precast-concrete bases should be of proper design and construction to withstand driving stresses without damage and must conform with the requirements of the plans and specifications. For inspection details see the subsection "Pile Material: Precast-Concrete Piles" for plant-produced bases or "Concrete for Cast-in-Place Piles" for bases made on the jobsite.

Base-to-Shaft Connection. The pipe or shell should be attached to the base so as to prevent the entry of soil or water. If the pile is to resist uplift loads, the joint between the base and the casing or the concrete filling must be designed and installed to transfer the tension load into the base. Joints between bases and any type of pile shaft must be capable of resisting all driving- and service-load stresses. For short piles the joint may be subjected to bending from lateral loads resulting from ground movements or construction activity. See "Piles off Location" in the subsection "Pile Installation."

Uncased Shafts. The use of uncased cast-in-place-concrete shafts with enlarged precast-concrete bases should not be permitted. The chances of installing an adequate foundation are quite remote. If such shafts are used, all the applicable control provisions of the subsections "Cast-in-Situ Pile," "Compacted-Concrete Pile," and "Enlarged-Base Pile" must be strictly enforced.

Heave. If ground or pile heave occurs (see "Pile Heave" in the subsection "Pile Installation"), check levels should be taken on the tops of all driven piles until driving progresses beyond heave range. For cased cast-in-place-concrete shafts, check levels should also be taken on telltale piles bearing on the bases.

Heaved piles may be redriven as necessary provided the joints between base and casing have not separated. If the joint cannot take the tension resulting from heave and if check levels indicate possible joint separation, the pile should be rejected.

Relaxation. If relaxation occurs (see "Relaxation" in the subsection "Pile Installation") and if pile bases are not driven to hard material, consideration should be given to changing the pile type or assigning a lower design capacity to each pile.

Reinforcing Steel. If internal reinforcing steel is required for cased concrete shafts, it should be placed in accordance with "Placing Reinforcing Steel" in the subsection "Pile Installation." If such steel is required to resist uplift loads, it must be positively connected to the precast base so as to transfer the tensile forces.

Concrete. Concrete for cased cast-in-place shafts should conform with the control provision of "Concrete for Cast-in-Place Piles" in the subsection "Pile Material." "Placing Concrete for Cast-in-Place Piles" in the subsection "Pile Installation" covers the placement of such concrete.

Lateral Support. The annular space between the soil and the pile shaft created by the enlarged base must be backfilled to provide lateral support to the pile. The natural sloughing off or caving of soils may not be sufficient to restore lateral support. Grout can be pumped into the annular space or clean sand washed down if the space remains open. If the space closes in with the possibility of voids below, the area around each pile shaft should be tamped and backfilled as necessary. In extreme cases, it may be necessary to remove the upper sloughed-in soil in order to place the backfill properly. These are generally high-capacity foundation units and require full lateral support for stability.

Records. In addition to the normal records of installed lengths and payment quantities, the inspector should keep an accurate record of the elevation to which each enlarged base was driven. Such elevations must be referenced to a permanent datum.

Installed Length.   The installed length of the pile shaft can be determined in accordance with "Pile Lengths" in the subsection "Pile Installation." To this length may be added the length or height of the base. However, if the measured length of the pile shaft includes a portion recessed into the base, the amount of the recess should not be included in the length of the precast base to be added.

Pay Quantities.   The pay length of an enlarged-base pile may not include the precast base. Bases may be paid for separately at a unit price.

Load Tests.   The actual capacity of an enlarged-base pile depends upon several factors such as the density, thickness, and physical properties of the bearing stratum, the degree of compaction of the soil resulting from driving the base into it, and the type and bearing capacity of the underlying soil.

If final penetration resistances vary and if the results of closely spaced reliable test borings are not available, the capacities of the piles should be checked by periodic proof-load testing. Piles to be tested should be selected at random by the engineer from among those installed.

PILE LOAD TESTING

(See Figs. 2.3-10 and 2.3-11.) Piles are load-tested to develop design data, to confirm the required load capacity of the pile (proof test), to establish installation criteria, or for a combination of these reasons. Since critical decisions are often made on the basis of load-test results, careful inspection and accurate recording and reporting of the data are essential. Piles can be tested in bearing (compression), in uplift (tension), under lateral loading, or in a combination of such loads. Piles may be tested individually or in groups.

Test-Pile Data

The pile to be tested should be properly identified (see "Identification of Piles" in the subsection "Pile Installation") and adequately described as to material, type, size, length, weight, and date installed (and concreted, if applicable). The elevation of the pile butt should be referenced to a fixed and permanent datum.

FIG. 2.3-10 Typical arrangement for a pile load test using reaction piles. *(Raymond International Builders Inc.)*

FIG. 2.3-11 Observing and recording butt movements of a test pile. *(Raymond International Builders Inc.)*

Driving Record

A complete record of the installation of the test pile, including the driving log, descriptions of the hammer, hammer cushion, pile cushion (if used), drive cap, follower (if used), and drill or jet (if used), and a record of the depths predrilled or jetted should be made. Any interruptions or unusual occurrences during pile installation should be clearly and completely described. (See "Driving Log: Vibratory Driving" in the subsection "Pile Installation".)

Reaction Piles

If reaction piles or other types of anchors are used, they should be described as to type, size, and lengths. Each reaction pile should have a unique designation. The driving log and the location of each reaction pile with reference to the test pile should be reported.

Test-Boring Data

The location of the closest boring with reference to the test pile should be recorded. The boring must be identified, and the boring log should accompany the test report. Ground-surface elevations for all test borings must be shown and referenced to the same datum used for the piles.

Instrumentation to Measure Pile-Head Movement

The movement of the pile head under load can be measured by dial gauges, by a wire-and-scale system, or by a remotely stationed surveying level or transit reading a scale attached to the pile or a target rod held on the pile. Both a primary and a secondary measuring system should be used to assure a check on all readings and continuity of readings in case one of the systems malfunctions or requires resetting. All instrumentation must be properly mounted and installed and be functioning accurately. For tests on pile groups the instrumentation or reference points will normally be on the pile cap instead of on the test pile as described below. Instrumentation and its supporting system should be protected from wind, extreme temperature variations, and accidental disturbance.

Dial Gauges.   At least two dial gauges, mounted on opposite sides of the pile, should be used. The required sensitivity of the gauges may be specified, but normally readings to 0.01 in (0.254 mm) are sufficient. Gauges should be mounted so as to measure movements at the sides of the pile near the butt relative to an independent reference system. Dial-gauge stems should travel freely and bear against a smooth surface.

Wire and Scale.   The scale should preferably be mounted on a mirror, which in turn is fixed to the side of the pile. Consistent readings are thus assured by lining up the wire with its image. The wire should be stretched across the face of the scale, kept taut at all times, and supported independently of the test setup.

Level or Transit.   The engineer's level or transit should be stationed a sufficient distance from the test pile so as not to be influenced by pile or ground movement during testing. If readings are taken on a scale, it should be fixed to the side of the test pile. If a target rod is used, readings should be taken on a fixed point on the side of the test pile. Readings should be referenced to a fixed bench mark, or the instrument can be mounted on a fixed object such as a pile for consistent readings.

Test Loads

For bearing tests, loads can be applied directly to the test pile or group with objects of known weight or applied with a hydraulic-jack ram acting against a suitable reaction such as a weighted platform or a steel frame tied to reaction piles or another type of ground anchor. For uplift tests and tests on batter piles, the load is generally applied with a hydraulic jack. For lateral-load tests the load can be applied with a hydraulic jack or some type of suitable pulling system. The amount of load applied to the pile during testing should be known within an accuracy of 5 percent.

Direct Load.   The amount of load applied to the pile can be checked by the volume and unit-weight method for the material involved. If necessary, test-load material can actually be weighed beforehand to determine the load being applied. Sometimes standard test weights are available. The weight of any test beam, platform, box, or tank should be included in the first load increment. The test load must be balanced on the pile and allowed to act without restraint.

Hydraulic Jack.   A calibration certificate should be submitted for each complete jacking system including the ram, pump, and pressure gauge. If multiple jack rams are used, they should be of equal piston size, connected via a manifold to a single pump and gauge, and, if possible, calibrated as a single system. If this is impractical because of the total jacking capacity or the limitations of available testing equipment, each jack ram should be calibrated separately with the pump and gauge. Adjustment factors may have to be applied for the complete system. Calibrations should be furnished for both increasing and decreasing loads.

Load Cell.   A load cell may be used to determine the amount of test load being applied. Load cells must be properly designed and constructed and accurately calibrated for both increasing and decreasing loads. They should be equipped with spherical bearing plates.

Dynamometer.   If a pulling system is used for lateral loading, a calibrated dynamometer should be installed in the system. If the load is applied with multiple-part reaving, the location of the dynamometer within the system should be carefully recorded along with a correlation of the dynamometer readings versus actual loads applied.

Reaction System

The minimum distances between the test pile and the anchor piles or supports for the reaction load will generally be specified. It is recommended that arrangements be made to take readings of the movements of anchor piles or other load-reaction systems during the test. This can be done with suitably mounted dial gauges or with a surveying instrument reading scales attached to the reaction system or a target rod held on fixed points.

Test-Pile Instrumentation

If special instrumentation of the test pile, such as strain gauges or telltales, is required, such instrumentation should be installed according to specifications. The installation of electric strain gauges and subsequent readings are generally handled by a specialist in this field. However, the installation of telltales or strain rods is often performed by the contractor, and subsequent readings are made with suitably mounted dial gauges or some other type of measuring system. Telltale readings should generally be referenced to the top of the pile to give direct measurements of elastic shortening under load. Measurements of telltale movements would normally be made as other time-load-movement data are recorded.

Testing Arrangement

Steel test plates having a minimum thickness of 2 in (50.8 mm) should be used on top of the test pile, the jack ram, and the load cell (if used). Eccentric loading must be avoided. All compression and testing loads must be applied directly along the longitudinal axis of the test pile. For lateral tests, the loads must be applied in line with the central axis of the pile. For group tests the loads should act on the center of the group. This requires careful positioning and alignment of all applied loads, loading devices, and special instrumentation such as load cells.

Testing Procedures

Normally the overall testing procedures including rate of load application, holding times, etc., will be specified. There are many different types of testing procedures, and there should be a clear understanding by all parties concerned as to what procedures will be used before testing begins. Testing procedures commonly used include the maintained load, the quick load, and the constant rate of penetration. The inspector should be familiar with the requirements of the testing procedure to be used.

Lateral-Load Tests

The lateral-load capacity of the pile or group should be determined under in-service loading conditions with the permanent dead load acting on the pile or group during the test. The test pile or group must not be restrained by the vertical load from free lateral movement. This can be achieved by applying the compression load with the direct-load method or by using suitable steel rollers between the test pile or group and the axial load.

Concrete Strength

For tests on cast-in-place-concrete piles, the concrete must be of sufficient age (strength) to carry the test loads without failure or excessive creep. Standard concrete cylinders can be tested at approximately the same age as the pile but may show strengths greater than the concrete in the pile. This is normal and results from the slower curing of the cast-in-place concrete especially when confined in a steel shell. Type III cement can be used in concrete for test piles. Sufficient time must be allowed between concreting and load testing.

Regain of Soil Strength

If test piles are driven in soils which could exhibit freeze or setup (see "Soil Freeze" in the subsection "Pile Installation"), sufficient time should elapse between pile driving and testing to permit the soil to regain its shear strength. The length of time necessary for the soil to set up could vary up to 30 days or longer. Prior experience in the area would serve as a guide. If test results are not up to expectations, the pile should be retested after additional elapsed time.

Special Testing Methods

The specifications may require that the pile be tested by using special methods in order to achieve specific objectives or to develop special data.

Casing Off. It may be required that the upper portion of the pile be cased off from the surrounding soil for various reasons such as to develop bearing-capacity data on underlying soils or to eliminate from the test results the frictional support of the cased-off soil. The outer casing should be of suitable diameter, installed to the proper depth, and thoroughly cleaned out. It may be necessary to insert support members at regular intervals along the unsupported pile lengths to eliminate buckling under load.

Cyclic Loading. To develop information on load distribution and transfer or the behavior of the pile under various load levels, the specifications may require that the pile be loaded and unloaded in cycles. The load level for each cycle and the number of loading cycles at each load level will be specified. The proposed design load should be one of the cycled load levels.

Failure Loading. The specifications may require that the ultimate capacity of the pile-soil system be determined by carrying the test to failure as evidenced by progressive movement of the pile under constant load. This may be difficult to accomplish for point-bearing piles. To determine the failure load would require a close estimation of the ultimate capacity of the pile-soil system so that sufficient testing capacity is furnished. The contractor may qualify this requirement by limiting it to a stated testing capacity that will be furnished.

Recording Data

A complete and accurate record should be made of all time-load-movement data (Fig. 2.3-12). Each gauge or measuring point should be accurately identified and marked so as to avoid any confusion or error in observing and recording data. Extreme care must be exercised to ensure that all readings are made accurately. If it is necessary during the test to reset gauges or scales, a complete record of exactly what was done should be made with a clear explanation as to the relationships between the old and the new readings. This is most important in order to maintain a continuity of data. Any adjustments made to field data should be thoroughly explained. Periodic readings should be made on the reaction and reference systems to determine any movement under loading. Such readings should be recorded.

Interpretation of Load-Test Results

In most cases the pile inspector will not be involved with the interpretation of load-test results. However, the inspector should be familiar with the acceptance criterion, which should be specified in advance so that all parties concerned, including the contractor, will know what constitutes a

FIG. 2.3-12   Measuring the final set. *(Raymond International Builders Inc.)*

satisfactory test. Some criteria may require that the inspector plot the load-movement data as they are developed in the field to ensure that sufficient data are recovered for application of the criterion.

Compression Tests.   Most pile load testing conducted at the start of or during pile installation is for proof testing only or to establish installation criteria. Under such conditions, the test load is carried routinely to only twice the proposed working load. The acceptance criterion is an arbitrary definition of what constitutes the *failure* load. Generally, the allowable working load is one-half of this arbitrary failure load. If actual failure of the pile-soil system occurs as evidenced by a progressive settlement of the pile under a constant load or if the pile fails structurally, a factor of safety of 2.5 should be applied in determining the allowable working load.

There are in use several acceptance criteria, many of which are based on a maximum permissible gross or net pile settlement as measured at the pile butt. The gross settlement is the movement of the pile butt under the test load, and the net settlement is the amount that the pile has permanently moved after it has rebounded upon removal of the test load.

Maximum permissible pile settlement may be expressed as a finite number or as either a function of the total pile test load or of the pile-tip diameter. The gross settlement permitted may be that measured after deducting the theoretical elastic shortening of the pile. The gross-minus-elastic-shortening settlement could be expressed as a finite number or as a fixed number plus a factor which is a function of the tip diameter. The acceptance criterion could be based upon a maximum permissible slope of the load-settlement curve combined with a maximum permissible gross settlement under the proposed working load, which should be in addition to the elastic shortening of the pile. This could be determined by removing the test load after applying the proposed working load and measuring the rebound.

There are several definitions of the arbitrary failure load which are rather indeterminate, such as "where the load-settlement curve shows a break," "where the settlement is disproportionate to the load," or "the point of intersection of tangents drawn to two parts of the load-settlement curve." Others are based upon the performance of the pile during test, such as "that load which shows a settlement on the curve equal to the rebound after application and removal of the full test load," "that load for which the settlement is twice the settlement under 90 percent of that load," or "that load determined by the intersection of the two straight portions of a curve resulting from plotting the load versus the settlement under that load during the last 30 minutes for which it was held."

Tension Tests. For uplift tests, there are no established acceptance criteria; the acceptance criteria will be specified. Generally, if the pile-soil system behaves elastically under the proposed test load, the test will be considered satisfactory. If pile upward movement is progressive under a constant load, the actual ultimate uplift capacity of the pile is determined.

Lateral Tests. There are also no established acceptance criteria for lateral-load tests; such criteria will be as specified. Again, if the pile exhibits elastic behavior during the test, the test is considered satisfactory. For lateral tests, the amount of lateral movement under the design load should be an important consideration, and the permissible amount would depend upon the structure involved. The amount of permanent lateral deflection of the pile butt (net movement after removal of the test load) may also be critical, and the permissible amount may depend upon the structure.

REFERENCES

Standards of Professional Societies

American Concrete Institute, P.O. Box 19150, Detroit, Mich. 48219

ACI 211.1-81, Recommended Practice for Selecting Proportions for Normal and Heavy-weight Concrete.

ACI 211-75/80, Recommended Practice for Selecting Proportions for No Slump Concrete.

ACI 212, 1R-81, Admixtures for Concrete.

ACI 212, 2R-81, Guide for Use of Admixtures in Concrete.

ACI 214-77, Recommended Practice for Evaluation of Compression Test Results of Field Concrete.

ACI 304-73/78, Recommended Practice for Measuring, Mixing, Transporting and Placing Concrete.

ACI 305 R-77, Recommended Practice for Hot-Weather Concreting.

ACI 306 R-78, Recommended Practice for Cold-Weather Concreting.

ACI 311-64, Recommended Practice for Concrete Inspection.

ACI 318-77, Building Code Requirements for Reinforced Concrete.

ACI 543 R-74/80, Recommendation for Design, Manufacture and Installation of Concrete Piles, *ACI Manual of Concrete Practice*, part III, 1974.

ACI 621, Selection and Use of Aggregates for Concrete.

American Society for Testing and Materials, 1916 Race Street, Philadelphia, Pa. 19103

ASTM A252-80, Standard Specification for Welded and Seamless Steel Pipe Piles.

ASTM C 31-80, Standard Method of Making and Curing Concrete Test Specimens in the Field.

ASTM C 33-81, Standard Specification for Concrete Aggregates.

ASTM C 39-80, Standard Method of Test for Compressive Strength of Cylindrical Concrete Specimens.

ASTM C 91-78, Specification for Masonry Cement.

ASTM C 94-81, Standard Specification for Ready Mixed Concrete.

ASTM C 143-78, Standard Method of Test for Slump of Portland Cement Concrete.

ASTM C 150-81, Standard Specification for Portland Cement.

ASTM C 172-77, Standard Method of Sampling Fresh Concrete.

ASTM C 470-79, Specifications for Molds for Forming Concrete Test Cylinders Vertically.

ASTM C 803-79, Method of Tests for Penetration Resistance of Hardened Concrete.

ASTM D 25-58, Standard Specifications for Round Timber Piles.

ASTM D 25-73, Standard Specifications for Round Timber Piles.

ASTM D 1143-81, Standard Method of Testing Piles under Axial Compressive Loads.

ASTM D 3689-78, Method for Testing Individual Piles under Static Axial Tensile Load.

ASTM D 3966-81, Method for Testing Piles under Lateral Loads.

American Welding Society, 550 LeJeune Road, N.W., Miami, Fla. 33135

AWS D 1.1-75/76, Structural Welding Code—Steel.

American Wood-Preservers' Association, P.O. Box 849, Stevensville, Md. 21666

AWPA C 1-81, All Timber Products—Preservative Treatment by Pressure Processes (Standard).

AWPA C 3-81, Piles—Preservative Treatment by Pressure Processes (Standard).

AWPA C 18-77, Standard for Pressure Treated Material in Marine Construction.

AWPA M 1-76, Standard for the Purchase of Treated Wood Products.

AWPA M 2-81, Standard for Inspection of Treated Timber Products.

AWPA M 4-80, Standard for the Care of Preservative Treated Wood Products.

AWPA M 6-75, Brands Used on Forest Products (Standard).

Books, Articles, and Reports

Bastian, C. E.: "The Effect of Vibrations on Freshly Placed Concrete," *Foundation Facts*, vol. VI, no. 1, Raymond International Inc., Houston, 1970.

Bruce, R. N., Jr., and D. C. Hebert: "Splicing of Precast, Prestressed Concrete Piles: Part I—Review and Performance of Splices; Part II—Tests and Analysis of Cement-Dowel Splice," *PCI Journal*, vol. 19, nos. 5 and 6, September–October and November–December 1974, Prestressed Concrete Institute, 20 North Wacker Drive, Chicago, Ill., 60606.

Chellis, R. D.: *Pile Foundations*, 2d ed., McGraw-Hill Book Company, New York, 1961.

Concrete Manual, 8th ed., U.S. Department of the Interior, Bureau of Reclamation, Engineering and Research Center, P.O. Box 25007, Denver Federal Center, Denver, Colo. 80225, 1975.

Davisson, M.T.: "Design Pile Capacity," *Proceedings*, Conference on Design and Installation of Pile Foundations and Cellular Structures, Lehigh University, Enuo Publishing Co., Inc., 1970.

———: "Pile Load Capacity," *Proceedings*, Seminar on Design, Construction and Performance of Deep Foundations, University of California, Berkeley, February 1975.

———: "Static Measurements of Pile Behavior," *Proceedings*, Conference on Design and Installation of Pile Foundations and Cellular Structures, Lehigh University, Enuo Publishing Co., INc., 1970.

Fuller, F. M.: "Pile Installation: Pitfalls, Problems and Solutions," *APF Piletalk Seminar Papers*, March 1979.

———: "Types and Selection of Concrete Piles," *ACI Pile Foundation Seminar*, New Orleans, April 1975 (unpublished).

Gendron, G. J.: "Pile Driving: Hammers and Driving Methods," *Highway Research Record*, no. 333, Highway Research Board, Washington, 1970.

Goble, G. G., and F. Rausche: "Dynamic Measurements of Pile Behavior," *Proceedings,* Conference on Design and Installation of Pile Foundations and Cellular Structures, Lehigh University, Enuo Publishing Co., Inc., 1970.

————and————: "Pile Load Test by Impact Driving," *Highway Research Record,* no. 333, Highway Research Board, Washington, 1970.

Hirsch, T. J., L. L. Lowery, H. M. Coyle, and C. H. Samson, Jr.: "Pile Driving Analysis by One-Dimensional Wave Theory: State of the Art," *Highway Research Record,* no 333, Highway Research Board, Washington, 1970.

Hoy, H. E.: "Pile Load Tests Including Quick-Load Test Method, Conventional Methods and Interpretations," *Highway Research Record,* no. 333, Highway Research Board, Washington, 1970.

Manual of Steel Construction, 7th ed., American Institute of Steel Construction, Inc., 1221 Avenue of the Americas, New York, N.Y. 10020.

Mosley, E. T.: "The Practical Application of the Wave Equation," *Proceedings,* Soils Mechanics and Foundation Engineering Conference, University of Kansas, Lawrence, 1971.

Mosley, E. T., and T. Raamot: "Pile Driving Formulas," *Highway Research Record,* no. 333, Highway Research Board, Washington, 1970.

Peck, R. B., W. E. Hanson, and T. H. Thornburn: *Foundation Engineering,* 2d ed., John Wiley & Sons, Inc., New York, 1974.

Portland Cement Association: *Basic Concrete Construction Practices,* John Wiley & Sons, Inc., New York, 1975.

————: *Principles of Quality Concrete,* John Wiley & Sons, Inc., New York, 1975.

Raamot, T.: "Analysis of Pile Driving by the Wave Equation," *Foundation Facts,* vol. III, no. 1, Raymond International Inc., Houston, 1967.

Smith, E. A. L.: "Pile Driving Analysis by the Wave Equation," *Transactions of the American Society of Civil Engineers,* vol. 127, part I, 1962.

Snow, R. K.: "Raycrete 800—A Proven Mix," *Foundation Facts,* vol. XI, no. 1, Raymond International Inc., Houston 1976.

Subsurface Exploration and Sampling of Soils for Civil Engineering Purposes, Report of Committee on Sampling and Testing, ASCE, SM&F Division, Engineering Foundation, United Engineering Center, New York.

Woodward, R. J., Jr., W. S. Gardner, and D. Greer: *Drilled Pier Foundations,* McGraw-Hill Book Company, New York, 1972.

Structural Concrete and Reinforcing

Lystre L. Sutcliffe, Jr., P.E.
Vice President and Manager of Construction Engineering Services Department
Parsons Brinckerhoff Construction Services, Inc.
Trenton, New Jersey

C. Gary Altoonian, Jr., P.E.
Assistant Vice President and Manager of Construction Engineering Services
Parsons Brinckerhoff Construction Services, Inc.
McLean, Virginia

Concrete is one of the most versatile and widely used building materials in the construction industry. It has an almost unlimited number of applications, which include construction elements from sidewalks, curbs, and roadways to the structural elements of buildings, bridges, and tunnels. Concrete elements can be poured in place by using forms that are set in place on site, or they can be precast elements cast off the jobsite, transported, and erected or incorporated in the structure. Concrete can be plain concrete with no reinforcement, or it can be reinforced with deformed steel bars. It can be pretensioned or posttensioned with high-strength steel bars and cables. No matter which of these applications is used, the production and placing of concrete require the utmost attention of the inspector.

This chapter is confined to the production and placement of structural concrete such as structural members of buildings, bridges, and tunnels. Further applications of concrete are treated in other chapters of the *Handbook.*

CONCRETE COMPONENTS

It is important that the inspector have a complete understanding of the various materials used in the manufacture of concrete. Concrete is basically a mixture of properly graded fine and coarse aggregate, portland cement, and water. Other additives, such as fly ash and various types of admixtures, i.e., air-entraining agents, accelerators, retardants, densifiers, and plasticizers, may be used. The inspector should be familiar with the various tests required for each component of a concrete design, such as gradation of fine and coarse aggregate, moisture content of fine and coarse aggregate, and cement-cube strength tests.

The task of the concrete inspector starts at the source of supply of the ingredients listed above. Before concrete can be incorporated into a structure, written confirmation that the various ingredients have been tested and found to conform to job specifications must be on file in the inspection agency's office.

The coarse and fine aggregates are usually tested at the quarry site. Normal tests for aggregates may include gradation, hardness, specific-gravity, absorption, and colorimetric tests for organic impurities. Other tests to check for resistance to environmentally destructive agents such as exposure to salt water may be required by specifications. Portland cement is tested at the mill that produces it, and the results are forwarded with each shipment. Water is tested at the source of supply. Normally if the water is potable, it is considered adequate for concrete production. Admixtures are considered acceptable by certification from the supplier.

When the above materials are delivered to the project site, the test results are checked, and if they are in accordance with the specifications, they are logged in at the inspection office and the field inspection team is notified that the materials may be used for the production of concrete.

The inspection force will make further spot checks of the aggregate and the mixing water at periodic times during construction. Their checks will be made in a field laboratory and will usually consist of gradation, specific-gravity, absorption, and colorimetric tests. Water will be tested periodically for salinity, especially if it is transported in barges for marine projects.

Upon delivery of materials that will be used for the manufacture of concrete, the inspector will check the manner in which the materials are stored at the project site. The method of stockpiling aggregate material must be checked to prevent harmful segregation, generally caused by coning of the material. The proper method for stockpiling aggregate is to deposit it in layers rather than by coning. Cement must be stored in a dry, moistureproof shed or container.

If it is necessary to barge water to the project, the barges must be kept in a condition that will ensure against saltwater intrusion.

Admixtures usually arrive in drums. Certain admixtures tend to have ingredients that settle in the solution if left in one position, and it may be necessary to remix these solutions by periodically rolling the drums or by using an agitator. In the case of manufactured admixtures as well as all other construction materials and manufactured products, the manufacturer's directions for the product's use must be thoroughly understood.

Once all the materials are on the jobsite and it has been ascertained that all of them conform to the specifications, the production of concrete may begin.

BATCH PLANT

The inspector's duties are now concentrated on the batch plant that will produce the concrete. The inspector should observe that the various types of aggregate are placed in their respective bins in such a manner that there is no spillage from one bin to another. The inspector should check the scales to see that they are sealed to assure calibration by the proper state agency and that they have been calibrated within the time limit set by the specifications. The inspector should check all admixture dispensers and, if necessary, make the required tests to ensure the proper batching quantity. It is also necessary to check water meters to ensure that correct volumes of water are added to the batches. The inspector should check the mixer for worn-out blades and hardened concrete.

When the plant has been fully tested and inspected and is ready for operation, the inspector must perform the following tasks, bearing local conditions in mind:

1. The free moisture in the fine aggregate must be ascertained. This free moisture is the surface moisture that is present in excess of the saturated surface-dry condition of the aggregate and will take part in the chemical reaction of the cement. Since the object is to achieve maximum-strength concrete for a particular mix design by striving for a low water-cement ratio, the water content of the mix must be minimized or compensated for, and therefore the amount of free moisture must be deducted from the normal water required by the mix design. Normally the free moisture in the coarse aggregate is not a concern; however, in certain parts of the United States where aggregates such as limestone are used, the absorption factor for coarse aggregate becomes important and must be considered. The absorption factor is important because some aggregate material such as limestone will absorb water intended to be used in the chemical reaction with the portland cement. Since this water is absorbed by the porous coarse aggregate, additional water must be added to the normal water required by the mix to prevent insufficient dispersion of the cement particles throughout the concrete mix. These tests should be made in accordance with the latest edition of the American Concrete Institute (ACI) *Manual of Concrete Inspection* and the latest American Society for Testing and Materials (ASTM) standards. The basic mix design must be altered to adjust for both free moisture in the fine aggregate and the absorption qualities of the coarse aggregate, if any. (See Fig. 2.4-1.)

2. The inspector will then check the scale settings to ensure that the final product will have the correct water-cement ratio and slump.

This completes the activities of the inspector in charge of checking actual production of the concrete. In the meantime, another part of the inspection force has been working on other extremely important areas necessary for the placement of this concrete. These areas are defined as follows:

Forms. The inspector must check forms for proper alignment (it may be necessary to call upon survey personnel to assure proper alignment and elevation). The inspector will also note that the forms are clean and free of hardened concrete from previous pours and other debris and that they are properly oiled to prevent the finished concrete structure from bonding to the form material.

CONCRETE-BATCH PLANT—INSPECTOR'S REPORT

Project _____   Contractor _____

Plant _____   Date/time _____

Truck no. _____ Yards this truck _____ Accumulated yards _____

Design-mix no. _____ Design strength _____

Cement _____

Coarse aggregate _____

Fine aggregate _____

Water _____

Admixtures _____

Moisture in sand _____ percent

Actual batch quantities:

Cement _____

Coarse aggregate _____

Fine aggregate _____

Water _____

Admixtures _____

Remarks _____

_____

_____

_____

Plant inspector   _____

Placing inspector _____

FIG. 2.4-1   Inspector's report for a concrete-batch plant.

Form Bracing.   Form bracing should be checked for conformity with the contractor's working drawings. The forms may be designed by the contractor on working drawings and consist of plywood facing with vertical timber studs and horizontal walers. Form faces will be held in position with form ties and wood struts. Alternatively, the forms may be patented steel forms manufactured by any one of a number of suppliers. In this case, the manufacturer supplies the contractor with working drawings to be reviewed by the engineer.

Reinforcing Steel.   The inspector must check for proper placement and sizing of reinforcing bars. A very critical check at this point is the clearance (concrete cover) between the forms and the first layer of reinforcing bars. This check becomes extremely important in environmentally harsh atmospheres, such as a saltwater environment or one exposed to various corrosive chemicals. The outside surface of concrete may develop shrinkage cracks due to temperature change or cracks due to vibration of the structure as in the case of bridge-deck slabs where flexure cracks appear. In a salty atmosphere, such as seacoast areas where salt fogs occur, or when bridge decks are deiced by salting, the cracks in the structure may allow harmful salts and water to penetrate through to the reinforcing steel. This will eventually cause rusting of the steel, which in turn causes the reinforcing bars to expand and the surface of the concrete subsequently to spall. Once this happens, the path for water infiltration widens, allowing more water and chemical salts to accelerate the rusting of the steel. Therefore, it is imperative that the design thickness of the concrete cover over the steel be adhered to minimize this situation. Some specifications call for coating reinforcing steel with any one of various types of epoxies. When such coatings are specified, the inspector should check for damage to the coatings due to loading, unloading, placement, and tying of the steel. These areas must be field-patched to ensure the integrity of the coating in accordance with the manufacturer's recommendations.

Embedded Items.   In most structural concrete, there are certain embedded items that must be inspected for proper positioning prior to placing the concrete. Embedded items include anchor bolts, drainage pipes, sleeves, anchor slots, and conduits. These items should be sufficiently anchored or secured to ensure that no movement occurs during the placement and vibration of the concrete. This is especially true of anchor bolts for columns, bearings, girders, and machinery. (See Fig. 2.4-2.)

CONCRETE PLACEMENT

Structural-concrete placement requires a minimum of two inspectors, the placing inspector and an inspector-technician. The duties of the placing inspector are to observe the following procedures (See Fig. 2.4-3):

1. Concrete must be placed as close as possible to its final position in the form by using conveyor belts, concrete buckets, pumping, or *elephant trunks* (see Fig. 2.4-4) to prevent the concrete from dropping in free fall for more than a 5-ft (1.52-m) vertical distance. In the placement of concrete, a free fall of more than 5 ft may result in segregation of the

---

FINAL CHECKOUT LIST FOR STRUCTURAL CONCRETE

Project ————————————————————————————
Contractor ——————————————————————————
Location of pour ——————————————————————
Description of pour
(slab, wall, etc.) —————————————————————

	Checked by	Date
1. Subgrade	———————————	———————
2. Forms (dimensions)	———————————	———————
3. Forms, oiled	———————————	———————
4. Tie clearance	———————————	———————
5. Bracing and supports	———————————	———————
6. Reinforcing steel	———————————	———————
a. Sizing and spacing	———————————	———————
b. Clearance	———————————	———————
c. Dowels	———————————	———————
7. Embedded items (bolts, sleeves, pipe, inserts)		
8. General cleanliness		
9. Remarks ———————————————————————		

——————————————————————————————
——————————————————————————————
——————————————————————————————

FIG. 2.4-2 Final checkout list for structural concrete.

coarse aggregate. This, of course, is undesirable because it causes a weak spot in the structure. In certain instances, for example, the placement of concrete in areas such as thin, high walls, an elephant trunk is used to avoid coarse-aggregate segregation or the formation of voids in the structure as the concrete falls through the layers of reinforcing steel. Honeycomb voids are formed when the coarse aggregate begins piling up on reinforcing steel or some other obstruction, thereby preventing the concrete mix from flowing around the reinforcing steel.

2.   Concrete should be placed and vibrated in layers no more than 18 in (457.2 mm) deep, except in large mass pours, where it may be necessary to increase the layer thickness to 24 in (609.6 mm).

STRUCTURAL-CONCRETE-PLACING CHECKOUT LIST

Project ————————— Contractor —————————
Location of pour ———————————————————
Description of pour ——————————————————
Start of pour ——————— End of pour ———————————
Total yards batched ———— Yards in place ———— Yards wasted ————
Ambient temperature   Start ——————— Finish ———————
Class of concrete ——————— Design strength ———————

1. Contractor's equipment   Checked by   Date
   a. Vibrator's operational   ———————   ————
   b. Buckets clean   ———————   ————
   c. Elephant trunks, chutes, etc. ———————   ————

2. Quality control (by contractor)   Checked
                                     a   b   c   by   Date
   a. Slump   —— —— ——   ——   ——
   b. Air entrainment   —— —— ——   ——   ——
   c. Cylinders made   —— —— ——   ——   ——
3. Quality control (outside laboratory)
   a. Slump   —— —— ——   ——   ——
   b. Air entrainment   —— —— ——   ——   ——
   c. Cylinders made   —— —— ——   ——   ——
4. Surface finish   ———————   ——   ——
5. Type of cure   ———————   ——   ——
6. Cold-weather protection
   a. Placing temperature   ———————   ——   ——
   b. Type of form protection   ———————   ——   ——
   c. Cover (insulation, test, etc.) ———————   ——   ——
   d. Temperature control in place ———————   ——   ——
   e. Ambient temperature   ———————   ——   ——
   f. Maximum and minimum temperature under protection

      Date   Maximum   Minimum   Checked by   Date

7. Remarks ——————————————————————————
   ———————————————————————————————
   ———————————————————————————————

                                              —————————
                                              Inspector

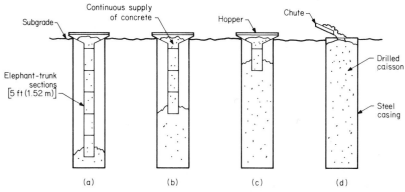

FIG. 2.4-4　Drilled-caisson-concrete placement. (*a*) Concrete pour begins with a continuous supply of concrete. (*b*) Pour continues with an elephant-trunk section or sections removed to allow concrete to flow upward, resulting from concrete head pressure. (*c*) Pour continues with the elephant-trunk section or sections removed again. (*d*) Pour is completed by removing hopper and remaining elephant-trunk section and chuting concrete to final elevation and putting dowels in place.

The purpose of vibrating concrete is threefold. First, proper vibration of concrete permits the concrete to flow sufficiently to surround the reinforcing steel completely and ultimately to achieve a high bonding capacity. Second, proper vibration prevents honeycombed voids within the concrete and at the formed surface. Quite often, the formed surface of the structural-concrete member is exposed as part of the architectural character of the structure. A honeycombed void in this instance would detract from the structure's appearance as well as the structural integrity of the member. And, third, when pours require that concrete be placed in 18-in (457.2-mm) layers, proper vibrating of successive layers of concrete assures that the new layer of concrete blends with the previous layer. In mass pours that cover a large area, each successive layer of concrete must be placed before the preceding layer begins setting, usually within 40 to 45 minutes. It is therefore wise to plan carefully the mass placing of concrete over a large area so that time is not wasted between layers.

One method of mass placing of concrete over large areas is to begin at a corner of the area and place a ±6-ft- (1.8-m-) wide strip of concrete, proceeding to the right until the corner of the area is reached, much as in reading the first line of a page. The next row is started proceeding to the left, as in reading the second line of a page backward. The third pass proceeds to the right, the fourth to the left, and so on. When the first layer of concrete is placed, the second layer is started at the same place as the first layer, and the placing sequence for the second layer follows the same sequence as the first. Successive layers are placed in a similar manner.

When a very large area requires the placing of multiple layers of concrete and it is impossible for the second layer of concrete to be placed prior to initial setting of the first layer, additional crews are necessary. In this case, the first crew should be far enough along on the first layer before the second crew begins the second layer of concrete, primarily to prevent either crew from being too close and reducing the efficiency and safety of the other. Concrete should be vibrated not only to blend successive layers of concrete and increase bonding to the reinforcing steel but to blend adjacent passes of concrete.

Sufficient blending occurs when the vibrator penetrates the previous layer by 6 to 8 in (152.4 to 203.2 mm) at approximately 12-in (301.8-mm) intervals in either direction.

3. An adequate number of vibrators should be on hand to keep up with the rate of concrete placement. Sufficient standby vibrators should be on hand to replace malfunctioning vibrators. The vibration of the concrete as it is placed is critical for compaction of the concrete and to prevent the occurrence of honeycombs in critical areas.

4. On very large pours, it is necessary to have a secondary source of concrete supply, such as another local supplier or another on-site batch plant, standing by in case the primary source breaks down. In any case, the secondary source of supply must receive the same preinspection and approval required of the primary source of supply.

5. Upon completion of the concrete placement and when the desired surface texture has been achieved, the concrete must be cured in accordance with the specifications. This may be a water cure or a manufactured liquid-membrane cure.

6. Upon completion of the concrete placement, the inspector should fill out placement record forms. Samples of these forms appear as Figs. 2.4-1, 2.4-2, and 2.4-3. These records should also contain information on concrete tests which are performed by the inspector-technician.

The duties of the inspector-technician are as follows:

1. Immediately at the start of a pour, an initial slump test is made (see Fig. 2.4-5). A slump test helps the inspector determine whether the water content of the concrete batch is too high or too low. The test is accomplished by using a slump cone, a metal cone with its top cut off so that it looks like a frustum. The cone is placed on a flat surface and filled with sample concrete in a manner similar to that described below for casting concrete test cylinders. Once the slump cone has been filled with concrete, carefully lift the cone with a slight twisting motion. Immediately place the cone next to the slumped concrete, and measure the slump of the con-

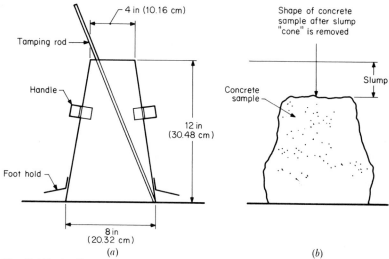

FIG. 2.4-5 (*a*) Slump-test mold (slump cone). (*b*) Slump test.

crete sample, the distance from the top of the slump cone to the top of the slumped sample concrete. The slump is generally determined when the concrete mix is designed.

Occasionally, a slump test will yield inaccurate results. For example, when a plasticizer admixture is added to a concrete batch to disperse the cement particles, the workability of concrete improves and the concrete flows much more easily. If a slump test is performed before the admixture is added, the test would yield normal results, but if the test were performed after the admixture was added to the concrete, a false slump over design requirements would result and the true character of the concrete mix would be suspect.

2. If the slump test is within specifications, the placement of the concrete can commence. The inspector-technician performs a complete set of tests including the measurement of slump and entrained air and the casting of test cylinders. Concrete test cylinders for a sample from a batch of concrete are 6 in (152.4 mm) in diameter by 12 in (304.8 mm) high and are tested after 7, 14, 28, and occasionally 60 days from the date of placing of the concrete. The test performed on the cylinder consists in applying an increasingly compressive force until the cylinder breaks. The final compressive force just prior to cylinder failure is compared with the designed strength, and appropriate action is taken. The proper method of casting a test cylinder of concrete is very important. Improper test-cylinder casting from a good batch of concrete could yield low compressive-strength-test results and falsely indicate a problem. The proper method for casting a concrete test cylinder is to place 4 in (101.6 mm) of concrete in the cylinder mold and randomly rod this layer 25 times, add a second 4-in layer, and rod the second layer 25 times while penetrating the first layer by 2 in (50.8 mm). Fill the cylinder mold completely, and rod the remaining layer in a manner similar to that of the previous layer, being careful to penetrate the second layer by 2 in. Carefully screed the excess concrete from the top of the mold, and subject the cylinder to the specified curing method: steam curing, insulated curing, or water curing (after concrete is set). A minimum of six test cylinders should be made for each 100 yd^3 (76.46 m^3) of concrete of each class of concrete placed during a day of concreting. Slump and entrained-air measurements should be made periodically during the pour. Air content should be checked with a pressure meter.

During the pour, the inspector-technician should also periodically check the placing temperature of the concrete. The temperature check is most critical in dealing with cold-weather and hot-weather concreting operations.

COLD-WEATHER CONCRETE PLACEMENT

In near-freezing or freezing ambient temperatures, the placement inspector-technician has several other concerns aside from the normal tasks described in the preceding subsection. To keep the concrete from freezing and to allow its temperature to be reasonably consistent throughout the concrete mass, it may be necessary, during cold-weather operations, to protect the concrete with insulated forms and proper cover or by tenting of the concrete and supplying additional heat inside the tenting. To protect the concrete during the placement operation, it may also be necessary to preheat the mix by using heated water in the design mix and/or heated aggregates. If appropriate action is not taken, variations in temperature throughout the concrete mass will produce shrinkage cracking.

The placement inspector will not only check placement temperatures but also check internal temperatures throughout the curing period until the internal temperature of the concrete is within 20°F (11.1°C) of the ambient temperature. The internal temperature-sensing devices will be set up by the contractor by contract specifications.

HOT-WEATHER CONCRETE PLACEMENT

During hot-weather concrete placement, the inspector-technician, in addition to the duties performed in normal concrete placement, must check to see that the contractor exercises proper control of mixing temperatures and monitoring the internal temperatures of the concrete after placement. This is especially true of large mass pours such as bridge foundations, bridge piers, and dams.

To slow down the heat of hydration (the heat developed during the chemical reaction between the cement and water in the mix) during hot weather, it is necessary to keep the placement temperature as low as possible. This can be accomplished with the partial or total substitution of ice for mixing water. Constant spraying of the coarse aggregate also is helpful. When this is done, be certain that the water-cement ratio is maintained.

On large mass placements, contract specifications should call for the placement of temperature gauges and monitoring of internal temperatures of the concrete.

Concrete placement should take place in the shortest time possible. All exposed surfaces should be finished with the required texture and the curing process started as soon as possible. The curing process should include keeping the exposed surfaces of the concrete saturated with a water spray. It is also desirable to keep the side forms sprayed with water.

Additional duties of the inspector include:

1. Checking to see that the coarse aggregate is sprayed well with water before the contemplated placing time

2. Checking scale weights to see that the correct allowance has been made for the substitution of ice for mix water

3. Checking to see that sides of forms and reinforcing steel have been sprayed with water

4. Checking the temperature of the concrete mix being placed

5. When the pour is completed, checking to see that the proper water cure is being applied

6. Checking the internal concrete temperature with previously set monitoring devices

TREMIE-CONCRETE PLACEMENT

The inspector should understand the basic principle of tremie-concrete placement. This is the placement of concrete underwater in such a manner that the bulk of the concrete is not contaminated with the saltwater or fresh-water environment where it is being placed (see Fig. 2.4-6). The ultimate object of the tremie concrete is to seal the cofferdam so that when the concrete has cured, the water within the cofferdam can be pumped

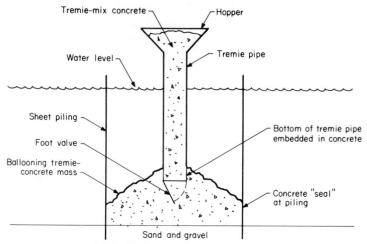

FIG. 4.2-6   Placing tremie concrete under water.

out. The following pours can be placed as normal concrete pours in normal-atmospheric-pressure air.

Tremie concrete is placed with the aid of a tremie pipe. The pipe is 12 to 14 in (304.8 to 355.6 mm) in diameter and is topped with a hopper to receive the concrete. The pipe may have a simple foot valve at the bottom to stop any inflow of water into the pipe while it is being lowered to the proper elevation. However, most contractors will lower the tremie pipe to grade without a foot valve and depend on an inflated ball (see Fig. 2.4-7) placed in the hopper so that when concrete is dumped into the hopper, it pushes the inflated ball down the tremie pipe, which in turn forces the column of water below the ball out of the bottom of the pipe.

The tremie pipe should be placed approximately 18 in (457.2 mm) above the bottom of the pour. The hopper and tremie pipes are filled with concrete that has a slump of 7 to 9 in (177.8 to 228.6 mm). Usually the mix will have a retardant densifier and an air-entraining agent for retarding the set of the concrete and providing a more fluid concrete respectively.

When the tremie-pipe foot valve is open or when the inflated ball comes out of the bottom of the pipe, the concrete will well around the pipe, stopping any influx of water into the bottom of the pipe. The hopper should be kept continuously filled with concrete. The concrete will continue to well out of the bottom of the pipe, building up around the pipe, and the surface of the concrete will expand outward and upward like the skin of a balloon being blown up. The only concrete that will be exposed to water will be the outside ballooning surface of the concrete. At

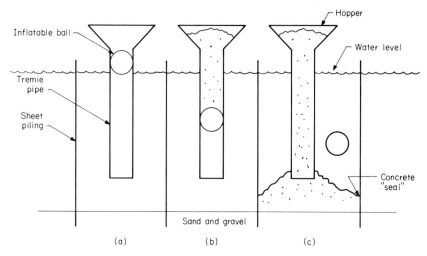

FIG. 2.4-7   Tremie-concrete placement (inflatable-ball method). (*a* Inflatable ball is placed in hopper prior to tremie pour. (*b*) Tremie-concrete pour has begun; column of water is forced downward. (*c*) Inflatable ball passes through tremie pipe; tremie concrete is dumped on bottom, and ball floats to surface of water.

times the downward pressure of the concrete in the tremie pipe will not be large enough to push the ballooning concrete outward and upward. When this occurs, the tremie pipe is lifted carefully 2 to 3 ft (0.6 to 0.9 m) and the operation is continued. Care must be taken that the tremie pipe has always at least a 3-ft embedment in the concrete. However, if the pipe is lifted too high and the seal is lost, the tremie pipe must again be sealed, as previously explained for the start of the pour. When all the concrete has been placed and cured and the cofferdam dewatered, the top 6 to 8 in (152.4 to 203.2 mm) of the surface, which contains concrete that was exposed to water, must be removed by jackhammering until design-strength concrete is exposed.

From this point on, the following pours will be made as in any structural-concrete pour.

In addition to the normal checks made by the inspector with normal structural concrete, the inspector should note the following.

1. Check to see that the correct number and placement of the tremie pipes are as shown on approved working drawings.

2. Check to see that an adequate supply of mixing machines is on hand to feed the hoppers continuously.

3. Check to see whether or not a standby source of concrete is fully operational.

4. Check to see that adequate soundings of the bottom have been re-

corded and the final grade of the tremied top concrete is part of this record. Both the contractor and the inspector should at all times be knowledgeable about the elevation of the concrete placed and the elevation of the bottom of the tremie pipe.

5. Frequent checks should be made during the pour to check concrete being placed against concrete in place by taking soundings as often as necessary. If the volume of concrete in place is greater than that batched out, then one or more of the tremie pipes has lost its seal and the cement has washed out of the mix, resulting in a bulking of aggregate, giving a false image of the in-place-concrete volume. If this situation occurs, immediate action must be taken to reseal the malfunctioning tremies. The only remedy for this problem is to drill and grout the affected areas. Properly grouting the voids in the washed-out concrete will increase the strength of the mass.

6. Once the tremie concrete placement has been completed, the concrete cured, and the cofferdam dewatered, the inspector must examine the surface of the tremie pour and check that all concrete laitance (that portion of the concrete that was exposed to the water and reduced in strength because of water infiltration) on the surface has been removed and that only sound concrete, as described earlier, remains.

Subsequent concrete pours will be placed as in a normal structural-concrete pour.

PRESTRESSED AND POSTTENSIONED STRUCTURAL CONCRETE

The first rule that an inspector should know in prestressing or post-tensioning is that of safety. The cables and rods involved in this type of operation are highly stressed and highly dangerous and have been known to fail during the tensioning operation. For this reason, the inspector must be stationed in a safe place away from the line of tensioning.

This operation normally concerns stressing a bed of four or more beams or stressing cables and rods for segmental construction. In either case, the inspector's work is as follows:

1. Hydraulic jacks used to tension the cables or rods must be calibrated.

2. The specified stress and the resulting elongation of the cables or rods must be given to the inspector and an allowance for *grip* setting must be added to the design elongation. Normally, a nominal initial load is applied to the cables or rods. This load will set the dead-end grips and, in the case of cables or strands, will straighten them so that an initial starting point

can be marked to ensure that all cables or strands are elongated uniformly. The jack load is then increased to the required specified load, and the required elongation is checked against the required load. To ensure that the grips on the live end of the cable or strand will set without losing stress or elongation, the design load and elongation are exceeded to allow for any slippage while the grips are setting.

Since posttensioning cables are usually placed in a conduit of some kind, it is necessary to grout the conduit with a sand-cement grout once the posttensioning process is complete.

3. In the case of draped cables, or cables that are tied down to frictionless pulleys to effect a change in elevation along the cables, it may be necessary to jack the cables from both ends. A simple proof of this necessity is to mark off 10-ft (3.05-m) sections of the cable with tape and check the elongation of the several 10-ft sections. Invariably, this simple test proves that the cable has to be jacked from both ends to distribute the stress in the cable evenly for the full length of the cable.

4. Forms should be well oiled before being set in place around the stressed wires. It is virtually impossible to oil the forms (especially I-shaped beams) after they have been placed without getting oil on the stressed cables.

5. The usual inspection requirements for casting structural concrete apply to prestressed units. Usually the concrete is a high-strength mix [over 5000 psi (34.47 MPa)]. Both internal vibrators and form vibrators are usually employed in placing concrete.

6. Most prestressed units are cured with a steam-curing process.

The inspector should be aware of the following items in the steam curing process (see Fig. 2.4-8):

Once the pour is complete, the forms are tented with tarpaulins. Before the tarpaulins are in place, the concrete test cylinders representing the pour must be placed under tarpaulins. A recording thermometer must also be in place under each tarpaulin to record temperature changes. The test cylinders should be cast in steel molds. Sheet-metal, plastic, or waxed-paper molds cannot be used.

There is a delay time of 4 hours before steam is applied. Steam is applied at a rate that will increase the temperature under the tarpaulin at the rate of 1°F (0.56°C) per minute until the specified maximum temperature is reached, which is on the order of 145°F (62.78°C). The length of time required for steam curing varies with the specified concrete strength requirements before releasing the cable tension and cutting the cables. Normally, it is more economical to have the casting yard set up on a 24-hour cycle with a casting each day.

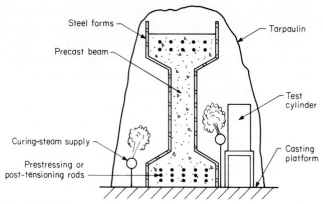

Steel forms

Precast beam

Tarpaulin

Test cylinder

Curing-steam supply

Prestressing or post-tensioning rods

Casting platform

Fig. 2.4-8   Steam-curing arrangement.

Cylinder test specimens are broken to check the strength of the concrete before steam curing is discontinued. It is necessary for the inspector to observe the removal of the test cylinders from under the tarpaulins. The cylinders must be protected against temperature shock between the time of removal and the time for testing the cylinders. Once the required detensioning concrete compression strength is reached, the steam-curing process is stopped and the concrete beams are allowed to cool. The stressed cables may then be severed and the beams lifted off the beds and stockpiled. The inspector should check to see that the beams are stockpiled so that the dunnage is placed at the same location at the ends of the beams that they will bear on the bridge seats.

Structural Steel

Gerald J. Hill
Consultant
Williamston, Michigan

Formerly

Neyer, Tiseo & Hindo, Ltd., Consulting Engineers
Jutton, Kelly Co., Bridge Construction Contractor
Michigan Department of Transportation

This chapter covers both shop and field inspection and testing procedures since most such procedures are generally equally applicable to
either shop or field practice.

The transition from riveted-steel construction to the electric-arc
method of joining metals took place over a number of decades. Each
segment of the steel industry made the conversion as the urgency of that
trade demanded. The pipe-line industry was one of the first, changing
from the oxyacetylene-welding method to the arc-welding process in the
1930s. Shipbuilding during the 1940s greatly escalated the advancement
of arc-welding methods. Welded building construction soon followed,
and by the 1960s most steel bridges were being fabricated by a variety of
arc-welding processes. The mid-1960s also saw the railroad companies
relenting to allow welded construction for their steel bridges, thus ending
the era of heavy riveted-steel construction, probably forever.

Although the history of electric-arc welding is relatively short, tremen-
dous growth and discovery have taken place. But not all that came to light
was favorable; many shortcomings surfaced. One of the most alarming of
these shortcomings is the fact that properly trained personnel is lacking at
all levels of responsibility.

From the owners who have ultimate control over the projects to the
architects and engineers who specify, design, and implement the work
and to the inspectors who must enforce the quality-control and quality-
assurance programs, education and improved performance are needed
throughout.

This chapter addresses each of the above participants to discuss and
outline some of the areas where upgrading is possible and should be

considered, starting with the owner and progressing through each level of responsibility to the inspectors on the floor and at the project sites who must pass on the final quality provided.

THE OWNER

The decision to strive for quality rests entirely with the owner. Without the owner's consent, backing, and desire for a quality end product, those working on the owner's behalf are quite helpless. Many owners try to keep the costs of projects down by eliminating quality-assurance (QA) inspection during fabrication altogether and calling for only a limited amount during erection. Such projects are rarely free from serious problems whose correction often exceeds the cost of what a good quality-assurance program would have required, had it been specified. These projects are also extremely fortunate if minimum standards are adhered to throughout the many phases of construction.

Owners should be convinced that requiring a QA program for their projects is one of the soundest investments they can make. The cost of the QA program is almost insignificant when compared with the overall cost of most projects, while the benefits derived are enormous.

THE ENGINEER

It is the engineer, with overall responsibility and control of the work, who must ascertain that contract documents for the fabrication and erection of structural steel are accurate and complete. All too often welding inspectors find themselves in the position of trying to obtain what they are sure the engineer intended and wants but are powerless to enforce because specifications and plans are weak and incomplete.

Many engineers adopt codes such as the American Welding Society's Structural Welding Code—Steel (AWS D 1.1) or the *American Institute of Steel Construction Manual* and do nothing more, thinking that the work is adequately covered. They fail to realize, however, that such codes are only general specifications to be used by the many disciplines of the steel industry and that each project must specify the separate tasks, scopes, and functions required to assure a final quality which will provide the service life intended.

The engineer must indicate clearly on the project drawings and in the specifications all areas where something more than standard practice is desired. The engineer must specify the type and quality of the base metal to be used; the pretesting of consumables, procedures, welders, and welding operations; the scope and acceptance-rejection criteria for all nondestructive testing (NDT) to be performed; the level of competence of personnel performing both quality control (QC) and QA; and numerous other changes from the normal.

The area of nondestructive testing is one that is repeatedly overlooked by those who prepare project specifications. The AWS code states: "When nondestructive testing other than visual is required, it shall be stated in the information furnished to the bidders. This information shall designate the categories of welds to be examined, the extent of the examination of each category and the method or methods of NDT used."

Many engineers specify that either radiography or ultrasonic testing may be used to verify the soundness of certain critical welds. Then they fail to indicate whether the welds should be tested according to Sec. 8 for buildings or Sec. 9 for bridges. If the girders involved are for a large overhead crane inside a heavy industrial building, the inspector is faced with a real problem. The crane railway girders will certainly be subjected to dynamic loadings similar to those of bridge girders, but since they are still part of the building, the fabricator will insist on being governed by the building part of the code. Needless to say, there are significant differences between the acceptance-rejection criteria of Sec. 8 (Buildings) and Sec. 9 (Bridges).

It is thus obvious that in some cases specification writers do not understand the AWS or American Institute of Steel Construction (AISC) codes or, for that matter, welding in general. Engineering performances, as a whole, have not scored very high over the past several decades in preparing welding specifications and detailing pertinent welding information on the plans. Of even greater concern is the fact that this problem continues to get worse instead of better.

THE DESIGNER

Since welded construction is not nearly as forgiving as the riveted construction it replaced, the designer must keep current with design details and geometries which have proved to be troublesome in the relatively short life span of welded construction. Experience has indicated that connections which were adequate for riveted construction may not work for welding. Riveted construction generally used multiple plates or shape components, and when one component cracked or failed, the crack did not go directly into the other plies but was arrested.

With welded construction, small flaws which escape detection can initiate cracks, and once the cracks have started, they will continue to grow to critical size (see Fig. 2.5-1). For this reason the modern-day designer

Fig. 2.5-1   Centerline crack.

must look into all aspects of the total design. Material fracture toughness may be a primary consideration for a nonredundant structure, as may normalized base material for cyclically loaded members or even cross-rolled plate if lamellar tearing is a possibility (see Figs. 2.5-2, 2.5-3, and 2.5-4). Below are listed some of the more important considerations that should be addressed in every design:

1. Make certain that the base metal specified is adequate for the intended use, i.e., normalized, cross-rolled, ultrasonically clean universal mill plates, minimum toughness for particular service temperatures, etc.

2. Above all, avoid square corners and fatigue-sensitive connections and geometries.

3. Provide for the smooth flow of stress from one direction to another especially when biaxial or triaxial stresses are present. Use gradual transitions for all critical connections, joints, and butt welds.

4. Allow members the room to flex by avoiding localized rigidity, or stiffen them for their full length without stopping short.

5. For dynamic structures require all backing bars to be continuous without any interruptions. This also applies to longitudinal stiffeners and other attachments welded to the main members.

6. Do not allow tack welding on any dynamically loaded structures unless they are totally re-fused in production welding.

7. Call for nondestructive testing compatible with the degree of safety and service life desired.

8. Specify the welding process desired, and eliminate all others. If submerged-arc welding is the only process wanted, say so.

9. Avoid using the E70XX designation on plans if low-hydrogen electrodes are the type wanted.

10. Specify the degree of smoothness for flame cutting and machining and the cleanliness for welding and painting, including the anchor profile desired for blast-cleaned or Wheelabrated surfaces which are to receive paint.

11. For bolted connections, be sure that there is adequate room to tighten the bolts by some means other than an open-end wrench.

THE SHOP WELDING INSPECTOR

Because shop welding inspectors are the individuals most directly responsible for assuring the quality of the end product, their qualifications, role, and duties will be discussed to a greater extent than those of some of the other participants in the chain of command. Shop welding inspectors are the official representatives of the owner or client for whom the fabrication plant produces work, but they usually report directly to the engineer.

Before being assigned to a project, an inspector should have a thorough knowledge of fabrication techniques, welding procedures and pro-

0204 ⓒ The Welding Institute UK 1975   5 mm

FIG. 2.5-2 Lamellar tearing.

FIG. 2.5-3   Lamellar tearing.

FIG. 2.5-4   Lamellar tearing of corner joint.

cesses, and the duties of an inspector. The inspector should be supplied with a complete set of design and shop drawings, proposal, and specifications for the contract and a complete set of inspection tools and gauges. Inspection of welding is similar to inspection of other work performed during construction: it consists mainly of seeing that the plans and specifications are followed.

Physical Traits.   The job of a welding inspector is physically demanding. It often involves difficult inspection conditions, requiring climbing in and around large fixtures and assemblies before, during, and after fabrication. During erection it may require working high off the ground in awkward and precarious positions much of the time.

While strength and agility are important, good vision is vital to quality inspection. Inspectors must look closely at welds as well as at the results of radiographic and other nondestructive tests. To be an AWS certified welding inspector (CWI) requires 20-40 vision, as read on corrective eye charts, and Jaeger J-1 near-vision acuity, with or without corrective lenses.

Equipment.   Equipment may be thought of as the testing, inspection, and protective apparatus used to perform the work. It should also include the contract documents which guide and regulate inspection tasks as well as the fabricator's work.

Among the actual tools and instruments needed to perform the necessary QA inspection are:

1. Contract plans and proposal
2. All pertinent contract specifications
3. Fillet-weld gauges
4. Measuring devices: tapes, calipers, etc.
5. 12-in (304.8-mm) straightedge; 1-ft (0.3048-m) and 3-ft (0.9144-m) levels
6. Undercut gauges
7. Surface-roughness comparator gauge
8. Instrumentaton for measuring voltage and amperage and for all NDT operations
9. Temperature-measuring devices capable of covering the range from 40 to 1500°F (4.4 to 815.5°C)
10. Required safety equipment: hard hat, shoes, glasses, welding hood, flashlight, etc.
11. Packet of forms for job documentation
12. Office supplies
13. Approval stamps and tags for shipping approved components
14. Office space, desk, and telephone supplied by the fabricator as a contract requirement

Painting inspection requires:

1. Testex Replica tape kit for measuring blasted-steel-surface profile

2. Steel Structures Painting Council (SSPC) *Book of Pictorial Blast Standards*

3. Temperature- and humidity-measuring instruments

4. Wet-film paint-thickness gauge

5. Dry-film paint-thickness gauges: Positector type and calibrated standards and Tooke gauge

Knowledge and Abilities. A welding inspector should have enough welding experience to be able to differentiate satisfactory and poor welding techniques on sight and to recognize and identify satisfactory welding procedures by description. The inspector should also have enough knowledge of NDT methods, techniques, and procedures to inspect welds and to know when to call for and how to use the results of nondestructive tests to guide the repair of discovered defects.

All decisions that the inspector is not authorized to make or is not capable of making because of limited experience and knowledge of engineering and welding theory or that would affect the function of any part of the structure in an important way should be referred to the engineer. The inspector in turn should convey the engineer's interpretations of the plans to the fabricator in such cases.

A good welding inspector will have a working knowledge of at least the following:

Fundamentals of welding

Fundamentals of metallurgy

Requirements of the AWS Structural Welding Code

Requirements of the applicable standard specifications of the American Society for Testing and Materials (ASTM)

Requirements of the SSPC code

Applicable requirements of the Occupational Safety and Health Administration (OSHA)

Defects to watch for in materials and equipment

Causes and acceptable methods of repairing defects

Cutting equipment and procedures used

Methods, procedures, and workmanship levels for production welding

Approved joint configurations

Approved joint tolerances

Basic NDT methods

Criteria for accepting and rejecting work based on NDT results

Inspector's Checklist.   The following checklist is suggested for use as a general guide in making welding inspections in the shop or in the field. The actual steps and their exact sequence will depend on the type of structure, the method of erection, and the qualifications of the welders who are to do the work. The checklist pertains particularly to welding and related operations and does not include all the items that should be checked.

1.   Obtain and review the mill-test analysis for steel; check the type of steel, quantities, dimensions, heat numbers, physical and chemical properties, etc., for specification compliance.

2.   Forward the required number of copies of the mill-test analysis and reports to the proper parties.

3.   Review approved shop drawings, plans, specifications, etc., for each project.

4.   Consult with fabrication-shop personnel to discuss requirements, procedures, quality control, production scheduling, certifications, qualification of welders, etc.

5.   Obtain shipping lists, and check shipments of steel as delivered for quantities, type, dimensions, markings, flaws, etc.

6.   Review joint-welding-procedure qualification tests.

7.   Review welding-personnel qualifications.

8.   Inspect welding equipment.

9.   Make periodic inspections of welding in progress for compliance with prequalified procedure and specification to requirements (preheat, machine settings, operator identification, interpass temperature, rod-flux combination, runoff tabs, dimensions, markings, workmanship, storage of rod, etc.).

10.   Inspect completed member for dimensions, flaws, errors, workmanship, identification of welds, heat-number identification, grinding, surface preparation, repair of defects, etc.

11.   Review paint test reports or certifications; check batch numbers, quantities, type, etc.

12.   Monitor painting process, check film thickness, visually inspect completed paint coat, and report on final inspection report.

13.   Make final inspection of completed members and components.

14.   If members comply with all specified requirements, stamp "Recommended for Use," and release for shipment.

15. If members do not comply with specified requirements, withhold approval until corrections have been made or reject the member as necessary.

16. Forward the required number of copies of the final inspection or shipping report to the engineer. Forward one copy of the beam and girder list with heat-number identification and location for each member. Forward radiographic film with proper identification when applicable.

17. The inspector will have full authority to suspend work or reject materials which, in the inspector's judgment, are inferior or deficient.

The inspector will document all inspection activities in a daily diary.

Duties of the Inspector. The preceding guide items are listed as just that and appear as brief statements similar to a checklist. Some of the more important operations deserve greater attention and explanation than are given above; therefore, to elaborate in greater detail, the following is offered:

Prior to Welding

1. At the fabricating plant, check the mill-test reports on the base metal for conformance with the specifications with regard to mechanical properties and chemical properties to the extent that they are specified. Develop a workable system for identifying the heat number of each piece of steel that is used in contract fabrication and recording its location in the structure. Obtain from the fabricator, if necessary, the shipping records, storage locations, and scheduling for each piece of steel that is to be used in connection with the assigned contract. Examine each piece of steel as it is received at the shop or construction site to see that it has no uncorrected mill defects, kinks, or bends which exceed the tolerance prescribed in the specifications, resulting from improper handling while in the mill or shop or in transit from mill to shop or from shop to construction site.

2. Check the records or other evidence of the welders' qualifications, and investigate the continuity of their work since the date of qualification tests. Have requalification or supplementary-check tests made of a welder's ability, if needed. Most specifications require that all tackers, welders, and welding operators be qualified prior to welding, either by direct testing or by a previous welding test that is acceptable to the engineer. In a new fabricating shop, previous records are not accepted, and a complete testing program is normally carried out.

3. Ensure that the welding procedures and sequences are agreed to and understood by the inspector, the contractor, the supervisor, and the welders performing the work. Make sure that the contractor has proper instructions regarding the number and type of procedure-qualification tests required and that such tests are satisfactorily performed and recorded. Many project specifications require that all welding procedures be qualified by test prior to any job welding. This qualification requirement includes all types of weld procedures, i.e., butt welding, fillet welding, seal welding, plug welding, etc. For these projects, no welding procedures are considered to be prequalified regardless of what AWS specifications allow or what previous procedure tests produced by the fabricator may indicate. See the supplemental specifications in the contract for testing requirements on the procedure-test welds. Post welding-procedure data, such as amperage, voltage, and travel speed, at each welding machine.

4. Make a general examination of the structural steel, and give particular attention to the quality of fabrication, including the accuracy of plate-edge preparation, that would affect control over welding. Require any necessary correction to be made before welded joints are fitted. Check the appearance and dimensions of shop welds, and make sure that no welding has been done previously at unspecified locations. Record and call to the fabricator's attention any unspecified welding. Also, notify the engineer so that the engineer may specify corrective measures.

5. Check the fitting of joints that are to be welded, including dimensions of root face, angle of bevel, cleanliness, match marks, alignment of parts to be joined, and uniformity and size of root openings. Recheck root faces and angles of bevel because trimming and rebeveling of plate edges are sometimes carried out during fitting. Check the prepared edges of the weld joints for evidence of possible undesirable internal defects such as laminations in the steel plate. Make dimensional checks of all critical measurements to assure a proper fit in the field.

6. Check the fixtures, clamping, and precambering arrangements used in the fabrication-assembly setup for adequacy. Make sure that tack welds are made by qualified welders and that the welds are small, smooth, and of specified quality. See that runoff or extension bars or plates are in place to ensure complete welding beyond the edges of the plates.

Welding in Progress

1. During inclement weather, see that suitable windbreaks or shields are provided and that welding is not carried out on surfaces that are wet or exposed to rain or snow. Check the temperature of steel at the start of and during welding to determine whether or not specified preheat and interpass temperature requirements are being observed. Use temperature-indicating crayons or equivalent means to check these temperatures.

2. Check to make sure that correct types and sizes of electrodes are available and that they are dried properly to prevent porosity and cracking in the final welds, especially if low-hydrogen electrodes are specified. (See Figs. 2.5-5, 2.5-6, 2.5-7, and 2.5-8.) If electrodes and fluxes have been stored improperly or exposed to humidity in excess of the tolerances prescribed in the specifications, require that they be reconditioned as

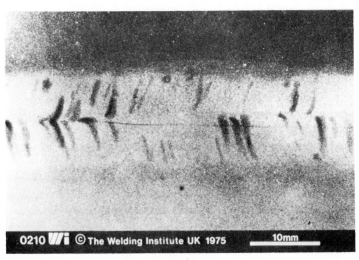

FIG. 2.5-5   Radiograph of wormhole porosity.

FIG. 2.5-6   Wormhole porosity.

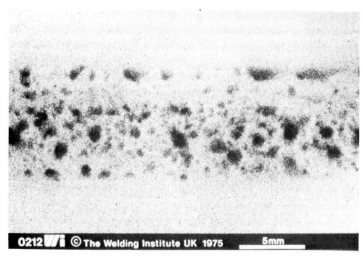

0212 ///i © The Welding Institute UK 1975   5mm

FIG. 2.5-7   Radiograph of group porosity.

0215 ///i © The Welding Institute UK 1975   20mm

FIG. 2.5-8   Linear porosity.

prescribed by the specifications before being used unless the exposure is so great that reconditioning and use are forbidden by the specifications.

3.   Observe the technique and performance of each welder, at suitable intervals, to be sure that approved welding procedures and suitable techniques are being used to conform to the requirements of the applicable specifications. For important joints, especially if some unusual condition warrants special attention, inspect multiple-pass welds at more than one stage of progress. Arrange for the welder or the supervisior to notify the inspector when such inspections at various stages are to be made.

4. Require all welding to be carried out by approved procedures and sequences, and make sure that electrodes are used with suitable currents and polarity and in positions for which the electrodes are intended to be used. Refer to the approved welding-procedure specification for all details of performing the weldment in question. Report any unusual or excessive distortion during welding, and take corrective measures agreed to by the engineer and the fabricator to hold distortion and locked-in stresses to a minimum.

5. Require that the arc be struck only in the groove or other area on which metal is to be deposited and not at random on the base metal outside the prepared joint. Arc strikes cause physical and metallurgical stress risers that can often result in fatigue failures (see Fig. 2.5-9). Do not permit any welding of ground bars, clips, and ties. Approval for such welding is given only by the engineer and only when it is unavoidable. When steel ground bars are used instead of ground clamps to carry the welding current to the base metal, make sure that the ground bars are carefully welded to the base metal at a runoff tab or securely clamped to an area where all mill scale has been removed. Keep the grounding lead as close to the point of welding as is practical.

6. Inspect root passes with special care because it is very important that the first welding deposited in the root of a multiple-pass weld be made properly. Closely examine the root pass in important groove welds, such as butt welds in flanges and webs, to make sure that it has been made

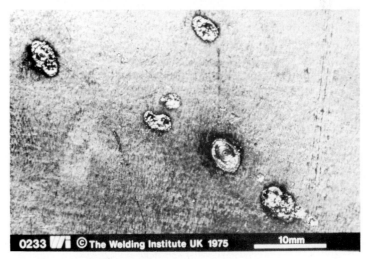

0233 ⬛ © The Welding Institute UK 1975   10mm

FIG. **2.5-9** Careless arc strikes.

properly and is free from cracks, inclusions, or lack of fusion. (See Fig. 2.5-10.)

7. Require the root pass and every subsequent weld pass to be cleaned by a wire brush and a chipping hammer to remove slag thoroughly between weld passes and to avoid inclusions before the succeeding weld pass is made. Have defects and substandard workmanship in any weld pass removed by chipping or gouging before subsequent passes of metal are deposited. Do not permit peening or consolidating of weld metal by hammering without the special approval of the engineer. Do not permit under any circumstances peening on root passes of final surface passes of a weld. Under conditions of very severe restraint, minimize weld cracking by other more acceptable techniques, such as using a cascade buildup sequence. Avoid any interruptions in the welding of a critical joint other than those necessary to change electrodes, and quickly clean the slag from a layer before the next one is deposited.

8. Take particular care not to create reentrants or local areas with high residual stresses in highly stressed parts of principal members. If beam flanges do not match well at butt-welded splices, require that the weld metal be deposited in such a way as to provide a smooth transition between the parts being joined. Be certain that temporary fitting aids, such as plates and angles, are not applied at highly stressed locations and that temporary tack welds are not allowed.

9. Check all members to make sure that the welds are of proper size and length, are being made in the proper location to conform to draw-

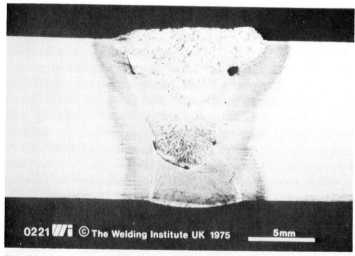

0221 ⚡ © The Welding Institute UK 1975   5mm

Fig. 2.5-10   Lack of interpass fusion and slag.

ings, and are performed in such a manner as to produce weld metal conforming to the requirements of the specifications. To determine whether the weld metal is being deposited in such a manner as to penetrate well into the root of a joint without producing excessive slag inclusions or porosity, a field test may be conducted by making a T joint with a fillet weld on only one side of the stem of the T; this joint can be broken open easily for visual examination. If welds are to be ground smooth and flush for any reason, have the grinding done so that grinding marks are not left transversely to the direction of the main stress in a member. Check to make sure that welds are not being overground so as to produce a "dished" surface. Require that the ends of welds be ground smooth on removal of the runoff tabs. (See also Figs. 2.5-11, 2.5-12, and 2.5-13.)

10. Identify with paint each splice of an important member with the symbol of the welder doing the work, but do not steel-stamp this identification on the member. If two welders work on such a splice, show the symbol of each and record in writing the work that each welder performed.

After Welding

1. Require welds to be cleaned of slag so that they can be given a thorough final examination. Be sure that the surfaces of the welds are reasonably smooth and of suitable contour without evidence of undercut, overlap, excessive convexity, insufficient throat or leg size, unfilled craters at the ends of welds, or other defects in excess of the limits prescribed

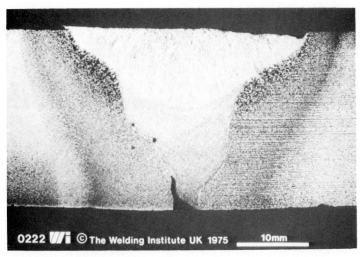

0222 ⓦ Ⓒ The Welding Institute UK 1975 ___ 10mm

Fig. **2.5-11**   Lack of root penetration.

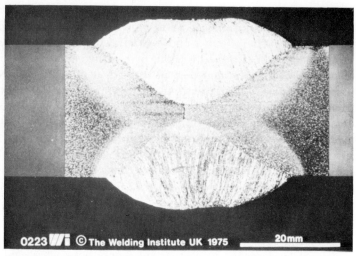

FIG. 2.5-12   Lack of penetration.

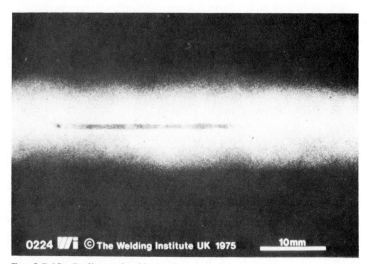

FIG. 2.5-13   Radiograph of lack of penetration.

by the specifications. Refer to the specifications for the appearance of welds containing these various kinds of defects. Have all scars and defects, such as undercutting or remnant portions of tack welds and other scars that are left after the removal of temporary fitting and erection clips, corrected to be within the tolerances specified for the quality of the steel. (See also Figs. 2.5-14 and 2.5-15.)

2.   Make certain that the required radiographic, ultrasonic, magnetic-particle, or dye-penetrant tests are performed as specified. Check to see

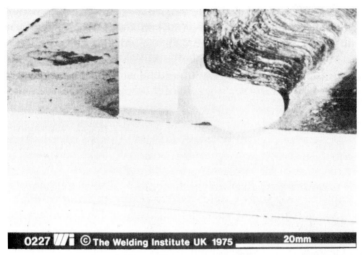

FIG. 2.5-14   Overlap of fillet weld.

FIG. 2.5-15   Undercut of fillet weld.

that the weld surfaces and adjacent plate surfaces are in satisfactory condition for the NDT process to be used.

3.   If the specifications require certain qualifications for NDT equipment or for operators, check records or obtain evidence of acceptable qualifications. If there are no specific requirements, request the engineer to specify what tests are necessary to ensure the adequacy of the testing equipment.

4. Check the performance of NDT operators at frequent intervals to see that approved procedures are being used, that all weld joints to be tested are examined in accordance with specified requirements, and that results are properly recorded and identified. The testing of critical flange and web butt splices by the contractor should be witnessed by the inspector.

5. Make certain that rejected welds are properly identified and marked for repair and that defect locations at the welds are clearly marked. Observe excavation defects, and use magnetic-particle tests to verify that no part of any defect remains. Require that repaired welds be inspected by the specified NDT method.

6. Check visually after blast cleaning for weld surface defects and general pickup such as grinding welds, where required, grinding edges, and cleaning holes. In any event, make a final visual inspection check prior to painting.

7. If welds are not blast-cleaned prior to painting, require that all welded areas be neutralized with a solution that will not interfere with the painting.

8. Check the storage, loading, blocking, and handling of the welded members to avoid distortion or structural damage. Do not permit any welding of braces and lugs to the members.

9. Check and report on appropriate forms the final camber and required curvature (or sweep) of all girders after all fabrication steps have been completed. Any members that measure out of tolerance must be noted for corrective action and rechecked after the correction has been made.

Duties of the Painting Inspector. The painting inspector is responsible for the enforcement of all contract specifications and requirements for the cleaning and coating of structural steel. Many steel contracts specify high-technology coating systems. Most steel structures are totally shop-coated (i.e., primer and final topcoats) by the fabricator. Advanced training in the application and evaluation of these systems is mandatory for successful inspection. The essential phases of painting inspection are summarized as follows:

1. *Check Environmental Conditions.* The contract special provisions for painting will include specific controls on environmental conditions, e.g., temperature, humidity, cleanliness, air movement, shading, etc. These specified conditions must be strictly adhered to.

2. *Inspection of Coating Materials.* All paints used must be carefully mixed, thinned, and handled in accordance with the specifications. Record all batch numbers used to be compared with the certification documents. Check the color numbers of the topcoat for conformance to the contract specifications.

3. *Inspection of Cleaning and Coating Equipment.* High-technology coating systems employ the most sophisticated blast-cleaning and spray-painting equipment developed. A thorough knowledge of their operation and use is required of the inspector. The inspector is responsible for evaluating the performance of the equipment prior to the coating of the structural steel. If any of the equipment is operating outside the specification limits, the coatings will not be properly applied and may fail (peel off) at some time after application.

4. *Inspection of Steel Surface Conditions.* All grinding, welding repairs, and fabrication steps must be completed before blast cleaning and painting. Any remedial work done after coating may be ground for rejection of the coating system. The steel must be free of all traces of grease and oil before blast cleaning.

5. *Inspection of Surface Preparation.* Contract specifications require an exact surface-cleanliness standard and a surface "peak" profile requirement. These must be measured with specialized equipment and be strictly adhered to. After these have been approved, the temperature of the steel and the surrounding air must be maintained within the specified limits. Humidity requirements (both maximum and minimum limits) must also be strictly observed.

6. *Inspection of Coating Application.* The inspector needs to be knowledgeable in the proper techniques of applying high-technology coating systems. Improper application techniques may appear to give an acceptable result but will lead to a greatly reduced performance life and possibly to an early coating failure (blistering and peeling). After each of the coatings is applied, it is the responsibility of the inspector to ensure that *temperature* and *humidity* are properly controlled (see contract specifications) over the required curing time. After each coating has cured, the inspector must check the dry-film thickness for conformance to the contract requirements before the next coat is applied. General appearance of the coating must be approved by the inspector, noting any objectionable runs, sags, rough texture, or dry spray. Corrective actions must be taken on each coat of the painting system before the next coat is applied. Be sure to observe the approved written coating-repair procedures on all remedial work.

Documentation. A log of the coating sequence may prove to be very valuable if a problem were to develop. It is suggested that the inspector keep such a log if at all possible. Documentation of an approved coating on structural steel comprises the inspector's test reports on the coating evaluations and submission of a certificate of compliance by the paint manufacturer on the coatings used.

Handling, Storage, and Shipping. The painting inspector must work closely with the welding inspector to ensure that all the contract special provisions concerning the handling, storage, and shipping of shop-painted steel are strictly observed. The steel is stamped "Recommended for Use" by the welding inspector only after the structure has been loaded for shipping and properly padded and secured to prevent damage in transit. All damage done to the paint during handling and loading by the fabricator must be repaired by using the approved procedures prior to the inspector's final stamp of approval. If this is not possible because of inclement weather conditions, the fabricator must submit to the inspector a written documentation of the damaged areas so that they can be distinguished from the coating damage done during unloading and erection of the structure.

Record Keeping. Finally, the welding inspector is responsible for *complete, accurate,* and *clear* record keeping through all phases of steel fabrication. The record keeping should also be timely: facts that are obvious and known to all at the time of writing will not be so easily remembered later on. A daily diary is maintained, recording any changes that deviate from the plans, major repairs to materials or equipment, pertinent conversations and telephone calls, and problems that arise (and how they are resolved). You should also register all results of nondestructive tests, including the filing of radiographic film. A history sheet for complete fabrication should be compiled, and all documentation should be turned over to the engineer or owner as appropriate.

Summary of the Role of the Welding Inspector. It should be evident from the foregoing that the duties and responsibilities of the modern-day welding inspector are more demanding than ever before, and the need for a high-quality performance cannot be overemphasized. The reputation of the shop welding inspector reached an all-time low during the late 1960s and the decade of the 1970s.

The problem of incompetent inspection personnel is directly related to the system of awarding inspection services to the low bidder in most cases. Unfortunately the two do not go hand in hand, and many inspection agencies are not bidding as equals when they submit their proposals. The best way to assure that all parties have the same degree of performance in mind is to require all inspection personnel to be AWS CWIs (American Welding Society certified welding inspectors).

It is difficult for the author to portray the real dilemma that has existed in the United States steel-inspection industry over the past several decades and how we are only now starting to make some small improvement. Owners and engineers are learning through unhappy experiences that inspection performances are only as good as what the customer is willing to pay for such services. Retaining well-qualified inspection personnel does permit first-class inspection agencies the luxury of being competitive when work is awarded strictly on a low-bid basis. If performance is a factor, good inspection agencies can offer high-quality inspection using well-qualified personnel at moderate rates.

PREFABRICATION CONFERENCE

There is probably no single requirement that can lead to an improved final product more than a prefabrication meeting. If a project were to be built with the absolute minimum of inspection, a prefabrication meeting should be one of the primary essentials. For it is such a meeting that gives all those responsible for the work the opportunity actually to build the job on paper. Preconstruction meetings have been standard practice for years; prefabrication conferences are just as important for a steel project.

As soon as possible after the award of the contract, the fabricator and/or contractor should make arrangements with the engineer for a prefabrication meeting. Experience has proved such conferences to be invaluable in getting projects off with the least amount of confusion, delay, or omission. They are usually held at the fabricator's plant and attended by fabricator or contractor personnel representing management, engineering, production, inspection, quality control, and field operations. Owner personnel taking part should include the structural-design engineer, welding engineer, quality-assurance engineer or the engineer's representative (the shop inspector), and a nondestructive-testing technician.

This meeting gives all parties the opportunity to discuss the overall shop fabrication, plans, specifications, quality control, quality assurance, etc., and to establish general ground rules for the entire job. Lines of communication which are agreeable to all and which give the most direct solution to each particular problem should be established. This is the ideal time to review the project schedule and head off any anticipated problems or delays related to prequalification tests, NDT procedures, the timing of quality assurance, inspections and testing, mill reports, and so forth.

The fabricator should be required, within the specifications, to submit an outline of the quality-control measures planned for the entire project. In addition, it is desirable that the inspector put in writing the detailed quality-control tasks that are planned to be performed and how and when the inspector plans to carry them out. Most fabricators do not want to include anything beyond what they consider to be minimum inspection in order to complete the job in the shortest time and on schedule.

The quality-control plan also should include information on:

- Materials
- Documentation
- Personnel qualifications
- Details of procedures
- Organization of the inspection and engineering staff
- Lists of equipment to be used in fabrication and inspection

Again, it is difficult to get all these details in writing from most fabricators, but it is important to obtain every possible commitment in the area of quality control.

Inspection tasks to be performed by the fabricator must be scheduled so that sufficient time is allowed for each task. All too often, inspection personnel are blamed for production delays which could have been avoided by proper scheduling. Proper scheduling also allows the owner's representatives to observe quality-control tests and inspections or to perform independent testing when warranted.

In any case, inspection functions should be as independent as possible from production or engineering functions. Inspection is usually last on a fabricator's priority list, but the qualifications of inspection personnel are just as important as the qualifications of other personnel working on the project. It is through the inspections performed that defective welds or materials are detected and then repaired in the best possible way.

Welding inspectors for quality control (fabricator's personnel) or for quality assurance (owner's personnel) should be certified by the AWS to ensure competence in reading, interpreting, and following plans and specifications. For critical structures, AWS certification should be a must. For less critical structures, inspectors should at least work under the direct supervision of a welding engineer or a CWI.

Since most major items of fabrication will be discussed and agreed upon during the prefabrication conference, it is imperative that the minutes of the meeting be recorded and become part of the project record, with copies sent to all who attend. Many projects undergo changes in staffing during the life of the work, and these minutes tend to preserve some continuity in both the quality-control and the quality-assurance program.

In summary, here is a list of some of the important items which should be taken up at the prefabrication meeting:

1. Review of the specifications, contract plans, and shop drawings (if available)
2. Quality-control organization, staffing, personnel qualifications, lines of communication, and responsibilities
3. Welder, welding-operator, and welding-procedure qualification (verification) or need for prequalification testing; test scheduling (actual complete testing) and length of time before test results can be expected
4. Verification of electrodes, wire, and flux, including care and storage
5. Mill certifications: timing of availablity, number of copies needed, and how distribution will be handled
6. Transfer of heat numbers for main-member material and identity-control program for all materials and NDT program
7. Assembly: for fitting tolerances, temporary fitting aids, tacking and tack size (including preheat), straightness, and distortion removal prior to assembly or final welding
8. Cleaning of joints prior to final welding, including removing slag and mill scale (when required)
9. Preheat prior to and during final welding
10. Conditioning of used flux (number of times of reuse)
11. Scheduling, notification, and witnessing of all NDT
12. Repairs (types and procedures used); need for consulting the engineer on repairs beyond the routine
13. Drilling from the solid, subpunching or subdrilling, full-size punching, and assembly for drilling or reaming field splices in their final position
14. Camber and camber adjustment (procedure for heat cambering or heat straightening)
15. Cleaning, painting, and handling methods (throughout fabrication)
16. Storage and shipping

To repeat, it is extremely important that the minutes of this prefabrication meeting be recorded and distributed to all in attendance. It is surprising how often these minutes will come into use during the course of the work. And they become the beginning of a well-documented project history which inspectors should maintain for their own protection as well as for the owner's benefit.

NONDESTRUCTIVE TESTING

No discussion of structural-steel inspection would be complete without touching on NDT. Nondestructive inspection of welds includes both tests and visual inspections. The major test methods are radiographic, ultrasonic, magnetic-particle, and liquid-penetrant. In all, however, over 30 individual testing techniques exist.

This chapter will not go into detail about test procedures or interpretation of results. Extensive coverage of the subject is provided in training courses. Included here is a brief description of each evaluation method: what it is and how and when it is applied.

Purpose.   The purpose of nondestructive tests is to detect flaws in welds without destroying or damaging the welds or the heat-affected zone (HAZ) adjacent to them. Then the type and severity of the flaws must be considered, in light of specified tolerances, to determine whether or not the material is acceptable. The idea is to determine serviceability: whether the work is good enough to do the job for which it was intended. Destructive testing exists but is not practical for most steel-fabrication inspection.

Visual Inspection.   Visual inspection is undoubtedly the most common nondestructive method of evaluating welds. It is performed before, during, and after the welding operations. It is easy to do, quick, and relatively inexpensive, and it requires only simple equipment. Through trained and experienced appraisal of welds and their flaws, the inspector can determine if the existing quality is acceptable, what probably caused the flaws, and what might be done to correct the problems and avoid repeating them.

Often, visual inspection is the only kind of inspection specified for a job. In these cases responsibility for ensuring that the final work meets all code and specification requirements rests heavily on the inspector. Also, while it is the fabricator's job to put the specified quality in the work, the inspector is the one who must judge whether or not it has been done. Therefore, when visual inspection is the chief or sole means of evaluation, the inspector's judgment must be based on the appearance of the welds. If a weld looks good to the trained eye, it usually is good.

Visual inspection during welding has the advantage of enabling the inspector to spot unacceptable workmanship and results in progress in time for corrections to be made. Timely correction of faulty production is one of the key functions of the welding inspector. Naturally, correcting one error in workmanship is much better than rejecting a whole series of completed welds. And visual inspection is the one method of nondestructive evaluation that can be performed routinely while work is under way.

Radiographic Inspection.   Radiographic inspection uses x-rays or gamma rays to penetrate welds and the adjacent metal and then produce an image on sensitized film or on a fluorescent screen. The image pictures are called radiographs, which become permanent records of the condition of the welds.

Radiographs are made by aiming the x-rays or gamma rays at the section of weld to be investigated. Some of the radiation gets absorbed by the metal: the thicker the metal, the greater the absorption. But some radiation passes through the weld and the base metal and reaches the film placed behind them. When there are voids in the weld (such as internal cracks and blowholes), there is less material to absorb the radiation.

So defective areas in the metal allow more radiation to pass through than do sound areas. These higher amounts of radiation reach the film and show up as black or darker areas, revealing the size and shape of the flaws. Only when a flaw is of rejectable size (according to the code) is it called a defect.

Surface discontinuities are detected by radiography, but the method is used mainly to reveal internal defects.

Slag inclusions (see Figs. 2.5-16, 2.5-17, 2.5-18, and 2.5-19) and weld porosity show up well on radiographs because of their shape and sizes. Internal cracks are not as easy to pick up. Their detection depends on their dimensions and orientation with respect to the direction of radiation. Flaws perpendicular to the plate surface usually produce fairly obvious images. Cracks that run at angles to or parallel to the plate surface may show up only faintly or not at all. It has been observed that cracks

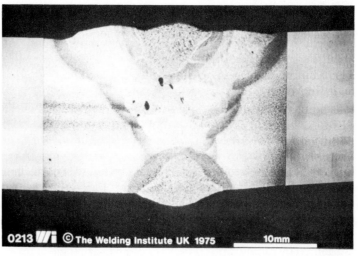

0213 *The Welding Institute UK 1975*   10mm

FIG. 2.5-16   Trapped slag.

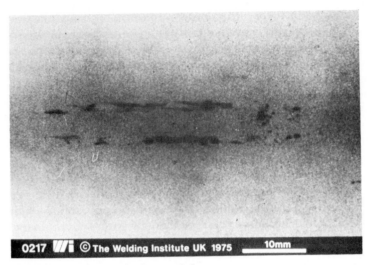

0217 ◫ © The Welding Institute UK 1975   10mm

Fɪɢ. **2.5-17**   Radiograph of trapped slag.

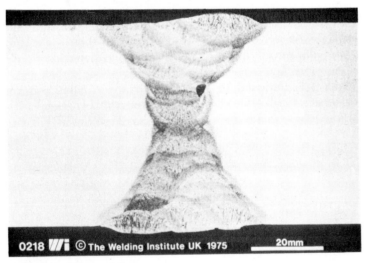

0218 ◫ © The Welding Institute UK 1975   20mm

Fɪɢ. **2.5-18**   Trapped slag.

appearing in the first pass of a weld may become less distinct or not show up at all in radiographs taken after later passes have been made.

Two factors affect the reliability of radiographic images and their value as interpretative tools: sharpness and contrast. These of course are critical qualities in general photography as well. A sensitivity of at least 2 percent must be attained by radiographs if they themselves are to be of acceptable quality. Tons of radiographs are rejected every year because they fail to provide such sensitivity. Sensitivity is defined as the smallest percentage

0219 *Wi* ©The Welding Institute UK 1975   10mm

FIG. 2.5-19   Radiograph of trapped slag.

of difference in weld thickness that can be seen on radiographs. The ability to see such a thickness difference depends on the sharpness of the image outline and its contrast with the background. So, for a fine crack to be positively identified on the radiograph, its image must have a distinctly recognizable outline and must contrast well enough with the background so as to leave no doubt as to its being a discontinuity.

Ultrasonic Inspection.   In ultrasonic inspection, a beam of acoustic energy at ultrasonic frequencies is directed into the test specimen. Discontinuities in the weld reflect the acoustic energy, which is then picked up and indicated on the cathode-ray tube (CRT). The ultrasonic beam travels with little loss through homogeneous material but is intercepted and reflected by discontinuities within a material, similarly to the way in which light is reflected from a mirror or other smooth surface.

The ultrasonic beam is directed into the material being inspected through a transducer connected to an electric-generating circuit. The transducer consists of a small piezoelectric element enclosed in a protective case. The piezoelectric element, or crystal, converts electrical energy into mechanical energy and vice versa. A couplant, such as glycerine or oil, is used to transfer the mechanical energy from the transducer to the surface of the material. The beam is sent in intermittent pulses such that the transducer has time to receive all or any part of the beam energy reflected from a discontinuity in the material. The reflected mechanical energy, converted to electrical energy at the transducer, is passed through an amplifier and produces a vertical trace on the screen of a CRT.

When the face of the piezoelectric element is parallel with the surface of the material being tested, the technique is called *straight-beam testing*. When the face of the element is at an angle to the surface of the material, the technique is called *angle-beam testing* or *shear-wave testing*.

In angle-beam testing, the ultrasonic beam passes into the material at an angle and is divided into a longitudinal wave and a shear wave. Each wave travels at a different refraction angle. When butt welds are inspected in plate, the shear wave will travel in a direction generally parallel to the surface of the plate but will, at the same time, be reflected back and forth between the plate surfaces. This beam will be reflected back to the transducer along the same path if it is intercepted by defects in the weld. The amount of energy reflected will depend on the orientation of the reflecting areas of the defect with the direction of the beam.

Most ultrasonic-test instruments can be calibrated so that the height of the indication on the CRT is a measure of the reflected energy and the horizontal position of the indication is a measure of the distance traveled by the reflected energy. From the horizontal position of the indication, the location of a defect within the weld can be accurately determined.

The plate is inspected for lamellar discontinuities by moving the transducer directly over the areas to be inspected. For angle-beam inspections of welds, the transducer is moved in a zigzag pattern along areas adjacent and parallel to the weld.

When the ultrasonic inspection of structural welds is made according to the AWS bridge specifications or any other specification that requires a sensitivity level or decibel rating for flaw indications, interpreting the indications as to the type of defect is not necessary for rejection or acceptance. However, knowledge of the type of defect can be very useful to shop personnel, and the experienced operator in ultrasonic testing can usually supply this information.

Magnetic-Particle Inspection.   In this method of inspection, a magnetic field is set up in the weld under test. If the weld section is uniform, the magnetic field will also be uniform. If there is a sharp change in the section, such as that caused by a flaw, local magnetic poles will be formed and a leakage flux will flow across the flaw. If finely divided magnetic particles are applied to the surface, the particles near the defect will be attracted to the local poles and will build up across the defect. When the surplus particles are removed from the area, the remaining particles will show the pattern of the defect. The maximum pattern is obtained when the path of the flux is normal to the lengthwise dimension of the defect. Subsurface defects, if not too deep, will also cause leakage flux, but the magnetic field will be broader and weaker.

The magnetic field can be set up by several methods. Two of these methods, *prod magnetization* and *yoke magnetization,* can be conveniently used on large weldments such as girders or bridge structures.

Liquid-Penetrant Inspection. Liquid-dye-penetrant inspection is a relatively simple process. First, the area to be inspected is thoroughly cleaned. Then a colored liquid penetrant is applied to the surface. It is left on the surface and allowed to penetrate any defects that are open at the surface. After the penetrating period, the excess liquid that remains on the surface is removed. Then the developer, a light-colored, powered absorbent material, is applied to the surface. This material acts as a blotter and draws out some of the penetrant that had previously seeped into the defect. As the penetrant is drawn out, it spreads into the coating of developer, forming a colored indication against the light background of the developer.

This process was originally developed for the inspection of nonmagnetic materials, such as aluminum, as a parallel to the magnetic-particle process for surface inspection.

The equipment in dye-penetrant inspection is relatively simple and inexpensive. All that is needed is a set of the inspection solutions and a supply of wiping cloths.

The inspection kits offered commercially contain the cleaner, penetrant, and developer solutions, all in pressure-spray cans and packed in a toolbox-type carrying container. The penetrant is bright red, and the developer is white, providing good contrast.

When this process is used, preparation of the area to be inspected is very important. All surfaces must be cleaned of dirt, rust, scale, grease, oil, paint, and welding flux and spatter. If cleaning is inadequate, the penetrant cannot enter the defect openings on the surface, or the poor surface condition may cause false indications to appear.

After the surface has been cleaned, the penetrant is sprayed on and allowed to remain for a penetration time of *at least 7 minutes.* Any penetrant remaining on the surface is then removed, and the developer is applied. Large defects or openings will show up immediately; finer defects, after a short time. Other things being equal, the time for an indication to develop is inversely proportional to the volume of the discontinuity. In other words, the smaller the flaw, the longer it takes to show up.

Interpretation of results from the use of this method requires relatively little experience or training. Surface defects that can be readily detected in welds are cracks, lack of fusion, and porosity.

Cracks and lack of fusion usually show up as a continuous line of penetration indication. The width and brightness of color depend on the volume of the crack. A crack that does not reach the surface for its entire length may produce an intermittent line indication. Porosity at the weld surface will show up as small red dots. Where weak indications are obtained, the area should be cleaned and the procedure repeated to eliminate the possibility of faulty technique.

One good way to estimate the depth of a defect is by the persistence of the indication. If it appears after the developer has been removed and reapplied, there must be a reservoir of penetrant present, indicating a deep defect.

Summary. To repeat, this has been just an overview of nondestructive inspection. Inspectors can and should obtain further information and training from the many training courses available on each of the methods. In summary, keep in mind the points listed below:

- Visual inspection tells most. Everyone can participate in it.
- Radiographic inspection permits looking into the weld for defects that fall within the sensitivity range of the process. It provides a permanent record of the results.
- Magnetic-particle inspection is outstanding for detecting surface cracks and is used to advantage on heavy weldments and assemblies.
- Dye penetrant is easy to use in detecting surface cracks. Its indications are readily interpreted.
- Ultrasonic inspection is excellent for detecting subsurface discontinuities but requires expert interpretation.

FIELD ERECTION

Field erection introduces slight variations and some new functions for the site welding inspector, but basically the same rules and requirements that were applicable for good shop practice also apply to work in the field. The weather, probably more than any other factor, determines the quality of the field welding and general erection phases of the work.

It is in the field that oversights and errors come to light and the inspector must retain good control of the fit-up and welding. Ironworkers take pride in their ability to make anything fit, but a cutting torch in an ironworker's hand can become a dangerous weapon in more ways than one. Often the ironworker's methods of correction are the most expedient and are not founded on good engineering practice or technique. Inspectors who observe the sparks of a cutting torch during erection should always investigate the problem immediately.

Correcting a problem by the torch in the early stages of erection usually compounds the problem throughout the erection process. It is best to take the time to determine the exact cause of all field problems and then refer them to the engineer for proper disposition.

Sometimes the corrective measures that ironworkers have used in the past for, say, a statically loaded member would be totally out of order for a dynamically loaded member, yet they fail to understand what all the fuss is about when an inspector halts work for good cause. Conscientious field welding inspectors have their hands full on most typical erection sites just trying to maintain average good quality. Some of the tasks involved in the work include:

Buildings

1. Before steel even arrives on a project site, the welding inspector should have coordinated the installation of the anchor bolts and leveling plates (if they are used), although the use of leveling nuts is a better and more effective method. Templates must be used if anchor bolts are to have the correct projection, pattern, and plumbness. Anchor bolts traditionally seem to provide an early and often major problem during the initial stages of erection. Great care and effort are usually needed to assure that proper fits will be attained.

2. Field inspectors should look for the "Recommended for Use" stamp on all main members shipped from the fabrication shop. This is their assurance that the steel was checked at the shop and should be ready for erection (that is, if shop inspection was part of the quality-assurance program).

3. Warpage of leveling plates and many column bases often presents problems in this first stage of construction. Do not let the problem be delayed for later correction because correction attempted after the part is in place becomes very complicated and good results are seldom achieved.

4. Plumbing of column lines and building sections should be provided as the sections are installed and as the work progresses.

5. Bolted column splices may not permit good bearing between lower and upper column members, resulting in the bolts' carrying the entire load. Shimming may be warranted in such cases when the gap exceeds the allowable tolerance.

6. Bolted splices may also require shim plates to compensate for differences between rolled sections of different weights. (This is a common occurrence.)

7. Many designs inadvertently call for bolted beam-to-column connections, which are impossible to tighten with impact equipment. The only method available is an open-end spud wrench. In many cases these connections cannot even be checked with torque wrenches because of the clearance restrictions. The inspector must resort to ingenuity in checking these bolts, which usually are found to be very loose.

8. Metal decking for floor-slab pours and those used in the roofing

system often have puddle welds which do not meet specification requirements for size or number of welds. Side-lap fasteners are often overlooked and omitted altogether, which means that the deck panels will deflect individually and not as a unit.

9. Pipe hangers for the heating system are often mistreated by the boilermakers in their methods of installation. Sometimes these hangers are fabricated with improper bend radii, but since they are considered miscellaneous metal, they never are checked before they reach the site.

10. Open-grid floor decking can present cracking problems if it is hot-dip-galvanized by the double-dip method. Problems are also quite common for all pipe or tube sections which are double-dipped. The practice of double dipping should be banned under most circumstances.

Steel Bridges. Dynamically loaded structures require inspection checks similar to those needed for other quality field erections, but their requirements go beyond those for statically loaded members. Notches, arc strikes, unfilled craters, and crater cracking, to name a few, become deficiencies which cannot be tolerated in tension members subjected to cyclic-loading conditions. Some items to check for such structures are:

1. Transverse welds in tension areas should not occur in good designs, but some designers do use them; therefore, the closest attention must be given to all such welds. Absolutely no undercut for fillet welds and/or butt welds should be allowed to slip by inspection. Reduced thickness and too much weld reinforcement both present fatigue stress-riser conditions which must be monitored and eliminated in the completed members.

2. Flame-cutting kerf notches and handling defects, especially plate-edge notches, must be eliminated completely.

3. Temporary fitting aids must not be tack-welded to primary members even if they are to be ground off at a later time. The grinding may remove the physical stress-riser conditions, but it will not remove the metallurgical stress riser in most instances.

4. Remember that in bolt-torque testing the element must be moving to obtain an accurate check. In too many cases the nut never moves, but the foot-pounds are exceeded, and the bolt is said to have the required minimum tension. In such cases the inertia of the threads has not even been overcome. This is especially true of hot-dip-galvanized bolts and nuts, which are supposed to be lubricated but often are not.

5. With the turn-of-the-nut method, starting from the snug-tight condition always presents a problem on what constitutes *snug-tight.* Also, when and how to slow down the ironworkers to permit the initial markings present scheduling and time delays which create additional problems in themselves. The turn-of-the-nut method is almost impossible to police properly and becomes a farce unless mandatory requirements detailing the exact procedure to follow in the field are spelled out in the contract.

6. Flame-torch enlargement of holes which do not fit should never be permitted, although it is quite a common practice. Enlarging holes by driving driftpins in misaligned holes should not be allowed either. In both cases, correction by reaming is the only method which should be considered and enforced.

7. The welding of end-welded stud shear connectors should not be attempted during inclement weather or when the members are wet and subjected to frost or snow.

8. Preheat and windshields to protect the welder and the weld puddle should be used when appropriate.

9. Field welders come and go quite regularly; therefore, it is necessary to check prequalification certificates closely.

10. Call for retesting of welders who provide sloppy workmanship and, in most cases, poor welding.

11. Insist on the chipping of all welds (deslagging) by the welder so that final visual inspection is possible.

12. Enforce the use of extension and runoff tabs so that welds do not begin or end on the main member.

13. Enforce all requirements for NDT and observe all repairs before, during, and after the repair. Follow up on retesting the weld repair itself.

The above are only some of the more important operations and tasks to administer during the field inspection quality-assurance program. There is much more.

CONCLUSION

This chapter has attempted to list and discuss some of the more basic essentials, test criteria, and observations that are necessary in every good-quality assurance program during each of the many phases of structural-steel fabrication and erection. If most of these are adhered to on the average steel-construction project, a giant step forward will have been taken in the industry.

It is very difficult to portray exactly how bad conditions have been during the past several decades or what caused them without pointing fingers and offending those involved in the separate areas of responsibility. It is to be hoped that all will review their roles in the total system and, if improvements are warranted, work toward the goal. Steel is an amazing product and, when treated in the manner intended, will provide the safe and long-lasting structures envisioned when its use was selected.

TERMINOLOGY

Air-carbon arc cutting   Arc-cutting process in which metals are severed by melting with the heat of the arc and an airstream is used to facilitate cutting.

Arc blow   Swerving of an electric arc from its normal path because of magnetic forces.

Arc gouging   Application of arc cutting in which a U groove is formed.

Axis of a weld   Line drawn through the length of a weld.

Back weld   Weld deposited at the back of a single-groove weld.

Backing   Material (usually metal) backing up the joint during welding to facilitate obtaining a sound weld at the root.

Bare electrode   Filler-metal electrode without a coating or covering other than that used for drawing the wire.

Base metal   Metal to be welded or cut.

Bead weld   Type of weld composed of one or more string or weave beads deposited on an unbroken surface.

Bevel   Type of edge preparation.

Blowhole   See GAS POCKET.

Butt joint   Joint between two members lying approximately in the same plane.

Chamfer   Contour prepared on the edge of a member to be welded.

Crater   Depression at the termination of a weld bead.

Crater crack   Crack in the crater of a weld bead.

Depth of fusion   Distance that fusion extends into the base metal from the surface melted during welding.

Downhand   Designating the position in which welding is done from the top and the axis of the weld metal is horizontal.

Electrode   In metal-arc welding, filler metal in the form of a wire or rod, either bare or covered, through which current is conducted between the electrode holder and the arc.

Faying surface   Surface of a member in contact with another member to which it is to be joined.

Filler metal   Metal to be added in making a weld.

Flux   Material used to prevent, dissolve, or facilitate removal of oxides and other undesirable substances.

Gas pocket (blowhole)   Weld cavity caused by entrapped gas.

Heat-affected zone   Portion of the base metal which has not been melted but whose mechanical properties or microstructures have been altered by welding.

Interpass temperature   In a multiple-pass weld, the lowest temperature of the deposited weld metal before the next pass is started.

Kerf   Space from which metal has been removed by a cutting process.

Manual welding   Welding in which the entire welding operation is performed and controlled by hand.

Notch effect   Abrupt change of contour or section or a defect or imperfection in workmanship which causes high local concentration of stress and constraint against ductile action, thereby affecting structural behavior adversely. Such notch effects are especially detrimental to fatigue or impact strength and resistance to brittle fracture.

Overlap   Protrusion of weld metal beyond the bond at the toe of the weld.

Oxygen gouging   Application of oxygen cutting in which a chamfer or groove is formed.

Parent metal   Metal that is to be welded or cut.

Peening   Mechanical working of metals by means of hammer blows.

Porosity   Gas pockets or voids in metal.

Postheating   Application of heat to a weld or weldment immediately after welding.

Preheating   Application of heat to the base metal immediately before welding.

Pressure welding   Any welding process or method in which pressure is used to complete the weld.

Resistance welding   Group of welding processes in which coalescence is produced by the heat obtained from resistance of the work to the flow of electric current in a circuit of which the work is a part and by the application of pressure.

Reverse polarity   Arrangement of direct-current arc-welding leads in which the work is the negative pole and the electrode is the positive pole of the welding arc.

Root opening   Separation between the members to be joined at the root of the joint.

Root face   Portion of the groove face adjacent to the root of the joint.

Root of the joint   Portion of a joint to be welded in which the members approach closest to each other. In cross section the root of the joint may be a point, a line, or an area.

Root of the weld   Point, as shown in cross section, at which the bottom of the weld intersects the base-metal surfaces.

Runoff tab   Plate having the same joint preparation as the joint to be welded that is placed on the end of the joint to carry the weld past the end of welded joint.

Semiautomatic arc welding   Arc welding with equipment which controls only the filler-metal feed. The advance of the welding is manually controlled.

Shielded-metal arc welding   Arc-welding process in which coalescence is produced by heating with an electric arc between a covered metal electrode and the work. Shielding is obtained from the decomposition of the electrode covering. Pressure is not used, and filler metal is obtained from the electrode.

Size of weld   (*a*) *Groove weld.* The joint penetration (depth of chamfering plus the root penetration when specified. (*b*) *Fillet weld.* For equal-leg fillet welds, the leg length of the largest isosceles right triangle which can be inscribed within the fillet-weld cross section.

Slag inclusion   Nonmetallic solid material entrapped in weld metal or between weld metal and base metal.

Spatter   Metal particles which are expelled during welding and do not form a part of the weld metal.

Straight polarity   Arrangement of direct-current arc-welding leads in which the work is positive and the electrode is the negative of the welding arc.

Stringer bead   Type of weld bead made without appreciable transverse oscillation.

Tack weld   Weld made to hold parts of a weldment in proper alignment until the final welds are made.

Underbead crack   Crack in the heat-affected zone not extending to the surface of the base metal.

Undercut   Groove melted into the base metal adjacent to the toe of a weld and left unfilled by weld metal.

Weave bead   Type of weld bead made with transverse oscillation.

Weld metal   That portion of a weld which has been melted during welding.

Welder   One who is capable of performing a manual or semiautomatic welding operation.

Welder certification   Certification in writing that a welder has produced welds meeting prescribed standards.

Welder qualification   Demonstration of a welder's ability to produce welds meeting prescribed standards.

Welding procedure   Detailed methods and practices, including joint-welding procedures, involved in the production of a weldment.

Welding sequence   Order of making the welds in a weldment.

Weldment   Assembly whose component parts are joined by welding.

Weldment defect   Failure of any weldment to meet the specifications.

Pavements

Earl R. Scyoc, P.E.
Chief Engineer of Construction
West Virginia Department of Highways
Charleston, West Virginia

Bill S. Hanshew, Jr., P.E.
Specification Engineer
West Virginia Department of Highways
Charleston, West Virginia

BASIC INFORMATION

The placing of pavements represents the end product in a long process of activities, from the original design to participation for use by the traveling public. Each activity requires experienced personnel adequately trained to exercise expertise in determining assurance of compliance with plans and specifications.

The standard method of inspection used by most agencies is to inspect each activity in detail as the work is being performed. However, in recent years some agencies have recognized the need to utilize the use of a statistically based quality-assurance method in the control and acceptance of paving projects. In these instances, the project engineer and inspector must be acquainted with the sampling, testing, and inspection methods but will not be required to perform these duties except on a random or spot-check basis. The contractor will perform these duties, take any required corrective action, and document the results for further evaluation. When work is performed by this method, the owner must have sufficient data to predict proposed results under a certain range of conditions. The owner should establish a minimum required frequency and testing to be adopted by the contractor for assurance of specification compliance. These data, combined with random sampling by the inspector, would provide sufficient information to maintain control as the work is being performed. As compared with the standard system of inspection, this method requires the inspector to take immediate action if actual results differ substantially from predicted results.

The success of a quality-assurance program depends on a number of things, such as the following:

1. An adequate data base must be established for development of a prototype specification, and the limits must be adjusted as needed when more data are obtained.

2. An adequate educational and training program must be developed for agencies and contractors' employees.

3. The contracting agency is required to control the process as the work is being performed. This prevents the work from being an end-result type of inspection and further prevents excessive removal and replacement should defective workmanship occur.

We will use the conventional, or standard, method of inspection for our discussion of pavement inspection.

In discussing roadway paving, the first consideration is to determine the type of pavement to be used. While many factors influence this decision, pavement can generally be classified as either flexible or rigid. Each of these types requires different inspection activities as related to the type of construction. However, many items are common to both types of paving.

See Table 2.6-1 for the sampling and testing of various types of paving materials.

TABLE 2.6-1 Field Sampling and Testing of Paving Materials*

Material and method	Minimum frequency	Size	Remarks
Bituminous materials, ASTM D 140	From each carrier.	1 qt for emulsions; 4 qt, 2 to 3 lb for solid material.	When field test equipment is available, perform the following tests or send to laboratory: emulsions (cationic), D 2397; emulsions (anionic), D 977; asphalt (penetration), D 946; asphalt (viscosity), D 3381; tar, D 490.
Bituminous-mixing plant, ASTM D 290	See ASTM D 290.	See ASTM D 290.	Also provides sample of inspector's daily plant report.
Aggregates for bituminous pavements, ASTM D 692, D 1073, D 1139, D 75	As specified or 1 for each half day of operation.	See ASTM D 15, Table 1.	Test for grading, abrasion, soundness, deleterious materials, and slag weights.
Cement, ASTM E 183	From 1 bag in 95; three 5-lb samples from each car or truck.	10 lb.	Send to laboratory for complete series of tests.
Aggregates for portland-cement pavement, ASTM D 75, C 88, C 117, C 123, C 131, C 136, C 142, C 535	As specified or 1 for each half day of operation.	See ASTM D 75, Table 1.	Test for grading, abrasion, soundness, deleterious materials, and slag weights.

Material	Frequency	Size/amount	Remarks
Portland-cement-concrete pavement, ASTM C 172	As specified or 1 for each 500 yd³.	See ASTM C 172.	Test for slump, T 119, air, T 152, yield, T 121.
Portland-cement-concrete pavement test cylinders or beams, C 31 or C 172	As specified or 3 sets of cylinders or beams for each day's operation.	3 cylinders per set or 3 beams per set.	Break cylinders or beams of 3, 6, and 8 days to determine when specified material is obtained.
Coated dowel bars and tie bars, ASTM A 615	As specified or a minimum of 24 bars.	....	Send to laboratory to test core steel properties and test coating as specified.
Wire fabric, ASTM A 185	1 for each 75,000 ft².	4 ft².	Send to laboratory.
Joint sealer; hot-pour plastic, ASTM D 1190, cold-pour silicone, manufacturer's specifications	1 for each batch or lot.	10 lb.	Send to laboratory.
Preformed joint filler, ASTM D 1752	2 ft² for each 1000 ft².	4½ by 4½ in	Send to laboratory.
Elastomeric joint seal and adhesive, ASTM D 2628, D 2835	1 for each lot of each cross section and 1 for each lot of adhesive.	9 ft and 1 qt.	Send to laboratory.
Curing compound, ASTM C 309	1 for each batch or lot.	1 qt.	Send to laboratory

*1 ft = 0.3048 m; 1 ft² = 0.0929 m²; 1 in = 25.4 mm; 1 lb = 0.4536 kg; 1 qt = 0.946 L; 1 yd³ = 0.7645 m³.

2.6.5

SUBGRADE

The excavation and embankment may have been constructed under a separate contract or under the present contract. In either case, the construction should have been performed and inspected with the best methods, equipment, and technology available. (See Chap. 2.1.)

Your responsibility, as inspector of the pavement section, is the review of the physical appearance of the former construction, particularly the embankments, to assure that there are no unstable conditions, poor drainage, etc., to prevent the pavement structure (subbase, base, and surface courses) from performing its designed function.

The subgrade, i.e., the upper portion [6 to 12 in (152.4 to 304.8 mm)] of the roadbed upon which the pavement structure and shoulders are placed, must be constructed of the specified material compacted to the required maximum dry density. Subgrade material ranges from suitable soil to crushed aggregate which is capable of being trimmed to a smooth surface. The best material would be a granular material composed of crushed rock, gravel, sand, or slag free of particles in which not more than 25 percent by weight pass the No. 200 sieve and a plasticity index of not more than 10.

The subgrade acts as a blanket between the embankment and the subbase or base to smooth the top of the embankment by filling the voids of broken rock or other material in the embankment. When granular subgrade material is used, it may serve to prevent the intrusion of fine soil particles or clays into the subbase or base.

Courses thicker than 6 in (152.4 mm) should be placed in two or more lifts with density tests on each lift. If subgrade material is paid by the cubic yard (1 yd^3 = 0.9144 m^3), depth tests must be made and width measurements checked to assure that plan quantity and dimensions are met.

Staking. Staking is the most important prepaving operation. Uniform staking methods will enable the contractor to produce uniform subgrades, subbases or base course, and surface courses. It is generally the responsibility of the contractor to perform all staking, but the inspector must know the method utilized so that information from the stakes can be used in daily inspection activities. Our discussion will consist of a common staking method.

Bench marks are permanent marks set throughout the United States that depict the elevation above sea level. They are the prime vertical reference points for all roadway construction.

Temporary bench marks are utilized by contractors to bring elevation reference points closer to the roadway area. These points are located from the permanent bench marks and are set along both sides of the roadway. These points should be spaced approximately 1000 to 1500 ft (305 to 457 m) apart and remain in place during the complete construction of the roadway. Therefore, they should be located out of the construction area.

Next, control hubs should be established from the temporary bench marks, and they too should be located out of the construction area. Because the hubs are used to control all staking for construction, they should be well guarded with guard stakes.

String lines are used to control line and grade. They should be set along both sides of the roadway at fixed distances above the final grade points of the pavement and from the edge of the pavement. The subgrade, subbase, and pavement should all be checked from one set of string lines. This procedure should allow the road to be constructed uniformly regardless of an initial error in surveying. When two projects are coming together, it is necessary to make sure that the string lines have been established from a common bench mark. String lines must be aligned properly. An inspector can perform a general check by sighting over the string, and if the lines seem out of line, they can be checked by a survey party.

Fine Grading.   The surface of the subgrade is trimmed to the plan cross section and grade with a motor grader or an automatic subgrade machine. Both methods utilize final grade stakes, sometimes called *blue tops*, to perform the fine grading.

When a motor grader is used, the surface is checked in a transverse direction from each grade stake, either by setting a string at a predetermined height above grade and measuring from the string down to the surface at random points or by reading elevation differences of selected points across the surface with a hand level from the grade stake.

With an automatic subgrading machine, a string or wire line is installed at a fixed distance above the profile grade and outside the pavement edge. Special sensing devices contact the line, actuating automatic controls which guide the subgrader and position the height of the cutting edge.

The subgrade must be built slightly higher than the plan grade so the motor grader or automatic subgrader can trim off the excess material. The final subgrade surface should not be more than ½ in (12.7 mm) above or below the theoretical elevation or other tolerance as specified.

SUBBASES AND BASE COURSES

Aggregate subbase and base courses are placed on a subgrade (1) to distribute the wheel load transmitted to the subgrade, (2) to provide a relatively non-frost-susceptible material on which to provide support for surface courses, and (3) sometimes to carry traffic temporarily. To fulfill these purposes, they must be constructed in the proper manner with approved material. Base-course material must be placed on an adequately prepared subgrade and shaped in accordance with the specifications and plan template section. Any soft or spongy areas in the subgrade should be removed and replaced with suitable material properly compacted. Any pipes or conduits across the roadway should be placed prior to final subgrade compaction and the placing of any base course.

Duties of the Inspector

As a base-course inspector, your responsibilities include the inspection of aggregates, stockpiling, mixing plants, road construction, and performance of aggregate-gradation analysis (see Fig. 2.6-1).

At the mixing plant your job will be to:

- Inspect equipment to determine that it has been properly calibrated and is operating in conformance with the manufacturer's recommendations
- Inspect plant operations to determine that materials are being proportioned in accordance with the job-mix formula and that quality material is being produced

On the jobsite the inspector will

- Inspect equipment to determine that it is functioning properly and adequately to provide proper use and end result
- Inspect the subgrade for assurance that it has been prepared and shaped according to the contract plans
- Inspect road operations to determine that the quality of materials and workmanship and the effectiveness of equipment on the road are acceptable
- Perform moisture-density tests as required

Many different types of base courses are used in roadway construction, but we will discuss only a few of the more common ones.

Cement-Treated Aggregate

Cement-treated-aggregate base is a mixture of aggregate material and measured amounts of portland cement and water that hardens after compaction and curing to form a durable base material. Its structural properties depend on the aggregate material, curing conditions, and age.

MATERIALS CONTROL, SOIL AND TESTING DIVISION

GRADATION OF EXTRACTED AGGREGATE

SAMPLE NO.   DATE   TECHNICIAN

- 200 MATERIAL

PAN	
FILTER (g-c) FROM PG. I	
ASH, LINE (n) FROM PG. I	
LOST IN WASHING	
TOTAL - 200	

WASHED GRADING

(1)   WT.   BEFORE WASH   _____

(2)   WT.   AFTER   WASH   _____

--(3)   LOSS   (1-2)   _____

TOTAL   AGGREGATE   IN   SAMPLE

(4)   AGGREGATE, IN PAN &
      TRAPPED IN FILTER
      (LINE I FROM PG. I)   _____

(5)   ASH (LINE n FROM
      PAGE I)   _____

(6)   TOTAL AGGREGATE (4+5)   _____

SIEVE SIZE	WEIGHT RETAINED	PERCENT RETAINED	PERCENT PASSING	
2"				
$1\frac{1}{2}$"				
1"				
$\frac{3}{4}$"				
$\frac{1}{2}$"				
$\frac{3}{8}$"				
NO. 4				
NO. 8				
NO. 16				
NO. 50				
NO. 200				
- 200 (TOTAL)				
TOTAL				

FIG. 2.6-1   Materials control gradation of extracted aggregate.

Mixing of the aggregate, cement, and water can be accomplished by a central-plant mix method or by a mixed-in-place method.

Central-Plant Mix.   The most common type of central-plant mixer is the pugmill, consisting of revolving blades or paddles on a shaft. The quantity of material in the mixer is controlled by batch weights or volumes in batch mixing and by adjustable vertical gates in continuous mixing.

Rotary-drum mixers of either the batch or the continuous type may be used. In general, these employ the same mixing principle as a concrete paver in which paddles, studs, or flights are made a part of the revolving drum, which affords a mixing action as the drum rotates.

The desired time for the addition of potable water into the mixing operation can be determined by observation and performance on the specific project. In continuous mixing, the water can be added as the aggregate and cement progress through the mixer following a preliminary dry mixing. Water, which may be added to the mixture by sprays, facilitates the mixing operation, improves distribution, offers increased production, and leads to a better spreading and compacting operation. The amount of water added is that necessary for hydration of the cement and subsequent compaction which is close to the optimum moisture content for compaction.

The addition of cement to the mixture in a uniform manner and in desired amounts is very important, as it establishes the quality of the finished product. Proportioning cement by weight in batch mixers is generally the most successful method of assuring that the required amounts are processed.

The feeding of cement on continuous-type mixers is generally performed with continuous-flight augers or vane feeders. Owing to the physical characteristics of cement, it is difficult to be assured of accurate delivery of the desired weight percentage. The more successful cement feeders now attempt to deliver cement from a constant-head receiver in which the cement is agitated by air or other means to keep it in a uniform condition for delivery to the mixer.

The materials for a mixture must be held in the mixer until thoroughly mixed to a uniform color. Usually they must be mixed for at least 30 seconds.

The right moisture content can be judged roughly by picking out the stones over ¼ in (6.35 mm) in diameter in a handful of material and squeezing the rest in the hand. If the remaining material makes a firm cast that can be handled without breaking and no moisture is left on the hand, the mixing probably is satisfactory. Judgment can be improved by making this test and then determining the actual moisture content by drying a sample of the complete mixture. The mixed material is then discharged into a holding hopper and then into haul trucks.

Each truckload of plant-mixed material should be covered with a tarpaulin while being hauled from the plant to the jobsite to prevent surface drying. If hauling time is more than 30 minutes, it will usually be difficult to compact the aggregate-cement mixture after it has been placed.

The mixed material is placed on a moistened subgrade without segregation and is spread by an aggregate spreader attached to a tractor, by two spreaders spreading side by side, or by an automatic string-line-controlled subgrader.

Mixed-in-Place Method. Aggregate can be mixed with cement and water on the roadway with a traveling-pugmill mixer. The aggregate will be formed into windrows of a uniform size to avoid variation in cement content, moisture content, and pavement thickness. The top of windrow aggregate should be flattened or slightly entrenched to receive the cement. The required quantities of cement shall be spread uniformly on top of the windrowed material. The aggregate windrow, water, and portland cement shall be mixed with a traveling-pugmill single- or multitransverse-shaft mixer. The mixer picks up the aggregate and cement and mixes them in place. The water is measured through a meter and is injected into the mix by a spray bar. The mixed material is left flat on the roadway for immediate compaction. Most single-shaft mixers are not designed to scarify; therefore, the aggregate may need to be scarified and prewetted before using this type of equipment.

Most contractors use electronically controlled equipment operating from an accurately placed reference wire or stringline for grade control.

Compaction. Compaction starts immediately after the materials have been mixed and spread. Vibratory steel-wheeled rollers are commonly used, although many types of compaction equipment may be employed to obtain adequate densification. It is extremely important to compact the edges of the roadway adequately.

If mixing or spreading has been carefully done, the compacted material should be smooth and at grade with required finishing. The finished surface should be dense and free of cracks, ridges, and loose material. A moisture-retaining cover should be placed over the base as soon after completion as possible to retain the moisture and permit the cement to hydrate. Usually a bituminous cure coat is used for this purpose. No equipment should be allowed on sealed cement-treated subbase or base until 7 satisfactory curing days have passed.

Certain weather conditions limit the construction of cement-treated subbase and base courses. The material should not be mixed or placed on subgrade that has a temperature lower than 40°F (4.4°C). When conditions indicate that the temperature will fall below 35°F (1.7°C) within 24 hours, the contractor must protect the base course adequately from freezing. Cement-treated aggregate should never be placed on frozen subgrade.

Hot-Mixed, Hot-Laid Bituminous-Treated-Aggregate Base Course

Bituminous base-course material consists of aggregate material and a measured amount of bituminous material mixed in a central plant and spread and compacted on a prepared subgrade. The inspector should refer to the subsection "Hot-Laid Bituminous Concrete" under "Flexible Pavements" for information on plant and roadway inspection.

Cold-Mixed Bituminous-Treated-Aggregate Base Course

Cold-mixed bituminous-treated-aggregate base course is a mixture of aggregate material and measured amounts of bituminous material generally mixed in place on the roadway. The equipment for road-mix construction falls into the following principal categories:

1. Traveling mixers that employ rotary tines or blades.

    a. The rotary pulverizer-type mixer with transverse shafts mixes the asphalt and aggregate with revolving tines under a hood. The number of rotors under one hood varies from one to four. Many mixers are equipped with a spray system which applies the asphalt and water, if needed, while mixing.

    b. The travel-plant mixer that receives the aggregate into a hopper from trucks, mixes it with asphalt, and spreads the mixture all in one pass of the machine.

    c. There is also a travel-plant mixer that takes the aggregate from windrows, mixes it with the asphalt, and usually deposits the mixture in a windrow behind ready for spreading and aerating by motor graders.

2. Motor graders, multiple-blade drags, and spring-tooth harrows.

3. The water distributor is used to dampen the aggregate.

4. The asphalt distributor is used to apply the asphalt when the mixer is not equipped to do so.

5. Rollers, self-propelled steel-wheel and tandem and pneumatic-tired, used to compact mixes.

6. Asphalt tank trucks, dump trucks, power brooms, windrow sizers, and other auxiliary equipment.

Spreading and Mixing. In several types of road-mix construction, it is necessary to place the aggregate in windrows. Windrow sizes should be used to ensure the placing of the correct volume for the desired depth of pavement.

Separate windrows should be used if two or more materials are to be combined on the roadway. These windrows should then be used to ensure the placing of the correct volume for the desired depth of pavement.

Separate windrows should be used if two or more materials are to be combined on the roadway. These windrows should then be mixed together thoroughly before the asphalt is added. The proper percentage of asphalt for the aggregate in the windrow must be determined and the amount needed per linear foot of windrow calculated. Nonuniformity of grading of the aggregate in the windrow will cause a fluctuation in the asphalt demand, and this should be avoided.

Asphalt is added to the aggregate from an asphalt distributor or from a travel mixer. Whichever method is used, close control of the quantity and viscosity of asphalt applied is necessary to ensure a proper mixture. Liquid asphalts, although already fluid, need some heating to bring them to the proper viscosity for spraying. The viscosity will quickly rise above that recommended for mixing unless mixing begins immediately after the asphalt has been sprayed. The volatiles in liquid asphalts keep them fluid long enough for compaction of road mixing if it is done properly.

An advantage of travel-plant mixing is that closer control of the mixing operations can be achieved. The proportioning of the asphalt with the material, as well as the uniformity with which the two can be incorporated, is of the greatest importance.

In performing this type of work, the mixing machine moves along the windrow, adding asphalt as it goes. If the windrow is so large that all the asphalt cannot be incorporated in one mixing pass, it should be split into two or more windrows and the asphalt added to each in one mixing pass.

Further mixing of the windrowed material after the addition of the asphalt may be necessary. Unless the travel mixer can be used as a multiple-pass mixer, this additional mixing usually is done with a grader; this procedure makes sure that all the windrowed material is incorporated into the mix, and it also aerates the mixture for the removal of moisture and volatiles. The number of passes with the motor grader varies with different job conditions. However, in general, a minimum of five or six passes is necessary. After the mixing and aeration procedure has been completed, the windrow should be moved to one side of the area to be surfaced in preparation for spreading.

A different type of travel plant operates by mixing asphalt and aggregate deposited directly into the plant's hopper by truck; it then spreads the mix in one pass. Except when using open-graded mixtures in this technique, care must be taken to ensure sufficient evaporation of moisture and volatiles from the spread mix prior to compaction.

The rotary type of travel plant combines the asphalt and aggregates under a hood by means of whirling tines or blades as the machine moves over the surface. Most of these machines are now equipped with a spray system which applies the asphalt while mixing. When using this rotary type of mixer, the following steps are recommended:

1. Spread the aggregate to uniform grade and cross section with motor graders.

2. Mix the aggregate by one or more passes of the mixer. When ready for the asphalt, the moisture content of the aggregate should not exceed 3 percent unless laboratory tests indicate that a higher moisture content will not be harmful when the asphalt is added.

3. Add asphalt in increments of about 0.5 gal/yd^2 (2.26 L/m^2) until the total required amount of asphalt is applied and mixed in. A total of 0.4 to 0.6 gal/(yd^2·in) [0.5 to 0.75 L/(m^2·cm)] of compacted thickness of the course is usually necessary. If the mixer is not equipped with spray bars, the asphalt may be applied with an asphalt distributor.

4. Make one or more passes of the mixer between applications of asphalt as necessary to mix it in thoroughly.

5. Maintain the surface true to grade and cross section by using a motor grader during the mixing operations.

6. Aerate the mixture by additional manipulation if needed.

If a motor grader is used for mixing, best results are obtained by adding asphalt to aggregate in multiple applications and by folding the asphalt into the windrows immediately behind the distributor truck.

As the mixing progresses, close attention should be given to uniformity of the mix in the windrows; the mixing of the material in the windrow should continue until all aggregate particles have been uniformly coated. During mixing, attention should be paid to the vertical and horizontal angles of the moldboard of the grader; this board should be adjusted so that the material is completely rolled when the windrow is manipulated. Also during mixing, care must be exercised to avoid cutting into the underlying materials and incorporating them into the windrow. After mixing and aeration are complete, the windrow should be moved to one side of the area to be surfaced in preparation for spreading.

In graded granular aggregate mixtures, moisture and volatile contents usually are not highly critical. However, for maximum compaction fine-grained aggregate mixtures should be aerated to the required moisture and volatile content. Proper aeration is reached when the volatile content is reduced to about 50 percent of that contained in the original asphalt and the moisture content does not exceed 2 percent by weight of the total mixture (2 to 5 percent for emulsified asphalt mixtures).

When fine-grained materials are used as a base course that will be surfaced within 30 days, the volatile content of the asphalt should be reduced by aeration to approximately one-third of the original amount.

Experience with the particular mixture being used and trail rolling are of value in determining the proper moisture and volatile contents when test data are not available.

Compacting. Open-graded mixtures may be compacted with steel-wheeled tandem and pneumatic-tired rollers immediately after mixing. The voids in the compacted open-graded mixture will allow the volatiles to evaporate in a reasonable length of time.

After one course has been thoroughly compacted and cured for a minimum period of 72 hours, other courses may be placed on it. Any loose material that will not compact should be wasted.

Good weather is important to the success of a road-mix job. It would be desirable to schedule road-mixing operations when weather conditions are likely to be hot and dry during the work and for a reasonable period of time after the work has been completed.

Crushed-Aggregate Base Course

The material shall consist of gravel, crushed gravel, crushed stone, crushed slag, chert, caliche, burnt culm (red dog), or any combination of these materials uniformly blended to conform to the requirements of the specifications.

Material should be placed by equipment especially manufactured to distribute it in a continuous uniform layer. When more than one layer is required, each layer shall be shaped and compacted before the succeeding layer is placed. The contractor should plan the hauling so that truck traffic is distributed over the entire width of the surface. Compaction should follow the placing operation closely. There are basically two factors which influence the compaction: (1) the moisture content of the material and (2) the compactive effort.

Compaction can be obtained with minimum effort when aggregate is at optimum moisture. Laboratory tests should be obtained to determine optimum moisture content. Water should be added if required in the amount necessary to provide optimum moisture content for compaction.

Equipment used to apply the compactive effort may be any one or a combination of the following:

1. Pneumatic-tired rollers
2. Vibratory rollers

3. Steel-wheeled rollers

4. Pan-type vibrating compactors

It should be the contractor's choice to select the type of equipment most adaptable to the material and work, subject to whatever requirements are specified in the contract.

Rolling should progress gradually from the side to the center, parallel to the centerline. Once the required moisture content and compaction have been achieved, they must be maintained. This can be accomplished by the continuous addition of small amounts of water to replace moisture lost. After the compaction operation, the surface of the top layer should be bladed carefully by a motor grader or an automatic fine-grading machine. The final duty of the inspector is to check the grade and shape of the finished aggregate surface to ensure that the entire surface area adequately conforms to the plan grades and templates.

Records. Document the inspection, construction work, and test results. Record keeping is a very important part of the inspector's work at the plant and on the project. The inspector's observations and measurements are an important part in justifying compliance with the specifications. Because much of the inspector's work is covered by subsequent construction, its results cannot readily be reviewed later. Written reports and records of observations and measurements are usually the only remaining evidence that the work was performed correctly. Emphasis should be placed on recording all portions of this work daily as it is performed. (See Figs. 2.6-2 and 2.6-3.)

The following specific information shall be recorded:

1. Station location of quality control and acceptance tests for compaction and the results thereof

2. Station location of samples for gradation purposes and represented quantity

3. Measurements for progress payment and final payment when applicable

4. Station locations and results of final depth checks

Soil-Cement Base Course

Soil-cement base consists of existing or selected pulverized soil or aggregate; uniformly mixed in place with a measured amount of portland cement and water, compacted to high density, cured, and sealed as the cement hydrates, the mixture becomes a hard, durable paving material. Soil may consist of existing in-place materials, approved selected material, or a combination of these materials, proportioned as directed within the gradation required by the specification.

The subgrade should be prepared and shaped in accordance with the governing specification. Selected soil, if used, should be hauled in and placed to an adequate depth. When this soil is mixed with cement and water and compacted, the procedure will result in the depth, width, and shape required by the typical section.

After the placement of the soil, if imported, the layer should be compacted to the extent that the equipment necessary to distribute the cement and water may be operated over the course. Existing embankment material may be used, in which case it should be determined that the material immediately under the soil-cement stabilized base course is acceptable and is compacted to the required density. If embankment material is used, the design depth of the layer should be loosened, with care being taken to assure that the material immediately under the design depth of the stabilized base course is not disturbed.

The preliminary design for the cement content of the layer is determined by an analysis of the soils available in the area. When the source of the soil is actually established, samples should immediately be obtained for a laboratory to determine the actual cement content and optimum moisture content for the soil. The testing requires approximately 30 days to produce the desired information before mixing may be started.

Usually the soil is analyzed before the award of the contract, and the quantity and rate of application of cement are shown on the plans. However, the engineer may review the above to meet changing soil conditions.

The preconstruction conference should include a discussion of the methods of procedure (see Fig. 2.6-4). The contractor should furnish a method of procedure, including the source of the soil to be used if known at that time, the paving pattern, the method of pulverizing the soil, the distributing of water, mixing, shaping, compacting, curing the layer, and controlling traffic.

When the cement is placed on the soil, the moisture content of the soil should be 2 to 3 percent below its optimum moisture as determined by the laboratory. The soil layer should be loosened to its full depth and thoroughly mixed so that no segregation takes place in the layer.

Tests should be continuously taken on the wetted mixture to ensure that the desired moisture is incorporated in the mixture. At least one set of test cylinders shall be cast for each day of mixing. After all mixing water has been applied, mixing shall continue until a uniform and intimate mixture of soil, cement, and water has been obtained, with a suitable mixture resulting. The percentage of moisture in the mixture should not vary by more than 3 percentage points above or 2 percentage points below the specified optimum, nor should it exceed that quantity which will make

Inspectors Daily Report
FORM HL-442 Rev. (T)

WEST VIRGINIA DEPARTMENT OF HIGHWAYS

Project No.		District	County		Weather		Temp.	Date

Item No.	Pay Item Code No.		Inspector		Reviewing Supervisor Signature	

INSTRUCTIONS: Place a check (√) in the block below for the applicable item of work being performed and inspected.

☐ Embankment   ☐ Drainage   ☐ Structures   ☐ Batch Plant Inspection

☐ Excavation   ☐ Bases   ☐ Seeding & Mulching   ☐ Survey

☐ Clearing & Grubbing   ☐ Pavements   ☐ Compaction Crew   ☐ Other_____

INSTRUCTIONS FOR COMPLETING DAILY REPORTS (Check (√) blocks below included in report)

☐ A.   Designate location and type of work being performed and beginning and ending time of inspection.

☐ B.   List men by classification, type of equipment and hours worked.

☐ C.   List idle equipment and arrival or removal of major equipment on project.

☐ D.   List visitors on project by name, title and organization. Record any instructions or pertinent comments by these visitors.

☐ E.   Record instructions given to contractor and protests, if any.

☐ F.   Record type of embankment material (soil, shale, rock) and lift thickness.

☐ G.   Unsuitable material (reason for removal).

☐ H.   Show arrival of material on project (show type and quantity).

☐ I.   Record CT numbers of material.

☐ J.   Designate location and visible condition of delivered materials on project and system of storage (example—Re-Bars stored above ground and covered).

☐ K.   List samples taken, time when taken and results when available. (Concrete, slump, air, moisture, compaction, etc.).

☐ L.   Calibrate testing equipment when necessary and record results.

☐ M.   Record sufficient data to show that work is being performed in accordance with specifications and that the daily report is an adequate record to document the quantity & quality of materials and workmanship. (For example—in placing pipe, show the number of joints laid, the CT numbers, the excavation performed, compaction tests, etc.).

FIG. 2.6-2   Inspector's daily report (face).

Measurements and quantities of observed work and sketch (measurements to be made to precision as required by applicable code no.)

dividual making measurements or sketch _____ _____
                                                    Signature   Date

FIG. 2.6-2   Inspector's daily report (back).

WEST VIRGINIA
DEPARTMENT OF HIGHWAYS

UNIT WEIGHT AND YIELD OF CONCRETE

PRODUCER_____DATE_____

Test Conducted by_____

Test No.		
Mix Design No.		
Class of Concrete		
Project No.		

Batch Weight in Pounds

(A) Cement		
Water		
Fine Aggregate		
Coarse Aggregate		
(B) Total Weight of Batch		

Weight of Concrete in Pounds Per Cubic Foot

Weight of Container Full of Concrete		
Weight of Container		
(C) Net Weight of Concrete		
(D) Container Factor		
(E) Weight Per Cubic Foot (C X D)		

Batch Volume Produced And Cement Factor

Specified Minimum Cement Factor (cwt/cy)		
(F) Batch Volume Produced (B ÷ E)		
(G) Yield (F ÷ 27)		
Actual Cement Factor (.01A ÷ G) cwt/cy		

Comment: _____

_____

_____

_____

_____

FIG. 2.6-3 Unit weight and yield of concrete.

FORM SC-428	Date
WEST VIRGINIA DEPARTMENT OF HIGHWAYS	
PRE-CONSTRUCTION CONFERENCE NOTICE	Project

| TO | FROM |
| | District Engineer-Assistant District Engineer |

A PRE-CONSTRUCTION CONFERENCE is being scheduled for the above mentioned project on the _____

day of _____ 19 ___ at _____ for ___ o'clock ___ M.
It will be appreciated if you will have made the following preparations prior to this
conference:

1. A preliminary plan and schedule of contract operations, utilizing network scheduling, such as PERT, CPM, or any comparable system.

2. Be prepared to outline sequence of operations such as Traffic Control, Utilities, Etc., so that possible conflictions will be recognized and discussed.

3. A list of the various types of equipment to be used in the construction stages.

4. Any questions arising from your study of plans and specifications and any problems which might be anticipated.

5. A letter with the names and responsibilities of your project personnel including (A) the designation of the Registered Professional Engineer supervising the Construction Layout Stakes' item, his West Virginia Registration Number, Resume of Experience and other States in which he has effected Professional Registration Status; (B) request for approval of project superintendent, with a resume of his experience; (C) designation of EEO Officer and (D) Representative(s) authorized to sign project documents.

6. Subcontract Forms HL-403, six (6) copies, if applicable, with attachment showing uncompleted workload of proposed Subcontractor(s).

7. Contractors Material Report, Form HL-454, three (3) copies, which is most important due to procedures necessary for the Materials Control, Soil and Testing Division to be of the most help in expediting your job. This particularly applies to pre-testing of materials.

8. Safety program including name of Project Safety Supervisor as well as Company Safety Officer. Name and phone number of Project Traffic Control person.

9. Knowledge and understanding of all labor and employment forms, along with necessary affidavits, required during life of contract.

10. Submission of On The Job Training Program in compliance with the specifications.

11. Quality control plans for asphaltic concrete, Portland cement concrete, embankment, base course and pollution control, when applicable.

The District Office will be glad to cooperate and provide assistance on any of the above in order that the Conference will be a success. We trust we will receive your cooperation in this matter and that a good and proper beginning will lead to a successful conclusion of this contract.

FIG. 2.6-4   Preconstruction-conference notice.

the mixture unstable during compaction and finishing. The color of the mixture will be predominantly the color of the aggregate.

Soil cement as compacted and finished should contain sufficient moisture for adequate cement hydration. A moisture-retaining cover is placed over the soil cement as soon as possible to retain moisture and permit cement to hydrate. In most cases bituminous material is used, but waterproof paper, moist sand, or dirt would be satisfactory.

FLEXIBLE PAVEMENTS

General.　Flexible pavements are constructed of various grades and mixtures of bituminous materials and of tar. With the ever-decreasing supply of crude oil for producing bituminous material and the increasing cost to purchase these materials, different additives, extenders, and substitutes are being incorporated in the flexible-pavement-construction process. Other ingredients are graded coarse aggregate, graded fine aggregate, and mineral filler, which are either supplied to the base through an aggregate spreader, mechanically mixed on the roadway, or mixed in a plant.

The project engineer or project inspector, of course, must ensure that the subgrade, subbase, and aggregate or stabilized base (see subsection "Subbases and Base Courses") have met all specified requirements to provide the best available foundation for the flexible pavement. Although the very nature of flexible pavement permits some deflection of the base, too much deflection often will reduce the design life of the pavement.

Inspector's Equipment.　Equipment should include the following:

Complete set of approved plans, specifications, and special provisions

Report forms, sample tags, cartons, cans, jars, and sacks for processing samples

Shovels, buckets, pans, and metal dipper for sampling

Thermometers to check both liquid bituminous material and plant-mixed material

Putty knife, calibrated rod, or other penetrating device to check the pavement depth

6-ft (1.8-m) rules, 50-ft (15-m) tape, and hand level

Survey stakes to set distance markers (stations) for application control

Specification straightedges to check joints and pavement-surface tolerances

Template or other devices for checking crown and/or cross slopes

Nuclear gauge or other density-measuring instrument

Pencils, field books, scratch paper, pocket calculator, etc., for documentation and checking application rates

If you are required also to perform field testing, you will need the following equipment:

Portable stove and fuel

Penetrometer and needles

Sample extractor, Marshall testing machine, molds, and tamper

Set of screens or sieves of the required sizes and wire brush for cleaning

Sample splitter and pans

Centrifuge

Supply of solvent for washing bituminous-concrete samples and cleaning testing equipment

One balance reading to 500 g and one balance or scale of 25-lb (11.3-kg) capacity, each with weights and pans

Preconstruction Procedures. The liquid bituminous material and aggregates usually are pretested and approved prior to arriving at the plant or jobsite. This approval should be indicated by a tag, certification, or other documentation accompanying each delivery. Material received without this documentation should not be used until it has been sampled, tested, and approved.

The testing laboratory will furnish you with the design-mix formula for high-type (bituminous-concrete) pavements. Observe the type of bituminous material, i.e., asphalt cement, cutback asphalt, asphalt emulsion, or tar, furnished by the contractor. This will govern the percentage to be used in the mix or the application rate and temperature.

On new construction or reconstruction, the pavement will be placed on a uniformly fine-graded aggregate base; however, when resurfacing an existing roadway, the present surface usually will have to be leveled and perhaps patched. If patching or leveling is required, you will have to make a prepaving survey to locate and mark the areas to be patched and leveled. The marking is accomplished by spray-painting the limits of the affected areas or by noting the areas by stations from the survey stakes, which have been placed earlier.

The paving equipment should be given a cursory inspection to discover any broken or contaminated parts, misalignments, and undersized or oversized features. This equipment consists of the many components of mixing plants, including bins, conveyors, screens, hoppers, dryers, scales, trucks, distributors, spreaders, brooms, paving machines, and rollers. The inspection will reveal the most evident conditions that would produce an unacceptable product. A quality finished product is what is being purchased, and any deviation from specified results may mean repairing, adjusting, or removing and replacing any equipment producing nonconforming results.

With increasing traffic volumes and speeds, everyone associated with a paving project must be keenly aware of the safety of the motorist and the workers. (See Chap. 1.2.) Traffic control, including adequate signing, cones, barricades, warning lights, and flaggers, must be in place before any work commences at the beginning of the day. Likewise, any traffic control that does not apply to the work being performed at this exact time, at night or on weekends, must be covered or removed. This gives the signing, etc., greater credibility when it is in effect.

Prime Coats.   These coats are applied to aggregate-base surfaces, with and without cover aggregates, to penetrate and seal the surface of the base and to provide some bond between the base and the bottom layer of pavement material. Be sure that the base is properly compacted and fine-graded to template, including width, elevation, and cross section.

The surface should be free of loose material. A slightly moist surface is better than a dry or dusty one. Cutback asphalts, asphalt emulsions, and lightweight tars are used for priming. Owing to environmental precautions, cutback asphalts are no longer permitted in some localities since the volatile distillates tend to accumulate in the atmosphere during evaporation.

Calibrate the distributor to determine the truck velocity for different application rates. The amount of bituminous material to be applied varies between 0.25 gal/yd^2 (1.13L/m^2) for very tight surfaces and 0.60 gal/yd^2 (2.72L/m^2) for loose surfaces.

See subsection "Hot-Laid Bituminous Concrete" for truck scale requirements.

The application temperature of the bitumen should be between 50°F (10°C) and 150°F (65.5°C) for cutback material but generally near the higher limit and between 75°F (23.9°C) and 140°F (60°C) for emulsions but generally nearer the lower limit. You will have to calculate the net volume of bitumen used by multiplying the volume used at the application temperature by a conversion factor to determine the volume to be paid for at 60°F. The appropriate conversion factor may be obtained from the contract specifications or an asphalt handbook. Approximate factors are 0.00034 for cutbacks and 0.00025 for emulsions. Subtract 60°F (15.5°C) from the application temperature, and multiply this difference by the approximate factor. Subtract this answer from 1.00000. Now multiply the difference by the gallons (1 gal = 3.785 L) applied to obtain the pay quantity.

Cover aggregate may be required to prevent migration of the bitumen or to permit traffic to travel on the prime coat while it is curing. The cover aggregate is generally AASHTO No. 8 coarse aggregate [⅜ in (9.525 mm) to No. 8 sieve)]. If cover aggregate is applied, it may need to be broomed and must be rolled, preferably with a pneumatic-tired roller, to seal the aggregate in the asphalt.

Most specifications will not permit applying bituminous material when the base temperature is less than 50°F (10°C), or when it is wet, foggy, or raining.

The curing period must be adequate to permit the evaporation of the distillates or water, or approximately 48 hours.

Tack Coat. This coat is applied to existing pavements or to very tight bases such as stabilized base. Application procedures are the same for the prime coat except as follows. The application rate of bitumen is very light [0.07 to 0.15 gal/yd^2 (0.32 to 0.68 L/m^2)]; therefore, the distributor must travel at a very fast speed or use a hand spray hose with a fog nozzle.

Asphalt emulsions are the preferred bituminous material since they "break" or cure faster than cutback asphalts. These emulsions can also be diluted up to 50 percent with water, which helps to keep the amount of bitumen applied at the lower rate. Observe temperature and weather requirements.

Cover aggregates are seldom used since the new pavement is placed while the existing surface is tacky or sticky.

Surface Treatment. This treatment is applied on base material or on existing surfaces. It may be placed in single or multiple courses.

Base material must be primed before placing a surface treatment. (See the necessary preparation procedures and application requirements in the subsection "Prime Coat.") Existing surfaces need not have a tack coat, although some specifications may require it. Potholes should be patched and depressions leveled well in advance of placing the surface treatment. This waiting period, preferably several days, will permit the curing of the deeper patches.

The key equipment for this work is the asphalt pressure distributor and the aggregate spreader. Also needed are a broom and a pneumatic-tired or steel-wheeled tandem roller. Be sure that the distributor is cleaned if a dissimilar material was used previously. Also be sure that each spray nozzle is clean and produces a uniform fan spray with no overlapping or with a double or triple lap. This is absolutely vital to eliminate bare spots (streaks) or rich (fat) areas. A tachometer visible to the driver is useful to maintain the correct speed of the distributor to produce the specified rate of application.

The bituminous application rate is similar to that of prime coat. You may be expected to determine the rate to be used. A guide to use at the beginning is 18 gal/ton (75.14 L/t) of aggregate to be spread, or 0.01 gal/lb (0.08 L/kg) of aggregate to be spread. Multiply 0.01 (0.08) by the pounds per square yard (kilograms per square meter) of aggregate to be applied to obtain the gallons per square yard (liters per square meter) of bituminous material. After the first application of bituminous material and aggregate it will be necessary to adjust the rate of bituminous material to provide just enough bitumen to "wet" or adhere to the bottom two-thirds or three-fourths of the larger particles.

Observe temperature and weather requirements.

Formulas are available to determine application rates of bituminous material and aggregate. These rates are based on the gradation of the aggregate. After the source of aggregate is known or the material has been delivered to the project, samples can be sent to the laboratory for tests and calculations.

The cover aggregate must be applied immediately after the bituminous material. It takes 1 minute or less for the temperature of the bituminous material to drop to a point at which the aggregate will not adhere properly. The aggregate must be applied ahead of the spreader or truck tires. (See subsection "Hot-Laid Bituminous Concrete" for truck scale requirements.)

The specifications may require a particular application rate or a calculation of the application rate on the basis of the actual gradation of the aggregate. This was discussed earlier in determining the application rate for bituminous material.

Succeeding courses of bituminous material and aggregate may be used in what is called *double-surface treatment* or *multiple-surface treatment*. The succeeding courses are used to fill the voids of the underlying course. The particle size of the second course is approximately half the size of the first course so as to perform the intended function of filling the voids and not necessarily increasing the thickness of the surface treatment.

The particle size of the first course usually determines the nomimal thickness of the surface treatment regardless of the number of additional courses. The plans or specifications will prescribe the thickness by calling for a certain size of aggregate, say, AASHTO No. 8, which will produce a thickness of approximately ⅜ in (9.525 mm), or No. 7, which will produce a thickness of approximately ¾ in (19.05 mm). The next course or two will serve only to fill the voids and seal or smooth the surface. Of course, successive applications of the same particle sizes will eventually build up a thicker surface if this is desired.

Rolling must immediately follow the spreading of aggregate. This rolling is intended to set or position the aggregate particles properly into the bitumen more than to compact the aggregate. Drag brooming or wire-mesh dragging may be necessary along with rolling to help achieve the set. Because the use of brooms or drags is somewhat controversial, be certain that the specifications allow it.

Penetration Macadam. This pavement is of a slightly higher type than surface treatment, and its use can achieve much thicker courses. Its construction differs from surface treatment in that the aggregate is placed before the bituminous material; therefore, the bituminous material must be capable of coating the aggregate from top to bottom.

To achieve the thicker courses, the first layer may use aggregate up to 4 in (101.6 mm) in size, although 3 in (76.2 mm) is a more practical top size. Be sure to avoid an excessive amount of $-\frac{1}{2}$-in (-12.7-mm) aggregate, fine aggregate, and dust in the layer. This material will prevent the bituminous material from penetrating.

The base should be prepared as described in the subsection "Prime Coat" and "Surface Treatment." It should then be primed. Existing pavements should be patched or leveled and tacked before beginning the penetration macadam.

To prevent lateral displacement of the macadam aggregate during rolling, the shoulders must be built up and compacted to a strength sufficient to serve as a containing form.

Be sure that the aggregate and bitumen have been pretested and approved. This precaution also helps to determine the proper application rates.

Observe temperature and weather specifications. Cool aggregates cause the bituminous material to congeal before it can thoroughly penetrate the aggregate. The minimum aggregate or ambient temperature is generally 50°F (10°C).

The aggregate should be placed with a mechanical spreader, although tailgating and blade graders are used. After the aggregate has been placed, some handwork with rakes or screed boards may be needed to true the surface. High spots and depressions must be eliminated by manipulating the coarse aggregate, not by adding finer aggregate. Pockets of fine aggregate or dust must be removed and replaced with properly graded coarse aggregate.

Rolling will compact and key the aggregate and assist in trueing the surface. The process of rolling macadam aggregate is very sensitive and must be watched carefully. Overrolling will fracture or round the aggregate particles and generate additional dust. Begin rolling at the outer edges and progress to the center, being careful to overlay the previous wheel path properly in straight lines. Avoid unnecessary reversing of the roller.

Bituminous material is applied in much the same way as the prime coat or surface treatment. The specifications will generally set forth an application rate for the bituminous material. If not, the material application rate can be estimated by multiplying the application rate of the first course of aggregate by 0.005 (0.4). This will provide the gallons per square yard (liters per square meter). Visual inspection will then determine whether or not the application was sufficient to penetrate the aggregate thoroughly. Adjust the application rate accordingly.

The second layer of aggregate must be spread immediately after the bituminous material. This layer is composed of aggregate approximately one-half the size of the first-layer aggregate and is intended to fill the voids of the larger aggregate.

Begin rolling immediately after spreading the second layer of aggregate, preferably with a pneumatic-tired roller. The rolling will position or "key" the aggregate into the voids and embed it in the hot bitumen. Broom or wire-mesh dragging may help to distribute this aggregate if the specifications permit dragging.

Place a second application of the bituminous material, which will penetrate and coat the second layer of aggregate. If the specifications do not give the application rate, it can be estimated by multiplying the pounds per square yard (kilograms per square meter) of aggregate actually placed in the second layer by 0.01 (0.08). This will provide the approximate application rate of bituminous material in gallons per square yard (liters per square meter). Adjustments may be necessary.

A third course of aggregate is applied before the bituminous material cools. This layer of aggregate, which is composed of particles approximately one-half the size of those of the second layer, will further fill the voids and begin to smooth the riding surface. Roll and drag if necessary.

Bituminous material is then applied for the third time. The approximate application rate will be 0.01 times the application rate of the previous layer of aggregate, which is no larger than the previous layer. This provides the final sealing and smoothing; drag, if necessary, and roll. This rolling can be carried out with a pneumatic-tired roller or a steel-wheeled roller. Be sure that all wheel marks are eliminated.

The pay quantity of bituminous material must be adjusted for temperature as described in the subsection "Prime Coat."

Road Mix.   Road mix utilizes liquid bituminous material, i.e., cutbacks or emulsions, and aggregate similar to that used in surface treatments, but there are two major differences. In road-mix operations the bitumen and aggregate are mixed together before final placing rather than being placed in two separate applications, and thicker surfaces are obtained in single courses.

Mixing is achieved with motor graders or special equipment, i.e., pulvimixers or rotary tillers and travel plants.

The contractor may elect or request to use a stationary plant and haul the mix to the project site. If so, mixing temperatures may need to be higher than for road mixing.

The bitumen and aggregate should arrive at the project site preapproved. Remember to check the approval and take a sample for laboratory testing if necessary. (See Table 2.6-1.)

Frequently, aggregates already in place as part of the existing roadbed may be used. If the existing aggregates are deficient in quality or quantity, however, new aggregate from an outside source may be hauled to the roadbed and blended with the existing aggregates.

Secure samples of the aggregates from the roadbed or the proposed outside sources to assure an ample supply of specification material, and submit these samples to the laboratory to complete a preliminary design. The results of these tests should be used to specify the characteristics of the aggregates and the type, grade, and estimated amount of the bituminous material. When construction begins, additional samples should be secured to check conformance with the preliminary design and with the governing specifications.

The bituminous material for this type of construction must necessarily be a liquid that will remain fluid at air temperature sufficiently long to permit completion of construction operations. The materials ordinarily used are cutback asphalts, emulsified asphalts, and tars. The type and grade of the material to be used on any project is generally determined by the characteristics of the aggregate, type of road-mixing equipment to be used, and climatic conditions.

The three principal types of travel mixers used in road construction are (1) the travel-plant mixer that receives the aggregate into a hopper from trucks, mixes it with bituminous material, and spreads the mixture, all in one pass of the machine; (2) the travel-plant mixer that takes the aggregate from a windrow, mixes it with bituminous material, and deposits the mixture behind the mixer in a windrow; and (3) the rotary pulverizer-type mixer with transverse shafts that mixes the bituminous material and aggregate with revolving tines under a hood.

The mixing mechanism of the mixer should be examined daily for excessive wear and broken or defective parts. The pressure pump and meter that deliver the bituminous material from the tank truck to the spray bar on travel mixes should be accurately calibrated to deliver the percentage of bituminous material specified for the mixture.

The motor grader or graders should be heavy enough to windrow, mix, and spread the material properly without lateral sliding or wheel spinning. The blade must be reasonably sharp, and the control unit should be capable of holding the blade to an established line and grade.

The rollers should be of the size and type specified for the project. On pneumatic-tired rollers all tires must be of equal size and equally inflated. Tire pressures and the loading of the roller may be varied to produce ground-contact pressures desirable for the particular mixture. Steel-wheeled rollers should be checked for excessive play in the steering and driving mechanisms, flat spots on wheels, and spray bars operating properly with wetting mats in satisfactory condition.

See the subsection "Hot-Laid Bituminous Concrete" for truck scale requirements.

Other equipment such as bituminous storage tanks, bituminous heaters, water trucks, disk harrows, tractors, power brooms, windrow sizers, and other auxiliary equipment may be required for use on the project.

The weather is critical in a road-mix operation. It should be hot and dry to facilitate evaporation of moisture and volatiles from the mixture. Cool or humid conditions will require extra manipulations of the mixture to remove the moisture and volatiles. Observe specified temperatures and weather requirements.

When the aggregate is to be blended with material from the existing road surface, the process is the same as in the preceding case except that, following the scarifying of the reshaped roadbed to the required depth, the new aggregate should be spread over the loosened existing aggregate in the required amount. The two types of aggregate should then be thoroughly blended by a travel mixer or by harrowing and blading, after which all the aggregate should be bladed to the side and the understratum prepared as a foundation, as in the preceding case.

When all-new aggregate is to be used in the mixture, it is necessary only to shape and compact the existing road surface to receive the mat and apply a prime coat if specified. If more than one new aggregate is to be used, these aggregates should be placed on the prepared surface in the required amount and blended as in the preceding case. Usually, one material is windrowed and spread to the width desired, and then one or more new aggregates are added onto this aggregate until the required amount of material is in place and ready for blending operations. If the construction is a retread mat over an existing hard-surface pavement, some patching of the pavement may be necessary and the application of a tack coat will be desirable.

The aggregate, whether new, blended, or salvaged from the existing road, should be bladed into a windrow along the center or one side of the roadbed. The cross-sectional area should then be measured, the volume computed, and the required amount of bitumen determined.

Immediately prior to applying bitumen, the aggregate should be checked for moisture. The recommended maximum moisture content at this time is 2 percent. If the aggregate is wet, it should be turned by blades, disk harrows, or a rotary travel mixer or otherwise aerated until the moisture content is reduced to 2 percent or less.

If the traveling-plant method of mixing is to be used, the aggregate should be left in the windrow from which it will be picked up by the machine, fed continuously through the plant, mixed with bitumen, and redeposited in a windrow behind the machine ready for aerating, spreading, and compacting. In the mixing machine the desired proportions are obtained automatically through devices which measure both the aggregate and the bitumen into the mixing chamber, where they are processed to uniformity and forced out of the rear in a continuous stream by the twin pugmill-type mixer. Another traveling-plant method of mixing is to receive the aggregate in a hopper from the haul trucks, feed from this hopper continuously through the plant, mix with bitumen, and deposit the mixture behind the machine to the grade and cross section prescribed for that course.

When the mixing is to be performed on the roadbed rather than by a traveling plant, the windrowed aggregate should be spread smoothly and uniformly over part of the roadbed to a width convenient for the application of bitumen. The bituminous material should then be sprayed over the aggregate in three separate applications of approximately 0.5 gal/yd^2 (2.26 L/m^2) each. Each application should be followed immediately by partial mixing with blades, disk harrows, a rotary travel mixer, or other suitable equipment until as little free bituminous material as possible is left. The intervals between applications depend upon the results of the partial mixing.

After the third application of bitumen and partial mixing have been completed, the entire mass should be windrowed and then bladed alternately from one side of the roadbed to the other, or otherwise manipulated by means which will produce equivalent results, until all particles of aggregate are coated with the bituminous material and the whole mass has a uniform color. During mixing, attention should be paid to the vertical and horizontal angles of the moldboard of the motor grader. This board should be adjusted so that the material is completely rolled when the windrow is manipulated. Also, during the mixing and the aerating and spreading operations to follow, care should be taken to avoid cutting into the earth or other extraneous matter. When specified, the mixing process shall be confined to part of the width or area of the road so as to allow traffic to pass.

Either method of mixing will produce satisfactory results, but the traveling-plant method has the following advantages: (1) more accurate control of bitumen content is possible, (2) heavier grades of bituminous material can be used, (3) a more nearly uniform thickness can be obtained, (4) delays caused by inclement weather will be shorter, and (5) the likelihood of partially mixed material getting wet is reduced.

If when the mixing process has been substantially completed, the mixture shows an excess, deficiency, or uneven distribution of bituminous material, the unsatisfactory condition should be corrected by the addition of the required aggregate or bituminous material and then remixing. The final bituminous content should be 4 to 6 percent by weight.

If, for some reason, mixing operations are not completed before the end of the day's work or if the operation is interrupted by weather conditions or otherwise, all loose material should be bladed into a windrow, whether mixing is completed or not, and retained in a windrow until operations are resumed.

Before the mixed material is spread on the road for compacting and finishing, it should be checked for moisture content and the amount of the volatile portion of the bituminous material remaining in the mixture. If the moisture content exceeds the maximum allowable for aggregate, the mixture should be aerated sufficiently by manipulation to remove the excess water.

The volatile portion of the bituminous material serves no useful purpose after the mixture has been prepared and placed, and it must be removed if the material is to develop the natural cementing properties of which it is capable and the expected mixture stability. The need to dissipate volatile material after the mixture has been compacted should be eliminated as far as possible before compaction begins. This should be accomplished by continued manipulation until the mixture is just sufficiently workable to permit satisfactory placing.

When the mixture is ready for placing, the windrowed mixture should be moved to one side of the centerline. Approximately one-half of the windrowed material is then split from this windrow, and the spreading process begins with the blade carrying this windrow across the centerline to the edge and back to the remaining half of windrowed material. This material should not be expended in this operation. The remaining material is then bladed to the other edge and back. Sufficient material should be left to continue across the centerline to the first edge and then back across the centerline to the second edge, completing the laying operation. A pneumatic roller of the size and type specified should begin rolling right behind the motor grader on the first spreading pass and continue to roll until blading has been completed. This procedure will compact the mixture from the bottom up, mostly eliminating grader tire marks from the surface. The finish rolling should be completed by a steel-wheeled roller of the size and type specified. Any loose material that will not compact should be wasted over the side. As a part of final finishing, the edges should be trimmed to neat lines and the surface straightedged in accordance with the governing specifications.

After one course has been compacted and cured, other courses, as required by the plans, may be placed on it. This operation should be repeated as many times as necessary to bring the road to the cross section and the grade shown on the plans.

No uncompacted mixture should be allowed to remain spread on the roadbed overnight or until resumption of operations following suspensions due to weather or other conditions. To avoid contamination, increase in moisture content, or damage by traffic, such loose material should be bladed into a windrow at the end of each day's work and at the beginning of any interruption and retained there until operations are resumed.

A seal coat or surface treatment may be specified, but the road mix must first be thoroughly cured.

Hot-Laid Bituminous Concrete. Hot-laid bituminous concrete is the highest type of bituminous base or pavement. It is composed of graded coarse aggregate, graded fine aggregate (passing a No. 8 sieve), mineral filler (passing a No. 200 sieve), and asphalt cement, asphalt emulsion, or tar, mixed mechanically in a plant. Samples of these materials must be submitted to the laboratory, where a job- or plant-mix formula will be designed. Only one plant formula will be designed for these materials and the plant (see Figs. 2.6-1 and 2.6-5).

If the producer proposes to change the source of aggregate used in the mix or if production problems occur to the extent that the plant-mix formula cannot be met by plant adjustments, a revision will be necessary. Once the correct amount of bituminous material has been set for the paving mixture, the gradation of the aggregate must be held as constant as possible.

Bituminous concrete usually contains asphalt cement rather than cutback asphalt or asphalt emulsion. The asphalt cement is generally graded by viscosity. The softer asphalt cement has a viscosity grade designation of AC-5, and the harder asphalt cement has a designation of AC-40. Most highway pavements use AC-10 or AC-20. When tar is specified, the heavier grade, say, RT-12, is generally used.

The harder grades of asphalt cement make more stable mixtures which are less likely to be pushed out of place by traffic. Harder-grade asphalt is used for sheet asphalt and other types of pavements where additional stability is necessary. In an asphaltic-concrete pavement classed as *sheet asphalt,* less than about 30 percent of the mixture consists of aggregate particles 1¾ in (44.45 mm) in size or larger. Such a mixture usually must

PLANT MIX FORMULA FOR
BITUMINOUS CONCRETE MIXTURES

THE WEST VIRGINIA DEPARTMENT OF HIGHWAYS
MATERIALS CONTROL, SOIL AND TESTING DIVISION
312 MICHIGAN AVENUE
CHARLESTON, WEST VIRGINIA

REPORT NO. _____   BITUM. CONC. MIXTURE TYPE _____

DATE APPROVED _____   PLANT NO. _____

PRODUCER _____,   PLANT LOCATION _____

COARSE AGGREGATE TYPE _____   FINE AGGREGATE TYPE _____

COARSE AGGREGATE SOURCE _____   FINE AGGREGATE SOURCE _____

MINERAL FILLER TYPE (IF NEEDED) _____   PLANT MAKE AND TYPE _____

MINERAL FILLER SOURCE _____

SIEVE SIZE	PROPOSED PLANT MIX FORMULA (THIS COLUMN TO BE COMPLETED BY THE PRODUCER)	APPROVED PLANT MIX FORMULA (THIS COLUMN TO BE COMPLETED BY M.C.S. & T. DIV)	ALLOWABLE PLANT MIX TOLERANCE ±
% Passing 2"			
% Passing 1 1/2"			
% Passing 1"			
% Passing 3/4"			
% Passing 1/2"			
% Passing 3/8"			
% Passing 4			
% Passing 8			
% Passing 16			
% Passing 50			
% Passing 200			
% Asphalt Cement			
Temp °F of Completed Mix			
REMARKS:			

FIG. 2.6-5   Plant-mix formula for bituminous-concrete mixtures.

2.6.34

be made with a harder asphalt cement because the mix lacks the stability furnished by the interlocking of larger aggregate particles.

The asphalt cement supplied to a mixing plant must be checked frequently to make sure that it is of the grade used in the design of the mixture and specified for the particular project. When a test sample of asphalt cement is obtained at a batch plant, it must be taken either at the point where the asphalt enters the weighing device or from the circulating line that carries the asphalt from a storage tank to the weighing device and back to the storage tank.

Aggregates used in asphaltic concrete must be stockpiled properly to minimize segregation (Fig. 2.6-6). Each stockpile must be formed on a hard, tight base which is graded to drain. Unless the stockpiles are widely separated, bulkheads are required between them to prevent intermingling. Each pile must be built up in layers which are not more than 3 ft (0.9 m) thick.

The aggregate is placed in cold bins (Fig. 2.6-7), from which it is blended so that the percentage of each size in the bituminous-concrete mixture falls within the limits of the job-mix formula. To obtain the proper blend, the gates or other controls on the cold feed must be set properly.

When checking the adjustment of the cold feed, two rates of feeding are important. One rate is the total flow of aggregate through the feed. This rate determines the rate at which the mixture can be produced by the plant. For instance, when the aggregates are wet, as after a heavy rain, and cannot be dried easily, the total flow must be kept below the capacity of the dryer. The other rate is called *proportioned flow*. The different sizes of aggregates must be fed to the mixer in the proportions called for by the job-mix formula. The plant screens control the gradation and assure the uniformity of the materials in each hot bin.

From the cold feed the aggregate is elevated to the dryer (Fig. 2.6-8),

FIG. 2.6-6 Separate stockpiles to prevent intermingling of different aggregate sizes.

FIG. 2.6-7   Cold bins with gates and conveyors to blend aggregate.

FIG. 2.6-8   Aggregates elevated to the drying drum.

where it is heated and dried to the required temperature and moisture content. After passing through the dryer, the heated aggregate and the collected dust are lifted by the hot elevator to the top of the plant. There the aggregate is separated into various sizes by the plant screens. Each size goes to a separate bin.

Dryer−drum mixers are becoming more widely used. They utilize a drying drum to perform also the mixing of bituminous material with the aggregate. This process eliminates hot-aggregate bins and the mixing unit of a batch plant. Dryer−drum mixers can also be modified to receive recycled asphalt pavement near the midpoint of the mixing drum, where the old asphalt is not directly exposed to the drying flame. (See Fig. 2.6-9.)

Dust collectors (Fig. 2.6-10) serve a twofold purpose: (1) to reduce the amount of pollution going into the atmosphere during plant operation and (2) to collect and incorporate the dust into the asphalt mix. New plants or newly relocated plants are required to install baghouses for the collection of dust. Baghouses serve the same function as dust collectors, but they are more sophisticated and do a better job of collecting free dust and channeling it into the mix. As far as the mix is concerned, the most important function of either system is to incorporate the dust uniformly into the finished product.

FIG. 2.6-9 Dryer−drum mixer modified to add recycled pavement near the midpoint of the drum.

FIG. 2.6-10   A dust-collecting unit.

Many modern hot-mix asphalt plants are equipped with surge or storage bins (Fig. 2.6-11). A surge bin is a bin connected to the pugmill by a conveying system intended to hold the mix for relatively short periods. Generally, it is not insulated because the holding time is expected to be only 2 or 3 hours. A storage bin is similar to a surge bin except that it is heated and insulated because it is intended for longer storage periods. Frequently, inert gases and additives such as silicone are used to regulate the rate of hardening during storage. Both surge and storage bins discharge by gravity to trucks through gates in the bottom on the bin (Fig. 2.6-12).

Hot-laid bituminous concrete is placed on any of the types of stabilized or nonstabilized bases or on existing pavement. The base or pavement should be primed or tacked as the case dictates (Fig. 2.6-13).

Bituminous concrete is placed in varying thicknesses from approximately ½ in (12.7 mm) up to 6 in (152.4 mm) or more. Generally, a bituminous-concrete base course in one or more layers is placed, followed by a wearing course. On existing pavements, a patching and leveling course may be necessary. In this situation, you have to locate and identify the areas to be patched or leveled.

FIG. 2.6-11 Surge or storage silos.

FIG. 2.6-12 Loading truck from a storage bin. Note the insulation between the ribs of the truck bed and covering material rolled above the cab.

FIG. 2.6-13   Existing pavement tacked ahead of the paving operation.

Truck scales are very important in determining the pay quantity of a material such as bituminous concrete. Check the scales for:

1. Seal of approval by the state department of weights and measures
2. Zero balance and free of unnecessary debris on the platform
3. Complete freedom of movement of pivot points and beams
4. 50-lb (22.7-kg) test weights available for spot-checking scale accuracy

Many agencies require automatic electronic digital-reading scales which produce a printed record of the weighing showing the gross, tare, and net weights and the time, date, truck identification, project number, and other desired information. (See Fig. 2.6-14.)

Truck beds must be insulated to prevent the loss of heat during transportation. They should also have provision for covering the load with tarpaulins. Check for accumulated material in the bottom and corners of the bed. The beds can be cleaned with a detergent solution or light oil. Avoid excess use or accumulation in the bed.

FIG. 2.6-14   Digital-reading scales with an automatically printed ticket.

A paving machine is capable of receiving the mix in a hopper, spreading, screeding, and lightly compacting the material, and pushing the unloading truck. (See Figs. 2.6-15 and 2.6-16.) Adjustment and operation of the screed are perhaps the most important feature of the paver. Check the screed and tamper bar for warping and wearing. The screed heater must be in good working condition, and the screed height-adjustment mechanism must be capable of producing and holding the desired material thickness.

Pavement alignment and grade are controlled either manually or automatically. Manual control is achieved by laying a string line at least 500 ft (152 m) ahead of the paver and a few inches off the pavement edge (1 in = 25.4 mm). The paver operator then uses the string as a guide. Material thickness is controlled by turning the screed adjustment up or down and measuring the thickness by penetrating the material with a putty knife or small-diameter [± $\frac{3}{16}$-in (± 4.762-mm)] rod. Automatic control is achieved by installing a string or wire line at a determined distance above the pavement grade and outside the pavement edge. The paving machine is equipped with sensing devices which travel along the wire and automatically adjust the direction of the paver and the height of the screed.

Observe the mix as it is being delivered and deposited in the paver. Look for stripping (incomplete coating) of the aggregate, segregation, nonuniform mixing, incorrect temperatures, slumping, and contamination. Material should not accumulate on the sides of the hopper, on the gates, or at the ends of the screed.

FIG. 2.6-15   Loading mix into the hopper of a paving machine.

FIG. 2.6-16   Spreading and screeding mix with a paving machine.

Compaction equipment includes steel-wheeled, pneumatic-tired, and vibratory rollers. All three types would normally be permitted. A three-wheel steel-wheeled roller is generally used for initial or breakdown rolling and "pinching" or rolling longitudinal and transverse joints. Final compaction is obtained with two-axle or three-axle tandem steel and pneumatic-tired rollers with and without vibratory action (see Fig. 2.6-17).

The timing of rolling and final compaction is critical, as there is a

FIG. **2.6-17**   Steel-wheeled vibratory roller.

temperature "window" for each type of mix and asphalt that produces maximum density. The minimum temperature at the time of final compaction varies from 175°F (79.4°C) to 225°F (107.2°C). Check the project specifications. A general rule is not to exceed 10 to 20 minutes between placing and final rolling. Rolling must be completed more quickly at cool temperatures.

In summary, the field inspector has the following responsibilities:

1. Areas for patch and leveling shall be designated. The roadway shall be marked or staked out.

2. The application rate of the tack or prime coat shall be checked. The surface should be covered uniformly, without running.

3. Potholes shall be patched according to typical sections.

4. Cold-mix or winter-grade patching shall be removed.

5. The condition of and adjustments for paving machines and rollers shall be checked.

6. Joints with existing asphalt pavements shall be properly heeled in.

7. Longitudinal joints shall be raked and compacted properly.

8. Rolling operations and sequences shall be as established for density requirements.

9. The mat behind the paver shall be constantly inspected for nonuniformity and for proper finishing operations.

10. Asphalt-concrete temperatures shall be constantly checked and recorded prior to lay-down and finishing operations.

11. The rate of application shall be constantly checked to assure that the thickness placed is as directed on the typical section. The rate shall be recorded every 1000 ft (305 m) or a minimum of 3 times per day. If, owing to field conditions, additional material is required, locations and application shall be recorded, as well as reasons for the additional material. The application rate for the day's production shall be recorded.

12. Results of testing shall be recorded.

13. When paving is permitted beyond seasonal limitations, record the air temperature, base temperature, and weather conditions prior to the start of paving each day and when noticeable changes occur.

14. Be aware of the need for proper traffic-control devices, flaggers, etc.

Recycling. Recycling existing bituminous-concrete pavement may be permitted. The mixing plant must be modified (Fig. 2.6-9) to add the recycled pavement in proper proportions and at the proper time. You must watch for excessive fines created by combining the old aggregate with the new aggregate. Overheating the old asphalt cement also tends to cause environmental problems.

Samples of the old bituminous concrete (Fig. 2.6-18) must be used with the virgin materials to design a plant-mix formula. After the proper plant modifications and mix design, the remaining plant and road operations are essentially like conventional methods.

Sulfur-Extended Asphalt. Sulfur-extended asphalt (SEA) uses sulfur to replace a portion of the asphalt cement, thus conserving the supply of crude oil. Sulfur is used to replace 20 to 30 percent by volume of the asphalt binder. Higher substitution values may be used, but such a mix will become sensitive to compaction temperatures.

The sulfur and asphalt may be added separately to the hot aggregates in the mixing unit, or provisions must be made at the plant to blend the hot sulfur and hot asphalt prior to introducing the SEA to the mix. Sulfur-storage tanks must be thoroughly cleaned of all asphalt residue to prevent the formation of toxic hydrogen sulfide gas. Likewise, all sulfur residue must be cleaned out before refilling with asphalt. Dome and vent pipes must be open to prevent trapping any gas formed.

Mixing is performed in the conventional manner, keeping the temperature of the finished project within the 225°F (107.2°C) to 300°F (148.9°C) range. Conventional methods are also used in laying and rolling the SEA

FIG. 2.6-18   Stockpile of recycled asphalt pavement.

pavement, final compaction being achieved between 185°F (85°C) and 250°F (121.1°C).

Remember that sulfur weighs 2 times the same volume of asphalt; therefore, tanks, supports, etc., must be capable of this extra weight. Sulfur is generally considered nontoxic at temperatures below 300°F (148.9°C).

PORTLAND-CEMENT-CONCRETE PAVEMENT

Concrete for Pavements.   The construction of concrete pavement is a highly mechanized operation which requires the inspection of a vast quantity of material and a working knowledge of numerous types of equipment (Fig. 2.6-19). Inspectors assigned to this work should be thoroughly familiar with the specifications, special provisions, construction details, and sequence of work.

Prior to the start of paving operations, a meeting should be arranged between the contractor's supervisory personnel and the project engineer to discuss specification requirements, quality-control program, source of materials, handling of materials, plant site, equipment, and methods of operations. The type of equipment used and the method of operation will depend on the contractor's choice of using forms or slip-form paving methods. A résumé of the meeting should be written by the project engineer, and the inspector should be thoroughly familiar with this information.

FIG. 2.6-19 Slip-form concrete-paving train with spreading machine, reinforcement carrier, reinforcement depressor, finishing machine, tube float, and curing machine.

The contractor is responsible for control of materials and batching operations. The plant inspector will be responsible for monitoring the contractor's plant operations.

A field laboratory should be available and located to permit the maximum number of operations to be observed while the necessary functions are performed in the laboratory. A concrete-mix design and quality-control plan should be furnished to the plant inspector so that proper inspection can be maintained during batching and mixing operations.

The information should include mix proportions, gallons of water per sack assumed in arriving at mix quantities (1 gal = 3.785 L) specific gravity, dry rodded weight per cubic foot of the coarse aggregate and percent absorption of the aggregates (1 ft^3 = 0.0283 m^3), target percent of air assumed in arriving at the mix quantities, and batch weights for a cubic yard of air-entrained concrete (1 yd^3 = 0.7646 m^3).

The equipment for the various types of paving method will vary considerably; therefore, we will discuss the type of paving equipment as we discuss the paving operation.

Preparation of Grade.   Prior to the start of paving operations, the inspector must ascertain that the subgrade and subbase are constructed in compliance with the typical section and are of proper density for the full width, including form line or track path for slip-form paving. It is recommended that the subgrade and subbase be constructed slightly higher than fine-grade elevation to allow trimming rather than filling to attain the correct finished surface.

Specifications usually state the minimum compaction requirements as a percentage of standard density. This minimum should be obtained at all locations. Tests of moisture content and density of the compacted subgrade and subbase should be taken at least every 500 ft (152 m) and evaluated. The maximum density and optimum moisture content of the various soils and subbase on a project should be determined in a laboratory by the use of American Society for Testing and Materials (ASTM) standard methods.

The action of subgrade and subbases under construction traffic and rollers should be observed for weak spots, which should be removed and the material replaced and recompacted before fine-grade trimming. See subsection "Subbases and Base Courses" for additional information on various types of material.

Setting Forms.   When forms are used, they should be checked to ensure that they meet the requirements for dimensions and are clean, oiled, and straight, that the face is perpendicular to the base, that flanges are not bent, and that locking devices are in proper working order. The foundation for forms should be cut true to grade, usually from a reference string line. When forms are set, they should be firmly supported throughout their length. Pins must be adequate in length to avoid measurable movement under equipment and locked-in stake holes. Locking devices must be properly fastened. Width between forms must be correct. Forms must be at the proper distance from the centerline and at the correct elevation, with a smooth grade line.

After forms have been set and properly tamped, it is advisable to sight along the top of the forms to detect any irregularities exceeding ⅛ in (3.175 mm) from true grade or ¼ in (6.35 mm) from true alignment. The foundation for the forms must be retamped if it is necessary to make any adjustments. Approved flexible or curved forms of proper radius should be used for curves of 200-ft (61-m) radius or less.

Slip-Form Paving.   When fixed forms are not used to contain the concrete and to provide a track for the paving-train equipment, a slip-form operation is used. The most noticeable difference in a slip-form operation is the absence of forms. The equipment contains wide tires or tracks which travel on the prepared subgrade just outside the edge of the pavement. When slip forming is to be used, the prepared base or subgrade must be built at least 2 ft (0.6 m) outside the proposed pavement edges to provide a stable foundation for the equipment.

The consistency, or slump, of the concrete must be approximately 1 in (25.4 mm) to prevent edge slumping of the pavement. If slumping occurs, it may be necessary to require the contractor to utilize longer trailing forms on the finishing machine.

Basically, all placing, screeding, finishing, floating, and curing are performed similarly to a fixed-form operation. Special care must be given to the construction of the edge keyway when one is required for additional lanes. This keyway is extruded as part of the finishing-machine operation and must be observed to be sure that the keyway is at the proper height and of the proper shape and that hook bolts have been installed as specified. Since no forms remain in place, the pavement edge must receive a coating of curing material no later than the application of curing compound to the pavement surface.

Fine Grading.   Prior to placing any pavement the base-course materials must be fine-graded. If base-course material consists of bituminous or portland-cement base courses, they will be placed to template section within the allowable tolerance in the initial operation. However, untreated subbases will require fine grading.

The two most common types of fine graders are automatically controlled fine graders and form-riding fine graders. Each of these fine-grading machines has cutting and trim parts with a final strike-off plate or template.

The machine usually consists of an auger with teeth which loosen the material near the desired grade. The elevation of the teeth should not extend below the finished grade or be allowed to operate below the grade of the rear auger. No auger teeth marks should be visible on the completed fine grade. The final strike-off blade should leave a smooth surface which conforms to the line and grade of the finished roadway surface. The strike-off blades should be checked to make certain they are set properly.

Many contractors prefer automatically controlled fine graders because they can trim subbases to closer tolerances and no forms are required for alignment. Alignment and elevations are maintained by electronic sen-

FIG. 2.6-20 String line and electronic sensors to control grading and paving equipment.

sors (Fig. 2.6-20) which ride on string lines set along roadways. The string line between the stakes must be taut at all times to assure proper grade excavation. The form-riding fine grader trims the subbase similarly to the automatic fine grader except that the machine rides on side forms.

After fine grading has been completed, the grade should be checked with a scratch template. This should be checked before final depth and compaction tests are made on the base course and before any dowel baskets have been set. These templates have prongs that scratch high spots in the subgrade base and should be inspected visually to make sure that wear or damage to the teeth has not caused the templates to be out of calibration. Then they should be set ¼ in (6.35 mm) shorter than the depth of the pavement. [Some specifications may call for ⅛ in (3.175 mm).]

The template is usually pushed by hand over the roadway by the contractor, and any high spots may be corrected by hand or by a motor grader. It must be ensured that the base course has the proper compaction and depth required before paving begins. These activities have been covered in the subsection "Subbases and Base Courses."

The base course shall be sprinkled with water before any concrete is placed to prevent loss of water in the concrete due to absorption from dry base-course material. Sprinkling should not result in ponding of water.

Dowels and Tie Bars. When dowel supporting assemblies are required for transverse joints, they must be laid out and marked so that the exact centerline of the assemblies can be reestablished. Generally they are held in the correct position by metal stakes or pins driven into the subbase (Fig. 2.6-21).

It is important that dowel bars be placed perpendicularly to the edge of the pavement so that cracking will occur at the proper location. Inspectors should check to make sure that the dowels are level with the surface of the roadway; a string line and a square can be used to check the angle with edge of roadway. Inspectors should check the distance between dowel baskets to make sure that the line or distance is constant.

Small wires used to hold dowel supporting assemblies together during fabrication and shipment should be cut after installation. Dowels should be free-moving, with an approved dowel cap or sleeve in place for expansion assemblies, and be coated with asphalt or other approved lubricant for both contraction assemblies and expansion joints. Dowel caps for expansion joints should be placed on the lubricated end of the dowel bars.

In areas where pavement lanes adjoin it is desirable to have the transverse joints continuous across all lanes, including any concrete median or shoulders. Deformed steel tie bars or tie-bolt assemblies should be placed parallel to the surface and at right angles to the longitudinal joints. They should be placed by suitable mechanical equipment and be rigidly

FIG. 2.6-21   A dowel basket secured by pins.

secured by approved supports to prevent displacement and ensure proper spacing. Tie bars should not be painted, coated, or enclosed in tubes or sleeves.

Batching Plants. Prior to the start of batching operations the plant inspector must thoroughly check, calibrate, and make certain that all mixing equipment is operating in an acceptable manner. Hoppers or bins should be set level and loaded at least 24 hours prior to calibration.

Bins for batching aggregates or bulk cement should be tight, be constructed so that there is a free flow of material with no accumulation in the corners, and be loaded to avoid segregation, contamination, or mixing of different materials. The weighing hopper should be of sufficient size to accommodate the batch being weighed without overflowing or coning against the bottom of the bin and should be constructed to empty completely. All working parts, such as knife-edges, shackles and weighing arms, should be in good condition, free from avoidable friction, and readily accessible for inspection and cleaning.

Batching plants equipped to proportion aggregate and bulk cement by automatic weighing devices of approved types may be used.

The contractor is generally responsible for furnishing all necessary equipment and labor for the calibration of scales with weights in accordance with an accepted standard method. A record of all calibration readings should be kept in the project documents.

The batching plant must be situated at a location with adequate storage facilities for the necessary aggregate stockpiles to be built without overlapping of different materials. Stockpiles should be built in layers not more than 3 ft (0.9 m) thick, with each layer being completed before the next one is started. Conical stockpiles, built by discharging the coarse aggregate at one point, or end-dumping over the sides of the stockpiles should not be permitted. The use of rubber-tired equipment on the stockpile must be held to a minimum to avoid contamination, breakage, and segregation; steel-track equipment should not be allowed on a stockpile. Extreme caution should be exercised when using the bottom layer of aggregate from a stockpile to avoid contamination of the mix by mud balls and other foreign material. The stockpile should be maintained in a saturated surface-dry condition to prevent the aggregate from absorbing mixing water from the batch and decreasing workability. Aggregates removed from the stockpiles and placed in the bins must be handled so as to assure relatively uniform moisture and to prevent segregation, degradation, and contamination. Regardless of whether aggregates are tested at the point of production or at the jobsite, a test report with numerical results must be available to show that the aggregates are acceptable prior to being incorporated in the work.

Cement must be handled and stored so as to prevent loss, wetting, or contamination. Cement is usually furnished from pretested bins at the cement mill. If no documentation accompanies the shipment of cement indicating that it has come from an approved mill, a preliminary test sample must be obtained and tested in accordance with required specifications and approved before using. Different types of cement must not be intermingled or substituted for the type specified.

The intake end of the pipe or hose used in pumping mixing water from a stream or standing body of water should be covered with wire mesh and located so that no foreign matter will enter it. Mixing water should be hauled in clean, covered containers. Assurance of using acceptable water should be verified by the plant inspector for on-the-job mixing.

Admixtures shall not be used except as shown in the mix design unless permission is given by the project engineer.

The importance of proper plant inspection cannot be overemphasized since proper proportioning of materials is one of the major steps in obtaining a satisfactory pavement. The inspector must be guided by the concept that the entire paving project is a line operation, from raw-material source to the finished slab. The quality of the end product depends equally on each step during production, and no amount of extra effort at one stage can compensate for errors, omissions, or inefficiencies at some other stage.

The specific duties of the plant inspector should include the following:

1. Observation of the stockpiling and handling of materials to assure compliance with the specifications. The inspector maintains report records to verify that all material is acceptable prior to incorporation into the work and periodically (at least weekly) check the amount of cement actually used by comparing the total amount of cement received with the theoretical amount used, taking into account the cement remaining on hand.

2. Familiarity with the physical characteristics of aggregates and control charts, design-mix proportions, method of determining batch quantities, scale weights, yield, effective water-cement factor, and procedures for adjusting proportions and yield when using air entrainment. The design mix as established and approved must be included in the permanent records of the project.

3. Calibration of weighing and measuring devices, balancing scales and checking calibration, and systematic and regular checking of scale setting for batches to assure that proper quantities are being dispensed. The inspector should not make scale settings, since these are the responsibility of the contractor's representative.

4. Free-moisture tests (ASTM C 70) at least 4 times daily and more frequently if, in the judgment of the inspector, there has been a change in the moisture content for fine aggregates. These tests are required so that batch weights may be adjusted to ensure that the maximum allowable water-cement ratio is not being exceeded. It is the contractor's responsibility to advise the operator at the plant immediately of any change in moisture content of the aggregates and of the maximum gallons of water that may be added at the mixer without exceeding specifications and design limits (1 gal = 3.785 L).

5. Ascertaining that central-mixed concrete is handled in vehicles meeting specifications and in a manner to avoid segregation and is delivered at the site before it starts to take its initial set. Agitating-type trucks are required if these conditions cannot be met.

Central Mixing. Mixers used for central or site mixing should be checked before construction begins. Principal points to be observed include the following:

1. Blades in the mixer should be measured for wear and repaired or replaced if they are worn by more than 10 percent. Most wear will occur at the center of the blade, with little wear at the ends; therefore, wear can generally be measured from a string line or a straightedge placed along the length of the blade. The inspector should have the manufacturer's brochure to show the original configuration and height of the blades.

2. Mixing drums must be in condition to avoid spillage of material or leakage of grout either on the ground or between compartments in multiple-batch mixers.

3. All joints and connections in the waterline should be watertight, and valves must close adequately to prevent leakage of water into the mixer before or after the measuring tank has been discharged.

4. Air-entraining agents must be added to the mixing water by a positive mechanical dispenser at the time that the mixing water is being discharged into the mixing drum. The supply tank should have a gauge which shows the amount of agent on hand at all times, and the supply line should permit visual observations.

5. The time and length of haul should not exceed specifications or allow loss of workability before finishing operations have been completed.

6. The size of the batch, speed of rotation, and mixing cycle should comply with specifications and the manufacturer's rating for the specific type of equipment.

If nonagitation trucks are used for the transportation of concrete to the jobsite, the hauling body shall consist of smooth, mortartight metal containers and shall be capable of discharging the concrete at a satisfactory controlled rate without segregation. Covers shall be provided when needed for protection.

Transit Mixing.   When truck-mixed concrete is permitted for concrete pavement, the following items should be checked:

1.   Mixers must be of an approved type in a condition to produce uniform and well-mixed concrete. They should have a legible plate supplied by the manufacturer showing the capacities of the drum and the recommended speed of rotation of the drum or blades. The batch size in relation to the capacities of the equipment must be in conformance with specifications.

2.   Water-measuring devices and air-entrainment-agent dispensers should be calibrated and checked in the same manner as for central or site mixers.

3.   Washwater should be carried in an auxiliary tank. If it is to be used in the succeeding batch, a device must be provided to measure this water accurately.

4.   Drums must be checked for excessively worn blades and hardened concrete.

5.   Drum or blade speed should be checked to determine that it is within the limits of the specifications and the manufacturer's recommendations.

6.   Mixing is controlled either by a specified time or by the number of revolutions at a specified number of revolutions per minute. Regardless of the method used for controlling proper mixing, it shall begin after all ingredients, including water, are in the mixer. Close cooperation is required between plant and paving inspectors to assure that the proper mixing time or number of revolutions is being observed and that concrete is placed within the designated time limit. This is normally accomplished by the plant inspector's issuing of a trip ticket, a copy of which is sent to the paving inspector with the truck driver. Trucks should be equipped with either a revolution counter or a device which will record the mixing time.

Mixing Concrete.   Regardless of how concrete is mixed in site mixers, it is the responsibility of the paving inspector to assure that it is properly mixed and meets requirements with regard to slump, air content, uniformity, and desired workability when delivered to the site. Wet and dry batches should be avoided and the slump held to within very narrow limits, normally not exceeding a ¾-in (19.05-mm) variation. A mixer should be regulated so that some water will flow into the drum in advance of cement and aggregates and continue to flow for a specified period after all the cement and aggregates are in the drum. When using central-mixed concrete, not more than 30 minutes should elapse from the time that water is added to the mix until it is deposited on the grade when hauled in nonagitation trucks, and not more than 60 minutes when hauled in mixing or agitator trucks.

Placing Concrete and Reinforcing Steel. The contractor is responsible for the on-site mixing and placing of the concrete and the finishing of the concrete slab. However, construction of a quality pavement with the desired riding qualities depends to a large extent on the inspector's constant attention to details as the work progresses each day.

The paving inspector is also responsible for a certain amount of acceptance testing to determine that the pavement meets the contract requirements. To do this, the inspector must have a sound knowledge of the plans and specifications, recognize good construction practices, have a working knowledge of the equipment used, and be fully aware of all required tests and reports. Concrete pavement must be placed on the subbase so as to prevent segregation and to require a minimum of redistribution. Concrete dumped in piles causes nonuniformity of consolidation and may permit the spreader to ride higher than the specified grade, causing unevenness in the finished surface. This in turn will probably necessitate additional finishing work to obtain a good riding surface. When concrete must be spread by hand, it should spread with a shovel instead of a rake or similar tool. Extreme caution must be employed when placing concrete around joints, dowel assemblies, expansion joints, etc., to avoid displacement.

Trucks deposit concrete on the dowel assemblies immediately ahead of the spreader in a slip-form operation (Fig. 2.6-22). This procedure will help to prevent misalignment of the dowel baskets. Concrete-hauling units performing this operation should be kept off the base course and haul on the shoulder area.

The mechanical equipment generally used for the finished concrete pavement consists of a spreader, a transverse finishing machine, and a longitudinal or transverse float. Detailed adjustment of each piece of equipment will be covered in the manufacturer's manual and should be available for the inspector's review. Also, the inspector's knowledge of these adjustments will be helpful through knowing the limitations of the machines' capabilities.

Spreaders consist of a screw or plow for distribution of the concrete and a strike-off (Fig. 2.6-23). The elevation of the bottom of the strike-off can be adjusted by the operator. The gauge maintaining the height of the

FIG. 2.6-22   Depositing concrete on dowel assemblies.

FIG. 2.6-23   Placing concrete with a traveling hopper and spreading with a screw and auger.

strike-off should be set at zero when it is even with the top of the forms or pavement finish elevation. The edge of the screed should be slightly higher than the rear to help facilitate consolidation and to provide material for finishing. When forms are used, screed end plates wear rapidly as they slide on the forms. They should be replaced when both sides have worn down as much as ⅛ in (3.175 mm). The spreader should be adjusted so that concrete is struck off uniformly across the entire area. When steel is specified, the concrete may be placed in two layers with the mesh hand-placed on top of the first layer and covered by the second layer, or the concrete can be placed and struck off to its full depth with the mesh placed on top and vibrated to its final position by a mesh-depressing machine, or the reinforcement can be secured in proper position before the concrete is placed. When reinforcement is placed by the two-layer method, not more than 30 minutes should elapse before the top layer of concrete is placed. If an approved mesh-placing machine (see Fig. 2.6-24) is used, it should be checked for proper adjustment to assure that the reinforcement is at the correct elevation and that it does not crawl during placement. The final pass of the spreader should leave concrete slightly high to provide a roll of material ahead of the first screed of the finishing machine. When hand methods for spreading are permitted, a template should be used to assure that it has been struck off to the desired elevation.

All dowels and reinforcing steel should be free of dirt, soil, paint, grease, and excessive rust when concrete is placed. Excessive rust is defined as a reduction in cross-sectional area and does not refer to normal mill scaling. Adjoining mats should always be lapped at least past the first

FIG. 2.6-24 A reinforcement depressor.

transverse wire except at joints. The location of the joints should be carefully marked, and sufficient space should be left between the mats to allow for sawed or formed joints to fall in the proposed space.

Final Strike-Off, Consolidation, and Finishing. Immediately after spreading, the concrete should be screeded and consolidated by using an approved finishing machine and vibrators or other approved equipment. The finishing machine should have at least two oscillating-type transverse screeds in proper adjustment. The purpose of this machine is to assist in consolidating the concrete and to leave the surface with a uniform texture at the correct elevation and cross section for final finishing. When the finishing machine is properly adjusted, there should be a uniform roll of concrete in front of each screed. The roll in front of the screed should be approximately 3 to 6 in (76.2 to 152.4 mm) in diameter and 2 in (50.8 mm) in front of the back screed to provide uniform finishing. If an excess of concrete is being carried, it will tend to lift the screeds off the forms or track path and cause surging behind the screeds, resulting in overloading the next equipment of the paving train. As the work progresses, the tilt and speed of the screeds may need to be adjusted to compact the particular mix being used, eliminate tearing, and control the amount of surge. With low-slump harsh mixes, the screed oscillating speed should normally be rapid, with a long stroke and a slow forward speed. With more fluid mixes, the screed action should be decreased in both speed and length of strokes, with the forward speed increased. The number of screedings will be determined by field conditions. Excessive screeding should be avoided since it tends to produce undesirable quantities of low-strength mortar on the surface.

Vibrators (Fig. 2.6-25),which are normally attached to the back of the spreader, the front of the finishing machine, or a separate carrier, may be of the pan type or the internal type with either an immersed tube or multiple spuds. They should be mounted so that they will not come in contact with reinforcement, base course, or forms. The entire width of the pavement must be thoroughly vibrated in an effective manner for the full depth. Concrete should be thoroughly vibrated along forms, dowel assemblies, expansion joints, and key joints. When equipment other than vibrators is used for consolidation, it must meet the approval of the engineer and produce satisfactory results.

After consolidation and screeding, the concrete is floated to remove irregularities left by previous operations and by shrinkage. This can be accomplished by the use of a properly adjusted longitudinal or transverse float (Fig. 2.6-26). The duration of floating will depend on field conditions, as it is desirable for initial settlement of the concrete to be complete. The final surface may be rough if the concrete has not been thoroughly

FIG. 2.6-25 Vibrators to consolidate pavement completely for the full width.

FIG. 2.6-26 A transverse-tube float.

compacted and is in the early stages of shrinkage when the float passes. Floating should be held to a minimum during the period of greater bleeding since working the surface in the presence of bleed water dilutes the cement paste on the surface of the slab and reduces its wear resistance and durability. The longitudinal float should be operated so that the entire surface area is covered at least twice. This is accomplished by overlapping the previous transverse passes by one-half of the length of the float. If excessive cutting or filling is required, all paving equipment should be checked and necessary adjustments made to eliminate this condition.

When operating properly, the longitudinal float should carry a small roll of concrete along the front half of the screed. When the transverse float is used, the duration of operation must be adjusted to field conditions as with a longitudinal float. The screed or screeds working ahead of the transverse float should carry a uniform roll of concrete so that the float will have a smooth, uniform surface free of screed marks with a minimum of surging.

Regardless of the type of float used, a continuous operation at a uniform rate of speed is necessary to obtain the most desirable finished project.

When hand methods of finishing are permitted, the surface should be floated with a hand-operated longitudinal float of specified size. The float should be straight and rigid enough to prevent flexing or warping. It is operated from a bridge spanning the entire width, worked with a sawing motion from one side of the pavement to the other while being held parallel to the centerline. Each pass should overlap the preceding pass by not less than one-half of the length of the float.

When it is necessary to smooth or fill in open-textured areas in the pavement surface after the preceding floating, it is permissible to use an approved long-handled float. In this operation, care must be exercised to avoid distorting the surface. This equipment should be limited to small areas and not be used to float the entire surface. The surface must then be tested for trueness with a 10-ft (3-m) straightedge which has been checked against a master straightedge. If high or low spots are observed, concrete should be added or removed and the area refinished and checked. The straightedge used for testing the surface should not be used for finishing or moving concrete. The surface must be checked until it conforms to grade and cross section and is free of irregularities.

Texturing and Curing.   Texturing should begin when the concrete surface is plastic enough to allow texturing to approximately $\frac{3}{16}$ in (4.762 mm) in depth but dry enough to prevent the plastic concrete from flowing back into the grooves being formed. This may be accomplished by the use of wire tines (Fig. 2.6-27). Texturing should be made in a transverse direction. Adjacent strokes of the comb should abut one another without appreciable overlap. All texturing should be made with only one pass per surface area. Tines should be checked periodically throughout the day to be sure that they are not missing, worn, or out of shape. Particular attention should be given when texturing in superelevated areas, where uniformity can be more difficult to obtain. Hand brooms about 4 ft (1.2 m) wide, made of wire comb as specified above, may be used on small areas. An alternative procedure or equipment may be used if it can produce the desired result.

An edger with a radius not exceeding ¼ in (6.35 mm) may be used on joints and other edges. The concrete should be adequately set to permit the edges to hold their shape after they have been finished. Care must be exercised to assure that the leg between the concrete and the form or joint is held vertical. Marks left on the pavement surface by edging may be removed by a wet paintbrush or a small piece of damp burlap.

After finishing operations have been completed and as soon as surface marring will not occur, the entire width of the pavement should be covered with a curing material (Fig. 2.6-28). The timing of the application of this material is extremely important. Curing material must be applied prior to the time at which the surface dries to avoid shrinkage cracks,

FIG. 2.6-27 Transverse-wire fine texturing.

Fig. 2.6-28   A curing machine.

which may occur if the concrete surface is left exposed to sun and wind, permitting a rapid loss of evaporation of the concrete-mixture mix water at the top surface of the slab. The concrete should not be left exposed for more than 30 minutes between stages of curing or during the curing period. Various methods of curing, such as impervious membranes, waterproof paper, cotton or burlap mats, or polyethylene sheets, are used.

Impervious membrane should be applied uniformly with fully atomizing tank-spraying equipment at the rate of 1 gal/125 ft^2 (3.785 L/11.6 m^2). Frequent checks of the quantity used in relation to surface area should be made and recorded to ensure the proper rate of application. Application should be made as soon as the water sheen disappears and before the initial set has taken place. Should the curing agent be damaged by rain or other causes, the impervious membrane must be repaired immediately by an additional application.

Burlap or cotton mats, when used, must be dampened prior to placement on the pavement and kept thoroughly wet throughout the curing period. The mats should be placed and weighted so that they will remain in contact with the surface.

If waterproof paper or polyethylene sheeting is used, it must cover the surface, be weighted to avoid displacement, and be airtight. The surface of the pavement should be thoroughly wetted by a fine mist spray prior to the placement of curing material. When placing the sheeting, care should be taken not to mar the pavement texture.

The minimum required curing period is generally 72 hours after placing the concrete. Cold-weather curing requires extra attention to the type and duration of curing.

When concrete is being placed and the air temperature is expected to fall below 35°F (1.7°C), during the curing period a sufficient supply of straw, hay, or other suitable blanketing material should be provided, and any time that the air temperature is expected to reach the freezing point during the day or night, the material so provided shall be spread over the pavement to a depth sufficient to prevent freezing of the concrete. Such concrete should be cured a minimum of 8400 Fahrenheit degree-hours (1680 Celsius degree-hours) when other than high-early-strength concrete is used. It should be cured a minimum of 6000 Fahrenheit degree-hours (1200 Celsius degree-hours) when high-early-strength concrete is used.

In no event should the surface temperature of the concrete be allowed to fall below 35°F before the curing period is completed.

Joints.   Joints are placed either longitudinally or transversely to control cracking caused by the contraction of concrete as it shrinks. Both types of joint are placed in reinforcing and nonreinforcing mesh, while continuously reinforced concrete does not need transverse but only longitudinal joints. Construction joints are placed between separately poured concrete slabs such as at the end of the concrete pavement placed each day. Expansion joints are found between such areas as bridge approaches, ramps, and other approach roads. As an inspector, you must be sure that all joints are carefully constructed at the location specified on the plans.

When sawing joints, the contractor must have sufficient saws and blades on hand to perform sawing operations at the proper time and so prevent cracking. Facilities for night sawing should also be available.

The time for sawing transverse and longitudinal joints may vary from 4 to 24 hours, depending on weather and atmospheric conditions. Joints should be sawed to a depth and width specified on the plans. Slight raveling is not objectionable and generally indicates that sawing is being done at the proper time.

Load transfer is accomplished by placing dowel-bar assemblies at transverse contraction joints. The dowel bars will carry loads across the transverse contraction joints without restricting the closing and opening of the joints as weather and temperatures change.

Joints must be sawed over the center of the load-transfer unit within 1 in (25.4 mm) of the midlength of the dowels and perpendicular to the surface to the required depth for the full slab width.

When a crack occurs ahead of a saw cut, sawing on the joint should be stopped immediately and the saw moved ahead several joints. A joint should be sawed at this location; then the saw should be returned to cut the joints that were skipped. Measurements of the depth and width of sawed joints should be made periodically to determine compliance with the requirements and the measurements recorded as a part of the permanent record.

Immediately after completing the sawing operation, all dust or slurry should be removed by flushing the joint with a jet of water under pressure. The joint should then be blown with compressed air to remove the water. When the joint has dried sufficiently, an adhesive polyethylene tape at least 2.5 in (63.5 mm) wide should be centered over the joint and pressed into place. The tape should extend over the slab edge at least 2 in (50.8 mm) below the bottom of the saw cut. This tape should remain in place until just before the joints are sealed.

Joints must be clean and surface-dry at the time of sealing. They should be sealed with approved material prior to opening to traffic, construction, or the public. If heated joint-sealing material is used, it should be stirred to avoid localized overheating and the temperature continually checked for compliance with the manufacturer's recommended temperatures. Low-modulus silicone sealant requires no heating and is installed from pressurized containers at a puttylike consistency. The joints must be absolutely clean and dry. Special measures such as sandblasting, wire brushing, etc., must be used. The shape of the installed silicone sealant is very important also. The width should not exceed twice the depth, with a Styrofoam backer rod used beneath the sealer to form a concave bottom and the top tooled to form a concave top. To prevent vehicle tires from contacting the material do not allow the sealer to be flush with the surface of the pavement. Poured joint-sealing material should not be placed when the air temperature in the shade is less than 50°F (10°C) unless such placement is approved by the project engineer.

Surface Test.   As soon as possible after the concrete has set, the surface should be checked with a straightedge or other specified device. Concrete may be considered to be hardened sufficiently when it can be walked upon without damaging the surface and, if a white membrane curing compound is used, as soon as the compound has dried sufficiently so as not to collect on the straightedge. This will permit early verification of compliance with specification requirements and provide an opportunity to make adjustments in construction operations where necessary.

Straightedging should be performed in the following manner:

1.   On mainline pavement, the rolling straightedge should be operated parallel to the centerline at distances of 3.9 ft (1.2 m), 15 ft (4.6 m), and 21 ft (6.4 m) from the edge of the pavement.

2.   On one-way ramps, the rolling straightedge should be operated parallel to the center of the slab 4 ft (1.2 m) on each side from the centerline of

the slab. This procedure will provide equal areas of influence on either side of the straightedge line in 16-ft (4.9-m) ramps.

3. On acceleration and deceleration lanes, truck lanes, and taper sections, the rolling straightedge should be operated parallel to the outside edge of the pavement at distances of 3 ft (0.9 m) and 9 ft (2.7 m) from the outside edge of the pavement.

4. Straightedging of ramp gores or other special types of areas should be adapted to the geometry of the area with consideration being given to the direction of traffic movement.

It is suggested that two rolling straightedges, when secured together 6 ft (1.8 m) apart, will greatly reduce the time required for the surface testing of concrete pavement.

Marred areas observed during straightedging operations should be retouched with a curing compound when the initial curing method has been white membrane curing compound.

All irregularities should be corrected as required by the owner.

Removing Forms. The removal of side forms, when used, requires good judgment since weather and temperature will affect this operation. Unless otherwise permitted, forms should not be removed from freshly placed concrete until it has set for at least 12 hours. In all cases, the concrete should be hardened to the extent that spalling or other damage will not occur.

Cold-Weather Concreting. When the temperature of the plastic concrete is less than 55°F (12.8°C), the provisions of cold-weather concreting apply. When cold-weather concreting exists as stated above, the temperature of the mixed concrete should not be less than 50°F (10°C) and not more than 85°F (29.4°C) at the time of placement. When it is necessary to heat mixing water or aggregates, or both, they should be heated to not less than 70°F (21.1°C) or more than 150°F (65.6°C) in such a manner that the mass is uniformly heated. Heating methods should be outlined in the specifications. The possibility of overheating areas must be avoided. No concrete should be placed on frozen subgrade, nor should frozen aggregates be used in the concrete.

Hot-Weather Concreting. When hot, dry, and windy conditions prevail, it may be necessary to take precautions to prevent rapid surface drying, rapid temperature changes, and undesirable high temperatures [(the recommended maximum is 85 to 90°F (29.6 to 32.2°C)] in the concrete during the early stages of hardening. These conditions may remove moisture from the pavement surface more rapidly than it can be replaced by normal bleeding and cause plastic shrinkage cracks to form. It may be desirable to cool the mixing water and aggregate stockpiles to lower the temperature of the concrete. Forms may be cooled by sprinkling them with water or by dragging a piece of wet burlap over them immediately ahead of the concrete pavement. The application of curing materials immediately upon completion of finishing becomes extremely important, and under some conditions it may be necessary to use wet burlap or cotton mats for the first 24 hours. The wet burlap or mats can then be placed for the remaining curing period or removed and replaced with other curing materials.

Protection in Case of Rain.   Before paving operations start, the inspector should be assured that the contractor has on hand sufficient material such as polyethylene sheeting to protect the pavement surface properly in case of rain. Sudden showers which might occur during paving operations or immediately after finishing operations require the exposed surface of the fresh concrete to be covered to prevent washing cement from the surface.

The mixing and placing of concrete should cease immediately in case of rain. If rain continues for only a short period, the protective covering may be removed and finishing completed. If rain continues, finishing may be accomplished by rolling back a few feet of the protective cover at a time and replacing it immediately after finishing is done. The covering should not be placed so as to allow the texturing to be destroyed. The pavement surface should be inspected as soon as possible to determine the extent of damage and the contractor advised immediately of any corrective action or removal necessary.

Opening to Traffic.   The pavement should not be opened to traffic until the curing period has elapsed, the concrete has attained the required strength, the joints have been sealed, the pavement cleaned, shoulders constructed, and adequate guardrails and signing installed.

Inspection and Safety Evaluation of Existing Bridges

Michael J. Abrahams, P.E.
Vice President and Manager of Structures Department
Parsons Brinckerhoff Quade & Douglas, Inc.
New York, New York

Bridge inspection covers a wide variety of tasks, which range from walking along a bridge deck looking for spalled concrete to using sophisticated instruments to detect cracks in steel structures and determining bearing wear in movable bridges. While the subject matter is wide-ranging, this chapter will in general be limited to the maintenance inspection of fixed bridges. However, in order to acquaint the reader with the full range of the subject, some discussion of the more technical aspects is included.

It is assumed that the reader has some technical background and knowledge but not necessarily an engineering degree. The reader should use this chapter as a reference to become familiar with bridge-inspection techniques and requirements to detect problems and defects by visually inspecting bridge structures. The prudent bridge inspector should report findings to a qualified structural engineer for evaluation of the bridge's structural adequacy.

TYPES OF BRIDGES

Although there are numerous methods for classifying and identifying the many different types of bridge structures, a four-element classification system will be used in this chapter. Those elements are:

- Span length
- Material
- Span configuration
- Structural configuration

SPAN LENGTH

Span length refers to the distance between the supports on which the bridge superstructure rests. The various types of supporting structures, i.e., substructures and superstructures, will be discussed later in this chapter. Recommended classifications and limits of span lengths are shown in the accompanying table.

Span Length

Classification	Limits
Short span	0−100 ft (0−30.5 m)
Medium span	100−400 ft (30.5−121.9 m)
Long span	400 ft (121.9 m) or greater

MATERIAL

The material which composes bridge structural elements can be one or more of the following types: stone or masonry, steel, wrought iron (circa late nineteenth century and early twentieth century), timber, reinforced or unreinforced concrete, or prestressed concrete. Details of the type of steel or the strength of concrete are discussed later.

SPAN CONFIGURATION

Span configuration defines a bridge in terms of its continuity over a support. Figures 2.7-1 and 2.7-2 illustrate examples of span configurations.

In either the simple-span or the continuous-span configuration, the number of spans is unlimited, and a single bridge can combine simple and continuous spans. The difference between the simple- and continuous-span configurations is determined by the continuity of the superstructure over the support. A simple-span superstructure is characterized by the presence of expansion joints in the bridge at a supporting substructure.

STRUCTURAL CONFIGURATION

Structural configuration classifies a bridge structure by its overall profile. Examples of structural configuration are the arch, stringer, girder, truss, suspension, slab bascule, swing, lift, draw, cable-stayed, and others that are limited only by the designer's imagination. Discussions will be limited to the arch, stringer, girder, and truss structural configurations, as these are the most common.

TYPES OF BRIDGES

Arch Bridges. Arch bridges can be stone, concrete, or metal; two types are shown in Figs. 2.7-3 and 2.7-4. Note the difference between an open

FIG. 2.7-1   Simple-span bridge.

FIG. 2.7-2   Continuous-span bridge.

and a filled spandrel. An arch by design carries its load by compression or thrust in the arch. At the bottom of the arch the thrust is resisted either by an abutment (Fig. 2.7-4) or by a tie, which holds the ends of the arch from spreading outward. When inspecting an arch, this basic means of restraint should be kept in mind. Bear in mind the following questions: What holds this thing together, and is it working properly? What would happen if the tie were to rust through? What would happen if a school bus were crossing the bridge when the tie broke?

FIG. 2.7-3   Open-spandrel concrete arch bridge.

FIG. 2.7-4   Filled-spandrel concrete arch bridge.

Stringer and Girder Bridges.   The next and probably the most common type of bridge is the stringer bridge, shown in Fig. 2.7-5. The stringers span between the piers or pier and abutment. The deck on top carries the vehicles and distributes the load to the stringers. Figure 2.7-6 shows a girder bridge in which the deck rests on transverse floor beams, which in turn are supported by girders. The girders may be adjacent to the roadway, as in a through girder bridge, or below the roadway in a deck girder bridge.

Both stringers and girders are beams that work in bending. At midspan,

FIG. 2.7-5   Steel stringer bridge.

FIG. 2.7-6   Girder bridge.

the top of the beam or the top flange is in compression and the bottom of the beam or the bottom flange is in tension. In continuous-span configurations, the reverse is true over the supports; i.e., there is tension in the upper portion of the beam or the top flange and compression in the lower portion of the beam or the lower flange. If the beam is reinforced or prestressed concrete, at midspan the compression in the top is taken by concrete and the tension in the bottom is taken by the steel reinforcing bars or by prestressing of strands. Again, in continuous-span configurations, stress distribution at a support is reversed from that of midspan stress distribution. The reinforcing or prestressing bars or strands that carry the tensile stress in a concrete beam are similar to the tie rod for a tied arch bridge. If the tie rod or the tensile bars or strands fail, the arch tie structure will inevitably fail as well. Therefore, when inspecting a girder or a stringer bridge particular attention should be directed to the tensile areas of a beam.

In addition to bending, the beam is also subjected to a shearing force which is greatest at the supports. To visualize this force, think of a beam bolted to a wall. What happens if the bolts are out? The beam falls down. The force which the beam applies to the bolts is a shear force.

Truss Bridges. The last structural configuration is a truss bridge (see Fig. 2.7-7). For this type of bridge, the truss members are either in tension or in compression. It is beyond the scope of this chapter to illustrate how those forces occur, but the inspector should be aware that every member is subjected to either a tensile or a compressive force. If a member fails, the truss could collapse. While it is easy to visualize a member failing in tension (remember the arch tie), compression failure requires some thought. Think about a straw in a soft drink. What happens if you push on each end of the straw—put it in compression? If you push hard, the straw will buckle or fail in compression. While it may be hard to imagine this happening to a steel bridge member, this is not an infrequent event and has occurred, particularly with older truss bridges, when one of their members has been struck by a truck and bent so severely that it has buckled. In practical terms, this means that the bridge inspector must consider the condition and, in particular, the alignment (or straightness) of truss members.

Fig. **2.7-7**   Steel truss bridge.

There are several other points which need to be covered. All bridges move either because the members expand or contract with temperature changes or when vehicles pass over the bridge. Bridges move up and down, except at supports, as traffic passes over them, and they move longitudinally along their length as the members are heated or cooled. These movements (particularly longitudinal movements) are computed and allowed for in bridge design. To allow for movement, every bridge has expansion joints. The joints occur both in the bridge roadway and at the bridge supports or bearings. Typically, one end of a span has a pinned or fixed bearing which allows rotation as the span moves up and down but does not allow longitudinal movement, while the other end of the bridge has an expansion bearing which allows both rotation and longitudinal movement. If the joints become clogged with debris or frozen or otherwise restricted, the expected movement cannot take place. If bridge movement is restrained (for example, if the expansion joint in a roadway is paved over), the forces generated at the point of restraint will be very large and eventually a portion of the bridge will fail. Thus it is most important to be aware of this possibility and to examine bridge joints and bearings critically.

The preceding discussion has been concentrated on bridge superstructures. In addition, the inspector must be aware of the bridge substructure, piers, and abutments and the bridge approaches. The preceding figures included a number of bridge piers and abutments. The difference between piers and abutments is that piers are intermediate supports while abutments are located at each end of the bridge. Piers serve primarily to support the vertical load from the bridge, although they also transfer lateral wind loads from the superstructure. By contrast, abutments not only support vertical loads from the bridge but also serve as a retaining wall to restrain the earth behind the wall. The forces of the earth against the retaining wall are referred to as *lateral (horizontal) forces.* Usually, the designer will reduce the additional lateral pressure caused by lateral water pressure on the abutment by introducing weep holes in the abutment to allow for water drainage. The inspector should bear in mind the forces acting on the substructure so that he or she can be aware of possible problems. For example, a tilting or sliding abutment could result from excessive lateral pressure, which may in turn be caused by plugged weep holes or by erosion of soil at the footing level.

The bridge substructure, both piers and abutments, will be supported either by timber, steel, or concrete piles driven into the ground or by spread footings which bear directly on the soil or rock. Usually, the inspector will not be aware of the type of footing, but there are occasions when this becomes important. If, during the course of an inspection, the bottom of a pier or abutment footing is exposed, particularly when the footing has been exposed by stream action, the inspector should be aware that the situation may be critical, as the means of support for the footing may be in question.

Another part of a bridge substructure is the fender system. Fender systems are used on bridges in navigable waters to minimize damage from ship impacts. They vary from a few timbers bolted to a pier to an elaborate system of piles and timbers. It is the intent of most designs to minimize damage from a ship, but rarely is it practical to design a fender to absorb the full impact of a large ship. The inspector will frequently be involved in inspecting fenders and should be conscious that the fender system is subject to constant abuse from ship collision. One important point: if fuel barges use the channel, the inspector should ascertain whether or not there is any exposed metal on the fender which could cause sparks.

Traffic safety, both vehicular and pedestrian, is another item of major concern. While the failure of a bridge or a bridge member is dramatic, a far more likely dangerous situation is produced by inadequate or missing guardrails or handrails, too narrow roadway widths, lack of median barriers or railings, unprotected obstructions along the side of the roadway, and dangerous approaches, sight distance, and speed limits. In some instances these hazards exist because of poor maintenance (e.g., a missing handrail), while in other instances a bridge is outmoded for present traffic. The inspector should observe and report these items. In many cases, just observing the behavior of traffic using the structure will point out a number of safety problems. Several of the references at the end of the chapter can provide additional guidance.

The preceding discussions have provided a general introduction to bridges and furnished the inspector with a basic knowledge of bridge types and their components. Prior to discussing inspection procedures, the terms frequently used in conjunction with bridges should be reviewed (see Fig. 2.7-8). While the use of standard terminology is helpful and tends to lend authenticity to a report, it is not essential. Field notes should be accompanied by good sketches and/or photographs of unusual situations. Good sketches and/or photographs will augment any discussion in a report and provide a clearer understanding of an unusual situation.

BRIDGE-INSPECTION PROCEDURES

The procedures to be followed in conducting a bridge inspection are dictated by the type of inspection and the type of structure. An inspection can be as brief as a visual check to see that a bridge deck is not spalled to an in-depth inspection, which can require a team of personnel for a period of weeks taking measurements of members or making survey checks. Usu-

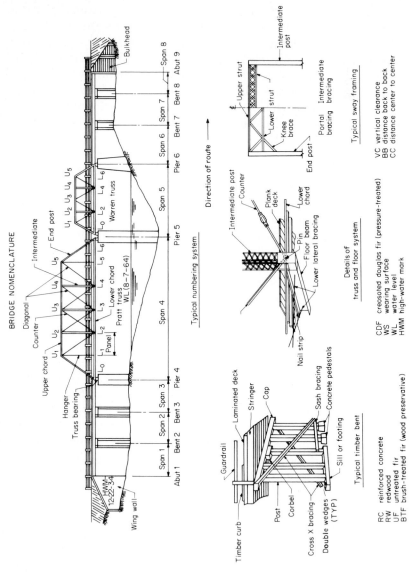

Fig. 2.7-8 Standard bridge nomenclature.

2.7.10

ally inspections are made as an annual or condition inspection and would require some time and effort at the bridge. The nature and purpose of the inspection is determined beforehand and is usually defined in a formal agreement between the owner and the inspecting agency, the exception, of course, being when the owner's forces are used for inspections.

While inspections can involve specialized instruments to detect cracks in steel, rust of steel reinforcing bars in concrete, concrete-deck delamination, and others, most inspections are based on visual observation, that is, looking closely and carefully at the bridge in a systematic, planned fashion. Typically, inspections will involve note pads, pencils, and a straightedge to record notes, one or more powerful flashlights, a folding ruler, a measuring tape, a ladder, hard hats, safety belts and ropes, a chipping hammer, and a brush to clean off areas. A camera with a flash and color-print film can also be very valuable, provided that the location and description of every photograph is carefully recorded. Beyond this basic material, there is a wide range of possible equipment.

If levels or distances are to be checked, survey instruments will be needed. If the structure is over water, a boat may be required. If traffic control is a problem, traffic-control devices such as cones or beacons are required. Every bridge is unique, and the bridge inspector must be resourceful to select the proper equipment.

On a larger bridge, specialized equipment will be required to reach portions of the structure, particularly the underdeck area. One particular device, called a snooper, has been developed for this purpose (see Fig. 2.7-9). Special rigging, such as that used by bridge painters, may also be needed.

To establish the equipment needed and the inspection sequence, most bridge inspections require a preliminary visit by the leader of the inspection team and, if necessary, other interested parties such as the owner. At that time one can briefly inspect the bridge to plan the actual inspection. It is important to get under the bridge to see how the underside of the deck and the substructure can be reached. Are ladders needed? Is a diver required? How deep is the water, and is there a current?

At the same time, one can plan how to sequence the work. For example, for the first day two inspectors will cover the roadway, sidewalks, and handrails, while one inspector takes notes. On the second day, the same group will inspect the west abutment, pier, and underside of the first span with two aluminum ladders; and so on, for the remainder of the bridge.

Notes are very important at this point, as it may be some time before the actual inspection is conducted. The notes should include a brief description of the bridge and an outline of the planned inspection, together with a summary of personnel and equipment required. If a camera is available, a photograph can be of great assistance, particularly if further discussions

FIG. 2.7-9   Snooper inspection platform being lowered below the bridge span.

are necessary with the client or others. Photographs are excellent briefing devices for the inspection team as to the type of structure, materials, span configuration, structural configuration, and other important factors that a camera's eye captures.

Prior to the inspection, it is helpful to locate the plans of the bridge. If the plans are available, they should be reviewed, especially to learn the nomenclature used (east abutment, Pier 1, etc.) and to determine various particulars such as the types of bearings. If the plans are not available, it does not affect the work required to make a survey and report on the general condition of the structure. However, if the inspection is for rating purposes, which will be discussed later, it may require measuring members to determine their exact lengths and sizes, information which would have been on the plans. This information will subsequently be used by a qualified engineer to calculate the load-carrying capacity of the bridge.

The preliminary inspection may also reveal special conditions which require some follow-up work prior to conducting the inspection. If entrance onto railroad property or private property is required, the owner must be contacted so that proper clearances can be obtained. In the case of railroads, it may be necessary to have flag signalers on the site to control train traffic and protect the inspectors. If special traffic-control measures are required, it may be necessary to advise the local traffic authorities. Since each bridge is unique, there is no rule of thumb for preliminary inspections, but it is important that the inspector be aware that prior arrangements must be made and, in some cases, that important legal requirements must be satisfied.

The actual inspection is usually a smooth operation if the proper preparation work has been done. Crew members should be well rested and have compatible personalities. Bridge inspection can be dangerous, and all members of the team must depend upon one another. Thus plan to arrive in the best of condition. If the site is at some distance, plan to spend the night in a nearby motel so that you can get a full night's sleep and eat a leisurely meal.

Upon arrival at the site, the team leader should walk the crew around the bridge, explain the method and order of inspection, and brief the team members on their respective duties. At this point, specific problems or plans of action, such as how to reach a particularly difficult joint, can be discussed.

The actual inspection usually involves one person carefully observing and identifying every defect while a second person takes notes on the observations. The notes should be kept in a neat and uniform manner, either in a bound field book or on prepunched coated paper which can be bound as a permanent record. The notebook should identify the bridge, date of inspection, inspectors, and weather and contain detailed sketches showing the bridge identification system as well as sketches of noted defects. Figure 2.7-10 is a reproduction of a page from an actual field notebook. The record of inspection is very valuable and should be carefully treated and stored.

While it is not possible to predict every defect that an inspector might observe, the following will serve as a guide when inspecting concrete, steel, and wood.

Concrete Structures.   Concrete when placed is a fluid mass and, unless there are obvious pour defects such as rock pockets, forms a relatively smooth product. After a time, a number of defects can develop. Cracks are part of every concrete structure because concrete is weak in tension and cracks. To help concrete resist tensile forces, reinforcing bars are added. Thus it is normal to see fine hairline cracks in tensile regions of concrete structures. This is not a problem provided the cracks are small so that water does not enter them. However, large cracks in concrete or spalls (loose pieces, particularly those which expose reinforcing steel or appear to affect load-carrying capacity) should be considered serious and be reported. For example, a report might state "large spall 2 ft by 1 ft by 3 in [0.6 m by 0.3 m by 76.2 mm] deep in face of curb. Steel is exposed for 6 in [152.4 mm]." Concrete bridge decks pose a special problem owing to the application of salt during the winter in many areas. The salt penetrates the concrete and sets up a galvanic cell in the reinforcing steel. As a

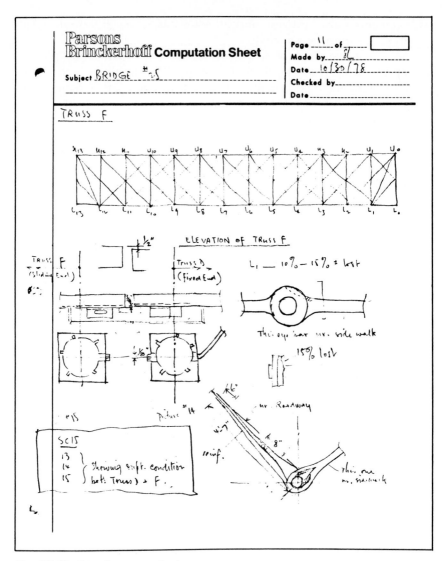

FIG. 2.7-10   Page from a notebook.

result, the reinforcing steel rusts and the rust expands, causing the concrete to spall, or delaminate. Specialized machines and techniques have been developed to inspect decks for delamination; one such technique is dragging a chain over the concrete deck to detect areas of lamination. For further information on the subject, refer to the *Federal Aid Highway Program Manual*, vol. 6, chap. 7, sec. 2, subsec. 7, "Concrete Bridge Decks"; and the American Concrete Institute publication ACI 201.R-68, *Guide for Making a Condition Survey of Concrete in Service.*

SUMMARY OF BRIDGE SURVEY REPORT

Bridge No.   Name:

Location: County:

Type: Single Span Truss Bridge   Dimensions: Length —   47 ft.-0 in.
                                                            Width —   33 ft.-0 in.
                                                            Roadway — 30 ft.-0 in.

General Description: Steel pony truss supported on masonry abutments

Date Constructed: Unknown   Date of Other Work: Strengthened - 1935

Date of Inspection: November 3, 1978   Date of Last Inspection: May, 1970 (report)
                                                                         July, 1976

Repair Work Since Last Inspection: Superstructure painted

Special Inspection Equipment Required: Ladder

Components	Material	General Remarks
Deck	Concrete	Cracks, leakage at edges - Gen. Fair Cond.
Approaches	Asphalt	Some patches, settlement - Fair Condition
Superstructure	Struct. steel	Heavy deterioration at fascias - Gen. Fair
Substructure	Stone masonry	Leakage at headers - Generally Good Condition
Channel	-	Appears adequate for flow
Highway Safety	-	Railings, walls unprotected

Ratings.   Truck Type (Tons)   H-15 (15)   3 (23)   3S2 (36)   3-3 (37)   Critical Member:
           Inventory   10.5   18   28.5   33.5   Fascia stringers
           Operating   15.5   26   41   48

Summary of Findings:
    The fascia stringers are seriously deteriorated at the floorbeam bearing
    seats due to heavy leakage around and through the edge of the roadway
    slab. The bottom chords of the truss are also deteriorated as are ends
    of stringers at abutment. There are no guide rails on approaches,
    leaving top of stone wingwalls unprotected.

Conclusions and Recommendations:
    This bridge is in generally fair condition with some major repairs needed.
    1. Post bridge for 14 ton weight limit
    2. Replace fascia stringers with new beams and install
        concrete barrier curbs along edge of roadway
    3. Repair truss bottom chords, clean and paint rusted
        structural steel
    4. Seal roadway joints above abutments
    5. Install steel beam guide rail on all approaches

FIG. 2.7-11a   Page from a bridge inspection report. (See pp. 2.7.21 and 2.7.22.)

On the underside of the bridge deck, water will seep through fine cracks in the roadway slab. The seepage carries dissolved salts which precipitate out on the underside of this deck, forming a characteristic pattern generally referred to as *effervescence*. The inspector will see this condition quite frequently. The presence of effervescence is not a problem, although it should be noted in the report. Spalling, large cracks, and exposed and rusting reinforcing steel are defects that should be reported.

Additional concrete-inspection techniques are possible, but they in-

SUMMARY OF BRIDGE SURVEY REPORT

Bridge No.   Name:

Location: County:

Type: Single Span Stringer Bridge   Dimensions: Length —   28 ft.-6 in.
                                                           Width —   32 ft.-6 in.
                                                           Roadway — 17 ft.-0 in.

General Description: Thirteen steel stringers supported on concrete abutments

Date Constructed: Unknown   Date of Other Work: Widened - 1932

Date of Inspection: October 23, 1978   Date of Last Inspection: September, 1976

Repair Work Since Last Inspection: Not Applicable

Special Inspection Equipment Required: None

Components	Material	General Remarks
Deck	Concrete	Roadway surface cracked, uneven - fair cond.
Approaches	Asphalt	Erosion at northeast shoulder - fair cond.
Superstructure	Struct. steel	Heavy rusting adjacent to south widening -fair
Substructure	Concrete	Spalling, scour at east abutment - fair cond.
Channel	-	Debris lodged against north fascia- marginal
Highway Safety	-	Fascia walls unprotected, no guide rails

Ratings.	Truck Type (Tons)	H-15 (15)	3 (23)	3S2 (36)	3-3 (37)	Critical Member:
	Inventory	0	0	0	0	Widened stringers
	Operating	2.4	3.2	4.9	6.0	

Summary of Findings:

    This bridge has no capacity for live load at inventory levels. There
    is heavy erosion at the northwest corner of the bridge with some under-
    cutting of the corner of the abutment.

Conclusions and Recommendations:

    This bridge should be replaced. The following repairs are needed if
    bridge is to remain open:
        1. Clear channel at north side of'bridge and rip rap embankment
            behind wingwall (high priority)
        2. Post bridge for 4 ton weight limit
        3. Install guide rails on approaches and across bridge span

Fig. 2.7-11*b*   Page from a bridge inspection report. (See pp. 2.7.21 and 2.7.22.)

volve some type of equipment or instrumentation. While these are valuable, inspectors should make primary use of their own natural instruments, their eyes and their common sense. The most valuable parts of an
inspection are careful observations accurately recorded by notes and
photographs. Sometimes concrete is sampled by taking cores, which can
then be examined in a testing laboratory for strength and, in the case of
bridge decks, for chloride content. The American Society for Testing and
Materials (ASTM) method C 42 can be used for this purpose. Concrete

strength can also be determined in situ with a number of proprietary test devices. However, these tests are generally considered to be less accurate than the testing of samples.

Structural-Steel Structures.   The inspection of structural steel is very similar to that of concrete. The primary technique is a close, careful visual inspection supplemented by written notes and color photographs, when possible.

Steel structures, if maintained by regular cleaning and painting, can be inspected in a straightforward manner. The inspector should be particularly attentive to looking for cracks, which in the case of steel can signal a major problem, the beginning of a failure in the member. The inspector should be aware that cracks may have occurred and been painted over. Typically, cracks occur at terminations of welds, at cuts, at joints, or wherever there is an abrupt change in the section of a member. Tests have shown that even a weld strike produces enough discontinuity to initiate a fatigue crack under some circumstances. The most likely places for cracking to occur are on members which make up the roadway deck, particularly around joints and under the traffic lanes, as they receive frequent heavy impacts from wheel loads.

If portions of a structure have not been maintained and are rusted or caked with debris, inspection is more difficult. In some cases, it may be necessary to arrange for the cleaning of the structure prior to inspection. When heavy rusting is encountered, the inspector should use a chipping hammer, such as the type used by welders to clean welds, to chip off the rust to reach sound metal. When chipping, it is imperative that safety goggles be used to protect the eyes, as each blow of the hammer can scatter fine metal particles in all directions. After the rust has been chipped off, the condition of the steel can be determined. If heavy loss of metal is suspected, the actual thickness remaining should be determined, usually with a set of calipers. If necessary, a small hole can be drilled through the member to determine its thickness. Alternatively, an ultrasonic device can measure the thickness. The thickness of rust can be deceiving. Rusted metal swells to approximately 8 times the thickness of unrusted metal. Thus ¼ (6.35 mm) of rust represents only a ⅟₃₂-in (0.794-mm) loss of steel. It is not practical to chip an entire bridge, but it is important that representative areas be chipped so that conditions of all areas of the bridge are adequately sampled. On older bridges, the inspector will encounter rusted rivet heads. Where loss of section is found, it should be reported.

On older bridges, especially those predating the American Association of State Highway and Transportation Officials (AASHTO) standard specifications, it may be necessary to remove one or more samples of metal for laboratory testing to determine the strength and, if necessary, the chemistry of the metal. The location and number and size of the samples should be determined by an engineer who specializes in bridges.

Occasionally, an inspector will encounter a bridge with a steel open-grid deck. Such a deck is generally used to minimize the weight on the structure and is made up with numerous small bars and plates. Several styles are available, each style from a different manufacturer. Grid decks have a limited life, and under heavy traffic the small members will crack and loosen. The inspector should be aware of the expected life of the deck and learn to recognize a grid deck which is nearing the end of its useful life as evidenced by numerous broken pieces and repairs. Grid decks can be equipped with small studs to aid in traction. The studs can be part of new construction or can be added later. Their presence or absence should be noted. Also, some grid decks are filled, partially or fully, with concrete to extend their life or improve traction. The presence and condition of the concrete should be noted.

Timber Structures. Except for fender systems, timber is infrequently used in bridge construction today. Nevertheless, the inspector will find timber decks, sidewalks, access stairs, and temporary bents, particularly in more rural areas. Although the timber is usually treated, it does not have the life span of concrete or steel and must be replaced more frequently. The inspector should note the general condition of the timber as well as its connections. The timber should be probed with a sharp blade to determine the condition of its interior. Loose or missing pieces should also be noted, particularly if they present a hazardous condition.

Bearings. Bearings and joints are two areas which require an inspector's particular attention, as they are the usual source of trouble. Previously, there was a discussion on bridge movement due to loadings and temperature and the reasons for bearings and joints. It was also mentioned that, whenever possible, the inspection team should review the plans of a bridge to determine the nature of the bearings, whether expansion or fixed. The inspector should be conscious of the importance of bridge bearings and joints, and during the course of inspection there should be close visual observation of all the bridge bearings or what is felt to be a representative sample of them. If there are expansion bearings, the inspector should determine whether or not they are working, i.e., able to move, remembering that on cold days the bridge has shortened while on hot days it has expanded. With 50°F (28°C) temperature change, a 100-ft- (30.5-m-) long bridge will move 3/8 in (9.525 mm).

On older bridges bearings are of all-metal construction, generally a combination of steel, bronze, and stainless steel. On newer bridges, erected since 1950, some shorter-span bridges have used bearings with neoprene, Teflon, and stainless steel. The edge of neoprene should be observed for splits or signs of aging.

On larger bridges bearings may be covered with a protective housing. To inspect the bearing, it may be necessary to remove a portion of the housing. This should be done with care so as to not dismantle the bearing proper.

If there is doubt that a bearing is working (i.e., that the bridge is expanding and contracting), it is possible to test the movement. On a hot, sunny day, make a mark on a bridge at its expansion end and a corresponding mark on the supporting pier or abutment, and record the temperature. It may be necessary to use a plumb bob to line up the marks. Then the next morning, when the bridge is cool, come back and check the mark, and record the movement and temperature. On the basis of the change in temperature and the length of the span, the measured movement should equal 0.000006 for concrete bridges and 0.0000065 for steel bridges times the length of the span times the change in temperature in degrees Farhrenheit ($1°F = 1.8°C$).

If signs of distress are determined at the bearing area (usually cracked concrete around the bearing seat), the inspector should attempt to ascertain the source of the problem. Is the bearing frozen? Has the abutment tilted? Has the bridge been hit and knocked out of line? The inspector should include the observation in the notes along with a photograph, when possible.

Expansion Joints.   Probably the most frequent source of problems with bridges is the expansion joints. While their function is clear, actual design and maintenance can present problems. The joint is expected to move and yet be able to withstand millions of cycles of load from wheels and, in many cases, wheel loads from large trucks moving at high speeds. In addition, many joints are designed to be watertight. The inspector should carefully examine the bridge joints. Are they loose? Are they clean? Are there broken pieces? Do they appear to be leaking? The cleanliness of a joint is important. The presence of a few stones wedged into a bridge joint can in effect freeze the joint from closing. The resulting pressure has been known to cause a bridge to move off its bearing.

As with bearings, joints have evolved from all-metal to modern devices which usually rely on neoprene to form a seal as well as part of the load-carrying capacity. Typically, the inspector should find the joint in a so-called open position; that is, it should be able to travel an additional distance. On a very hot day, when a bridge has fully expanded, there should be additional space for the joint and bearing to travel; otherwise, the bridge has overtraveled. Conversely, on a very cold day the joint should have a rather large gap to allow for expansion. While these are subjective judgments, the inspector should be aware of the joints' function and relate the joints' position to the temperature. If time permits, it is helpful to record the bridge temperature and the position of the joints, particularly if trouble is suspected.

Bridge Substructures. Inspection of a bridge also includes the substructure, the piers and abutments. Since the substructure is usually of concrete or masonry construction, the inspection would be concerned primarily with the condition of the concrete or masonry and the inspector would look for cracks and spalls. In addition, the inspector should ascertain whether or not there has been any tilting or moving of the substructure. This is usually detected at the superstructure bearings. If movement is suspected, then the substructure should be surveyed to check its position with respect to the as-built plans, if they are available, or the design plans. A simple check for tilting is to place a level on any surface which should be horizontal or vertical. When inspecting abutments, the inspector should ascertain whether or not there are weep holes in the face of the abutment and whether or not they are functioning. If the weep holes become plugged, a large buildup of lateral water pressure on the abutment develops and should be corrected.

If the bridge spans a body of water, the bottom of the substructure may be underwater. If the water is a stream or river, scour may occur around the footing. Provided that the water is not too deep, the inspector can use a probe to determine whether or not there is scour and possibly the general condition of the portion of the structure below the waterline. If the use of a probe is not possible or if a more detailed inspection is needed, a professional diver experienced in this type of inspection should be employed to conduct an inspection and a written report on the diver's findings be provided. Underwater photography is common, and it could be requested as part of the inspection. The inspector should be present at the underwater inspection to confer with and direct the diver as well as to keep record notes of the diver's observations. Underwater diving is hazardous, particularly if there is a current, so the task should be undertaken with great care and by a specialist.

The inspector should also observe the general condition of the waterway. Is it clogged with debris or clean?

If the bridge is over a navigable body of water, there usually will be a fender system. In some cases, the fender system will consist only of a few timber rub strips, and inspection effort will be minimal. However, if boat traffic is significant and the bridge piers flank a channel, there will be a substantial fender system. Usually the fender system will be treated timber fastened together with steel bolts and cables. The inspection is best conducted from a boat, preferably at low tide. The wood should be probed for condition and inspected for signs of deterioration due to impact. An underwater inspection is called for if scour or other underwater problems are suspected. Also, underwater inspections should be undertaken if there has been a relatively long time since the last inspection, say, 10 or 15 years. Finally, fender inspection should include a check of the navigation lights. Arrangements should be made to turn the lights on so that any deficiencies will be obvious.

Bridge-Inspection Reports.   While inspection of a bridge is important, the results of the inspection are not of great value unless they can be properly recorded and then conveyed to others. Thus a report becomes a vital part of the bridge-inspection process. It is essential that the report be prepared in large part by the inspector, who, after all, is the actual observer of the conditions being reported.

The report of a bridge inspection can include a range of presentations, from a one-page memorandum or letter to a multivolume work complete with calculations of bridge capacity, charts, graphs, and photographs. The product obviously depends upon the needs of the client, the depth of the inspection, and the complexity and size of the bridge. The more elaborate reports are prepared by consulting firms that specialize in bridge capacity and evaluation, and it would be beyond the scope of this chapter to discuss those reports. This discussion will be limited to a report associated with a small- to medium-span bridge.

A suggested format for reports is as follows:

1. *Letter of Transmittal.*
2. *Introduction.*   It describes the reason for the inspection, names the persons involved, and then describes the content of the report.
3. *History.*   This is optional, but on an older bridge it can be quite useful, particularly if there have been modifications or renovations.
4. *Findings.*   This is a report on what was found. A general plan of the bridge at the start of this section is most valuable.
5. *Rating.*   This is required on some bridges and involves detailed load-capacity calculations.
6. *Recommendations.*   These may be requested by the client and may include cost estimates for repairs.
7. *Conclusions.*   This is a summary of the report.
8. *Appendix.*   This may include photographs, calculations, and reduced plans.

The report should be very specific and should describe exactly what was done and what was found. For example, state in the introduction: "On June 18 and 19, 1982, I. M. Looking and I. Foundit conducted an inspection of the Cos Cob River Bridge, Greenwich, Connecticut. The inspection was conducted by observing the deck, stringers, bearings, abutments, and piers of the bridge. No inspection of the underwater portion was made. . . . " Thus concise language leaves no question in the reader's mind as to what was done.

The findings portion requires some organization, and one usually starts with the superstructure and works down. Sketches are helpful in locating and identifying areas under discussion and should be included when practical. For example, state "On the lower chord of the north truss from panel point L2 to L3, there was heavy rust and three lacing bars were rusted through." Again, the language is concise, and there is no question in the reader's mind. Pages from a typical report are included earlier as Fig. 2.7-11*a* and *b*.

After covering the findings of the inspection, the report may include a rating section on the capacity of the structure based on detailed engineering calculations. For a highway bridge, rating calculations would be in accordance with the governing code such as the AASHTO *Manual for Maintenance Inspection of Bridges* or the American Railway Engineering Association (AREA) *Manual for Railway Engineering*, chap. 8, part 19, and chap. 15, part 7.

Additionally, the report may include a recommendations section to discuss possible repairs, e.g., "The bridge needs to be cleaned and re-painted, and all cracks in the deck should be sealed by epoxy injection." Further information may include a detailed estimate of the cost of the repairs.

Or if, for example, the report is to be brief, the report may make no recommendations and merely draw a general conclusion: "The bridge is in generally good condition provided that normal maintenance is continued."

If possible, color-print photographs should be included to provide a very powerful description of the conditions found, particularly if there are serious conditions. The picture of a missing handrail or smashed fender can have a strong impact in a report. If prints are included, glossy prints are preferred and in a large format, say, 5 by 7 in (127 by 177.8 mm) or 8 by 10 in (203.2 by 254 mm). The photographs can be mounted on heavy stock with an appropriate description given below.

Finally, all records associated with the inspection should be assembled, cataloged, and saved. The inspector of a bridge assumes some liability and should preserve an accurate record of his or her efforts.

SPECIAL BRIDGE-INSPECTION PROCEDURES

As suggested earlier, there are a number of special bridges whose inspection is beyond the scope of this chapter. Movable bridges are quite common where there is a navigable waterway, and they are an economical alternative to a high-level bridge. There are three unique types of movable bridges: lift bridges (Fig. 2.7-12), swing bridges (Fig. 2.7-13), and bascule bridges (Fig. 2.7-14), typically of steel construction. All types have drive machinery and controls including motors, brakes, reducers, shafts, and gears to open and close the bridge. While the inspection of the structure is similar to that of other steel bridges discussed previously, the inspection of the machinery and controls is highly specialized. The reader is directed to the U.S. Department of Transportation publication *Bridge Inspector's Manual for Movable Bridges* for particular details.

Other specialized bridges include suspension and cable-stayed bridges (see Figs. 2.7-15 and 2.7-16). Like movables, these bridges require a level of inspection beyond the scope of this chapter, particularly for the cable elements.

FIG. 2.7-12   A vertical-lift bridge.

FIG. 2.7-13   A swing bridge.

FIG. 2.7-14   A bascule bridge.

FIG. 2.7-15 A suspension bridge.

FIG. 2.7-16 A cable-stayed bridge.

REFERENCES

For additional information, the reader is referred to the following:

Johnson, Sidney, M.: *Deterioration, Maintenance and Repair of Structures*, McGraw-Hill Book Company, New York, 1965.

Manual for Bridge Maintenance, American Association of State Highway and Transportation Officials, Washington, 1983.

Manual for Maintenance Inspection of Bridges, American Association of State Highway and Transportation Officials, Washington, 1983.

Park, Sung H., P.E.: *Bridge Inspection and Structural Analysis: Handbook of Bridge Inspection*, Trenton, N.J., 1980.

U.S. Department of Transportation, *Bridge Inspector's Manual for Movable Bridges*, Washington, 1977.

———: *Bridge Inspector's Training Manual*, Washington, 1970.

White, Kenneth, John Minor, Kenneth Derocher, and Conrad Heins, Jr.: *Bridge Maintenance Inspection and Evaluation*, Marcel Dekker, Inc., New York, 1981.

CHAPTER 2.8

Electrical Construction

Kenneth D. Pendergrass
Senior Quality Assurance Consultant
F & M Technical Services, Inc.
Dallas, Texas

This chapter presents a general discussion of typical electrical construction and an outline of basic field inspection criteria.

SAFETY PRECAUTIONS

During performance of inspection activities on any electrical-construction project, appropriate safety precautions must be exercised. Contact with exposed energized electrical-circuit components can result in personal injury and death. Most projects utilize safety tagging procedures during start-up and energization of the circuits and equipment constructed. All personnel should read and become familiar with safety procedures. Failure to follow such procedures can result in injury not only to yourself but also to your coworkers. Always approach exposed circuit components as though they were energized until it can be verified that power is disconnected.

GENERAL DISCUSSION

The construction of practically all industrial facilities includes varying scopes and magnitudes of electrical construction. Electrical construction will vary from simple lighting circuits to complex high-energy power, control, and instrumentation systems.

Complex electrical power, control, and instrumentation systems and equipment are required in electrical-power-generation plants to control the process of transforming thermal or mechanical energy into electrical energy. Power plants vary in generating capacity from a few thousand kilowatts to several hundred megawatts. Power-plant electrical systems and equipment are generally well defined by the engineer in project plans, drawings, and specifications. The project drawings and specifications define the applicable codes, construction standards, and, in many cases, field inspection requirements.

Electrical-power transmission lines may be constructed overhead or underground. Transmission voltages of 10 kV to over 500 kV are used to carry electrical power from the power-generation plants to distribution substations. Substations step down the transmission voltages to a range of 220 to 880 V and control local distribution of electrical power to the various industrial and residential users. Facilities for power transmission and distribution are generally well defined by the engineer in project plans, drawings, and specifications, which also specify the applicable codes and construction standards.

Industrial plants such as steel mills, petrochemical plants, heavy-equipment-manufacturing plants, and similar facilities require complex and high-energy electrical systems and equipment to produce their respective products. These facilities and the required electrical systems and equipment are defined in the engineer's plans and specifications.

The above discussions briefly present three typical examples of electrical-construction projects, each of which has differing requirements for industry-unique systems, equipment, and construction standards. Therefore, it must be recognized that the scope of work for both construction and field inspection will vary on each project depending upon the complexity and the industrial type of the facility to be constructed. Prior to the start of each project, the inspector should review the engineer's plans and specifications to determine the project's scope of work, unique requirements, and applicable codes and standards.

It is not within the scope of this chapter to attempt to discuss the various industry-unique requirements for electrical construction. The electrical installations and respective field inspection criteria presented in this chapter are generally common to all industrial and residential electrical-construction projects. Should any of the criteria defined herein conflict with specific project requirements, the project requirements shall govern.

The **National Electrical Code**®, NFPA No. 70*, is in general the recognized industry code applicable to the design and construction of electrical service for industrial and residential facilities. The **National Electrical Code**® was established and prepared by the National Fire Protection Association under the auspices of the American National Standards Institute. The requirements of this **Code** were used as a guide to define several of the field inspection criteria presented herein. The electrical field inspector should be knowledgeable of the requirements and criteria defined in the **National Electrical Code**®.

****National Electrical Code**® and **NEC**® are registered trademarks of the National Fire Protection Association, Inc., Quincy, MA.

MATERIAL CONTROL

Appropriate controls should be established and actions taken to assure that only correct and acceptable parts, materials, and equipment are used for construction. Early detection and correction or replacement of incorrect or defective items significantly helps to eliminate substantial delays.

Procurement. Project personnel assigned responsibility for purchasing must assure that only items specified by the engineer's drawings are procured from competent suppliers and subcontractors. Projects may require procurement of special control and/or processing of specific items such as nondestructive examinations, material analysis and traceability, maintenance of a special environment on an item prior to operation, and others. These requirements must be imposed on the affected suppliers and appropriately specified in the purchase orders. The field inspector should review these purchase orders to verify that special requirements are appropriately specified and that certificates and other required data are supplied with the items.

Receiving. All purchased parts, materials, and equipment should be examined by designated project personnel upon receipt for:

- Evidence of shipping damage
- Compliance with purchase-order requirements relative to the proper number and type of items received

The field inspector should perform surveillance inspections to assure continued performance of the previously described receipt verifications.

The field inspector may be required to perform receiving inspections on selected purchased items. These items should be determined and selected according to the following:

- Special processed or controlled items as defined in the subsection "Procurement"
- Long-lead delivery items, high-cost items, or other factors that may significantly affect schedules, such as failures or nonconformance conditions occurring during construction

Receiving inspection criteria can be determined from the engineer's drawings and specifications, applicable codes, and/or manufacturer's data. The established receiving inspections should be written in the form of inspection plans or checklists.

Storage. All parts, materials, and equipment must be appropriately stored and protected to prevent damage and/or deterioration. Storage areas should be maintained separately from construction areas and activities. Storage-area requirements are generally classified in four levels, defined as follows:

Level I. Outside storage which is well drained and preferably gravel-covered or paved. The items stored in this area should be placed on cribbing or its equivalent to allow air circulation and prevent the trapping of water.

Level II. The same as Level I requirements except that items stored in this area must be protected from wet and inclement weather. These items may be stored in a suitable building or securely covered with weatherproof and tear-resistant coverings so that water, salt spray, and dirt do not reach the items.

Level III. Weatherproof inside storage which provides protection from temperature extremes, moisture and condensation, dust, dirt, and chemical vapors. This facility should include appropriate electrical power for heaters enclosed in motors, motor-control centers, and similar equipment.

Level IV. The same as Level III except that temperature and humidity control is additionally required.

The field inspector should perform periodic surveillance inspections of the storage areas to assure that storage levels and items in storage are maintained and protected.

Handling. Electrical parts, materials, and equipment should be handled and transported consistently with good material-handling practices to prevent damage. Special rigging, hoisting, and handling procedures should be implemented for specific items because of weight, size, or susceptibility to shock damage. The field inspector should perform surveillance inspections of handling operations and activities. Periodic inspections of hoisting, rigging, and handling equipment should be conducted according to the following:

- Frayed, worn, or otherwise deteriorated rigging must not be used.
- Rigging items such as hooks, shackles, and turnbuckles that appear to have yielded or are distorted must not be used.
- Hoisting equipment and rigging must be kept clean, properly serviced, and free of conditions that could damage the equipment being handled or impair safe operation.

Equipment Maintenance. Several types of electrical equipment normally require maintenance tests and checks during storage. Specific storage and maintenance required for each item of equipment will be specified by the manufacturer or the engineer. The normal types of maintenance tests and checks are listed as follows:

- Items pressurized with inert gas must be monitored at specified intervals.

- Desiccant humidity indicators must be monitored and the desiccant changed or reprocessed when specified.

- Insulation testing of electrical equipment must be performed on a scheduled basis in accordance with the manufacturer's recommendations.

- Shafts of rotating equipment must be rotated as specified, and the shafts must not reset to previous positions after rotation.

The field inspector should maintain an appropriate maintenance log to assure and verify that required maintenance tests and checks are performed.

CONSTRUCTION AND INSTALLATION

Only the latest applicable revision or change-level engineering drawings, specifications, and applicable codes or other documents shall be used for construction and inspection. Tools, gauges, and measuring and test devices used during construction and inspection must be adequate and appropriate.

Typical electrical installations commonly required on construction projects are addressed in the following paragraphs, along with checklists containing the respective recommended inspection criteria.

Embedded Metallic and Nonmetallic Conduit.   Concrete placement is outside the scope of this subsection. The following checklist items address inspection of conduit installation prior to and after concrete placement.
Prior to Concrete Placement

1. Conduit and fittings are the correct size, type, and material as specified by the engineer's drawings.

2. Conduit routing and elevations are according to the engineer's drawings.

3. Expansion sleeves are installed in conduit runs which cross building expansion joints.

4. Minimum-bend radii comply with requirements defined in Table 2.8-1 unless otherwise specified by the engineer's drawings.

5. Each conduit run does not contain more than the equivalent of four quarter bends (360° total) unless otherwise specified.

6. Each conduit run follows, as closely as possible, the routing shown on the engineer's drawings without additional bends.

7. Conduit and/or sleeves terminating at wall or floor surfaces are installed with couplings or plugs as specified by the engineer's drawings.

8. Conduits are separated by at least 2 in (50.8 mm) sidewall to sidewall when run parallel and 1 in (25.4 mm) when crossing to allow for concrete encasement unless otherwise specified.

9. Conduit is installed so that it will be encased in concrete with a 2-in (50.8-mm) coverage unless otherwise specified.

10. Conduits are properly secured and anchored to prevent floating and maintain alignment during the concrete pour.

11. Conduit ends are appropriately plugged or protected to prevent the entrance of concrete during the pour.

12. Damaged or cut areas in the galvanized coating on steel conduit are touched up with an appropriate repair coating or paint.

TABLE 2.8-1 Radius of Conduit Bends, in
(Reference **NEC** NFPA N. 70, Table 346-10)

Size of conduit, in	Conductors without lead sheath, in*	Conductors with lead sheath, in*
½	4	6
¾	5	8
1	6	11
1¼	8	14
1½	10	16
2	12	21
2½	15	25
3	18	31
3½	21	36
4	24	40
4½	27	45
5	30	50
6	36	61

*1 in = 25.4 m.m.

Reprinted with permission from NFPA 70-1984, National Electrical Code, Copyright © 1983, National Fire Protection Association, Quincy, MA 02269. This reprinted material is not the complete and official position of the NFPA on the referenced subject, which is represented only by the standard in its entirety.

Exception: For field bends for conductors without lead sheath and made with a single-operation (one-shot) bending machine designed for the purpose, the minimum radius shall not be less than indicated in Table 2.8-1 Exception.

TABLE 2.8-1 Exception   Radius of
Conduit Bends, in

Size of conduit, in	Radius to center of conduit, in*
½	4
¾	4½
1	5¾
1¼	7¼
1½	8¼
2	9½
2½	10½
3	13
3⅓	15
4	16
4½	20
5	24
6	30

*1 in = 25.4 m.m.
Reprinted with permission from NFPA 70-1984,
National Electrical Code, Copyright © 1983,
National Fire Protection Association, Quincy, MA
02269. This reprinted material is not the complete
and official position of the NFPA on the referenced subject, which is represented only by the
standard in its entirety.

NOTES:

1. The radius of the curve is measured to the
   inner edge or surface of the conduit bend.

2. Bends shall be made such that the conduit is not
   damaged and the internal diameter is not effectively reduced.

3. For additional conduit-bending information,
   refer to **National Electrical Code,** NFPA No. 70,
   Arts. 346 and 347.

After Concrete Placement

1. Each conduit is swabbed or otherwise checked immediately after the
   pour to ensure that no concrete has entered it.

2. Conduit ends are appropriately capped and protected.

3. Each conduit run is identified as specified by the engineer's drawings.

Exposed Conduit.   Exposed-conduit installations as addressed herein include both rigid metal and rigid nonmetallic conduit. The following
inspection criteria are applicable unless otherwise specified by the engineer's drawings and/or specifications.

1. Conduit, fittings, and associated pull, junction, and outlet boxes are the correct size, types, and materials.

2. Conduit routing and elevations meet all requirements.

3. Conduit bend radii comply with requirements specified in Table 2.8-1.

4. Each conduit run does not contain more than the equivalent of four quarter bends (360°).

5. The cut ends of all conduits are appropriately reamed or trimmed to remove rough or sharp edges.

6. Appropriate bushings are installed where a conduit enters boxes or other fittings to protect the wiring from abrasions unless the boxes or fittings are designed to provide equivalent protection.

7. All conduit couplings and connectors are made up tight. In wet locations, couplings, connectors, and associated boxes are of the raintight type.

8. Expansion joints are installed in conduit runs where necessary to compensate for thermal expansion and contraction.

9. Where the ends of a conduit run are exposed to widely different environments, there are provisions to seal conduit ends to prevent the entry of moisture, vapors, fumes, etc.

10. The required pull and junction boxes are installed and supported as required.

11. All conduit runs are adequately supported with conventional clamps, straps, and, as applicable, racks and braces which are securely fastened to building structural members.

12. All conduit is supported within 3 ft (0.9 m) of each outlet, pull and junction box, cabinet, and fittings.

13. Rigid metal conduits are supported as follows:

    a. Horizontal runs are supported at least every 10 ft (3 m), and vertical runs are supported at least every 20 ft (6 m), or

    b. If conduits are made up with threaded couplings, straight runs may be supported according to the maximum distances between supports defined in Table 2.8-2.

14. All rigid nonmetallic conduit runs are supported according to the maximum distances between supports defined in Table 2.8-3.

15. All conduit supports are of sufficient size and capacity to support conduit loads adequately.

16. When used, anchor bolts in concrete are installed according to the manufacturer's procedures.

TABLE 2.8-2   Support of Rigid Metal Conduit

(Reference **NEC** NFPA No. 70, Table 346-12)

Conduit size, in	Maximum distance between conduit supports, ft*
½–¾	10
1	12
1¼–1½	14
2–2½	16
3 and larger	20

*1 ft = 0.3048 m.

Reprinted with permission from NFPA 70-1984, **National Electrical Code,** Copyright© 1983, National Fire Protection Association, Quincy, MA 02269. This reprinted material is not the complete and official position of the NFPA on the referenced subject, which is represented only by the standard in its entirety.

TABLE 2.8-3   Support of Rigid Nonmetallic Conduit

(Reference **NEC** NFPA No. 70, Table 347-8)

Conduit size, in	Maximum spacing between supports, ft*
½–1	3
1¼–2	5
2½–3	6
3½–5	7
6	8

*1 ft = 0.3048 m.

Reprinted with permission from NFPA 70-1984, **National Electrical Code,** Copyright © 1983, National Fire Protection Association, Quincy, MA 02269. This reprinted material is not the complete and official position of the NFPA on the referenced subject, which is represented only by the standard in its entirety.

17. Welding of support installations complies with the welding code and/or specifications delineated by the engineer's drawings.
18. Damaged or cut areas in the galvanized or other protective coating on metal conduit are touched up with an appropriate repair coating or paint.
19. Metal conduit installations are properly grounded.
20. Each conduit run is properly identified.

Flexible Metal Tubing and Conduit.   Installations addressed herein include flexible metal tubing, flexible metal conduit, and liquidtight flexible metal conduit. Flexible tubing and conduit are normally required in raceway installations where frequent disconnection and connection of equipment may be required or where vibration isolation is required as in raceway connections to motors. The following inspection criteria are applicable unless the engineer's drawings and/or specifications specify otherwise.

1. Conduit, tubing, and fittings are the correct sizes and types specified by the engineer's drawings.

2. The length of flexible metal tubing used in each installation does not exceed 6 ft (1.8 m).

3. The sizes of flexible metal tubing used are ⅜-in trade size minimum to ¾-in trade size maximum.

4. The bend radii of flexible metal tubing as measured to the inside of the bend comply with Table 2.8-4A or Table 2.8-4B as applicable.

TABLE 2.8-4A Minimum-Bend Radii for Flexible Metal Tubing Which Will Be Infrequently Flexed in Service after Installation
(Reference **NEC** NFPA No. 70, Table 349-20b)

Size, in	Minimum radii, in*
⅜	10
½	12½
¾	17½

*1 in = 25.4 mm.

TABLE 2.8-4B Minimum-Bend Radii for Flexible Metal Tubing Which Will Not Be Flexed in Service after Installation
(Reference **NEC** NFPA No. 70, Table 349-20c)

Size, in	Minimum radii, in*
⅜	3½
½	4
¾	5

*1 in = 25.4 mm.

Reprinted with permission from NFPA 70-1984, **National Electrical Code,** Copyright© 1983, National Fire Protection Association, Quincy, MA 02269. This reprinted material is not the complete and official position of the NFPA on the referenced subject, which is represented only by the standard in its entirety.

5. The sizes of flexible metal conduit used are ½-in trade size minimum to 4-in trade size maximum. The nominal trade size of ⅜ in may be used in lengths that do not exceed 72 in (1828.8 mm).

6. Liquidtight flexible metal conduit is used in wet locations, storage-battery rooms, or any hazardous-environment-locations.

7. Flexible metal conduit is secured with conventional and appropriate clamps or straps at intervals not exceeding 4½ ft (1.37 m) and within 12 in (304.8 mm) on each side of every box or fitting. Exceptions to the above are:

   a. Conduit lengths of not more than 3 ft (0.9 m) where vibration isolation is required or other conditions where flexibility in service is necessary.

   b. Conduit lengths of not more than 6 ft (1.8 m) from a fixture terminal connection for tap connections to lighting fixtures.

8. Each run of flexible conduit does not contain more than the equivalent of four quarter bends (360° total) including those bends located immediately at the outlets or fittings.

9. Flexible conduit installations are grounded in accordance with the engineer's drawings.

Cable Trays.   A cable-tray system is defined as a unit or assembly of units or sections and associated fittings, made of metal or other noncombustible materials, which forms a rigid structural system used to support electrical cables. A cable tray, as used herein, includes both ladder and solid-bottom types. The following inspection criteria are applicable unless the engineer's drawings and/or specifications specify otherwise.

1. The tray installed is the type, size, and material as specified by the engineer's drawings.

2. The tray routing and elevations comply with the engineer's drawings.

3. Tray sections are securely jointed, and tray runs are attached to supports with appropriate fittings and hardware as specified by the manufacturer's instructions and/or the engineer's drawings.

4. The cable-tray surfaces that contact electrical cable and wiring do not present sharp edges, burrs, or projections injurious to cable insulation.

5. All cable-tray runs are supported with horizontal, vertical, and/or diagonal braces of sufficient size and capacity to support tray loads adequately.

6. Cable-tray supports are securely fastened to building structural members.

7. Spacing of tray supports does not exceed 10 ft (3 m).

8. When used, anchor bolts in concrete are installed according to the manufacturer's procedures.

9. Welding of support installations complies with the welding code and/or specifications delineated by the engineer's drawings.

10. Damaged or cut areas in the galvanized or other protective coating on the cable trays are touched up with appropriate repair coating or paint.

11. Sufficient space is provided and maintained about the cable trays to permit adequate access for installing and maintaining the required cables and wiring.

12. Appropriate supports are provided where cables enter or leave cable trays to prevent stress and damage to the cables.

13. Cable-tray covers are provided for those portions of tray runs where additional cable protection is required, such as runs under walkway gratings and vertical runs through floors.

14. Cable-tray installations are grounded in accordance with the engineer's drawings.

15. Cable-tray runs are identified as specified by the engineer's drawings.

Raceways: Surface and Floor. Raceways as used herein include metal and nonmetallic surface raceways and underfloor raceways.

1. Raceways are the sizes and types specified by the engineer's drawings.

2. Raceway routings comply with the engineer's drawings.

3. Surface and floor raceways are not used in wet areas.

4. Raceway surfaces that contact electrical cable and wiring do not present sharp edges, burrs, or projections injurious to cable insulation.

5. Appropriate raceway covers are provided to protect cable and wiring adequately after installation.

6. Appropriate supports are provided where cables enter or leave raceways to prevent stress or damage to cables.

Equipment Installations. General types of equipment normally installed within the scope of an electrical-construction contract are as follows:

Switchboards	Machine tools
Panelboards	Transformers
Control centers	Switch gear
Motors	Lighting fixtures
Capacitors	Switches

Generators   Storage batteries
Cranes and hoists   Resistors and reactors
Data-processing equipment   Communications equipment
Elevators, escalators, and similar items   Heating, air conditioning, and refri-
                                                    geration

Prior to performing field inspections of equipment installation, the specific requirements should be determined from the engineer's and manufacturer's drawings and specifications. General inspection checklist items are as follows:

1. Equipment is located, aligned, and leveled in accordance with the engineer's drawings.

2. Mounting bases and/or mounting methods are in accordance with the engineer's drawings and/or manufacturer's instructions.

3. As applicable, welding associated with the equipment mounting is in accordance with the engineer's drawings and welding-code requirements.

4. When used, anchor bolts in concrete are installed according to the manufacturer's procedures and instructions.

5. Sufficient access and work space is provided around the equipment to permit safe operation and maintenance. Unless otherwise specified by the engineer's drawings and/or specifications, the following guidelines apply:

    a. Not less than 30 in (762 mm) is provided in front of electrical equipment where there are no exposed live parts.

    b. The minimum headroom for working spaces around equipment should be 6¼ ft (1.9 m).

    c. When equipment is likely to require examination, adjustment, servicing, or maintenance while energized, working clearances from live parts are as indicated in Table 2.8-5.

6. Equipment is permanently identified with the manufacturer's name or trademark and the operating voltage, current, wattage, and/or other data required by the engineer's drawings.

7. Live parts of equipment operating at 50 V or more must be guarded against accidental contact by enclosure in appropriate cabinets or access controlled and guarded by barriers, screens, partitions, or doors with appropriate caution or warning signs. Doors or other openings to live parts of equipment operating at over 600 V should be equipped with locks.

8. Unguarded live parts must be mounted above work areas at elevations that are not less than those defined in Table 2.8-6.

TABLE 2.8-5 Working Clearances
(Reference **NEC** NFPA No. 70, Tables 110-16A and 110-34a)

Voltage to ground, V	Minimum clear distance, ft*		
	Condition 1	Condition 2	Condition 3
0–150	3	3	3
150–600	3	3½	4
601–2,500	3	4	5
2,501–9,000	4	5	6
9,001–25,000	5	6	9
25,001–75 kV	6	8	10
Above 75kV	8	10	12

*1 ft = 0.3048 m.

Reprinted with permission from NFPA 70-1984, **National Electrical Code**, Copyright© 1983, National Fire Protection Association, Quincy, MA02269. This reprinted material is not the complete and official position of the NFPA on the referenced subject, which is represented only by the standard in its entirety.

Condition 1: Exposed live parts on one side and no live or grounded parts on the other side of the working space or exposed live parts on both sides effectively guarded by suitable insulating materials. Insulated wire or busbars operating at not over 300 V are not considered live parts.

Conditon 2: Exposed live parts on one side and grounded parts on the other side. Concrete, brick, or tile walls are considered to be grounded surfaces.

Condition 3: Exposed live parts on both sides of the work space (not guarded as defined in Condition 1) with the operation in between.

NOTE: Working space is not required in back of equipment where there are no replaceable or adjustable parts and where all connections are accessible from locations other than the back. Where access is required to work on de-energized parts of enclosed equipment, a minimum working space of 30 in (762 mm) horizontally should be provided.

TABLE 2.8-6 Elevation of Unguarded Energized Parts above Working Spaces
(Reference **NEC** NFPA No. 70, Table 110-34e)

Nominal voltage between phases, V	Elevation, ft*
601–7,500	8'6"
7,501–35,000	9'
Over 35,000 or 35 kV	9' + 0.37≡ per kV Above 35 kV

*1 ft = 0.3048 m.

Reprinted with permission from MFPA 70-1984, **National Electrical Code**, Copyright © 1983, National Fire Protection Association, Quincy, MA 02269. This reprinted material is not the complete and official position of the NFPA on the referenced subject, which is represented only by the standard in its entirety.

9. Raceways (rigid conduit, flexible conduit, flexible tubing, wireways, etc.) are properly routed and secured to the equipment as specified by the engineer's drawings.

10. Appropriate bushings are installed at conduit terminations and in conductor openings in metal enclosures, cabinets, and boxes as required to prevent damage to cables and wiring.

11. Equipment enclosures, cabinets, frames, panels, etc., are properly grounded as specified by the engineer's drawings.

12. Adequate space is provided inside equipment enclosures, cabinets, and boxes for cable and wire routing and bending. Recommended minimum wire-bending spaces are presented in Table 2.8-7.

13. Any damage to the equipment during installation has been properly repaired, including paint or finish touch-up.

14. Leveling and alignment of mechanical equipment such as motors, cranes, and hoists and machine tools are normally completed by a mechanical contractor and are not within the scope of the electrical contract.

TABLE 2.8-7   Minimum Wire-Bending Space at Terminals and Minimum Width of Wiring Gutters, in*
(Reference **NEC** NFPA No. 70, Table 373-6a)

AWG or circular-mil wire size	Wires per terminal				
	1	*2*	*3*	*4*	*5*
14−10	Not specified				
8−6	1½				
4−3	2				
2	2½				
1	3				
0−00	3½	5	7		
000−0000	4	6	8		
250 MCM	4½	6	8	10	
300−350 MCM	5	8	10	12	
400−500 MCM	6	8	10	12	14
600−700 MCM	8	10	12	14	16
750−900 MCM	8	12	14	16	18
1000−1250 MCM	10				
1500−2000 MCM	12				

*1 in = 25.4 mm.

Reprinted with permission from NFPA 70-1984, **National Electrical Code**, Copyright© 1983, National Fire Protection Association, Quincy, MA 02269. This reprinted material is not the complete and official position of the NFPA on the referenced subject, which is represented only by the standard in its entirety.

NOTE: Bending space shall be measured in a straight line from the terminal or termination point (in the direction that the wire will leave the terminal) to the wall or barrier.

15. Installation, assembly, and trim-out of oil-filled equipment such as power transformers are completed in accordance with the manufacturer's instructions and procedures.

16. Equipment installed in a wet area or outside a building is enclosed in a weatherproof enclosure or cabinet.

17. Externally operable switches and circuit breakers are enclosed in boxes or cabinets.

18. Knife switches are mounted so that gravity will not tend to close them, or they are equipped with a locking device to ensure that the blades remain open when so set.

19. All switches and circuit breakers used as switches are located so that they are readily accessible for operation.

Cable and Wiring Installation.   The following checklists contain basic items and factors to be considered during installation to help ensure that cables and wiring are properly installed without damage and degradation. The field inspector should perform the necessary surveillance, observation, and inspection actions to verify compliance.

Prior to Cable Installation

1. Raceways are checked to ensure that they are clean and free of debris and other foreign materials that could damage the cables or interfere with the installation.

2. Conduits should be swabbed to ensure that they are clean and free of obstructions.

3. Cables should not be installed or pulled when the temperature is below $-40°F$ ($-40°C$). Cable reels should be stored at normal room temperature for 24 hours to facilitate installation in extremely cold weather.

4. When power-assisted cable pulls are used, the maximum allowable pulling tension for the size and type of cable to be pulled must be determined and the expected pull tension must be calculated for the conduit configuration and other conditions affecting the pull. The mechanical stress placed upon a cable during installation must not be such that the cable is excessively twisted, stretched, or flexed. Maximum allowable pulling tensions for the various types and sizes of cables and the methods for calculating expected tensions are beyond the scope of the *Handbook* but can be obtained from most major cable manufacturers.

During Cable Installation

1. Areas in which cable is being handled and pulled are maintained free of debris and materials that could damage the cables.

2. Cable reels are positioned to train the cable as directly as possible into the respective raceways without excessive bending. During and after installation, nonshielded cable must not be bent in a radius of less than 8 times the overall diameter. Shielded cable must not be bent in a radius of less than 12 times the overall diameter.

3. Appropriate pull lines (hemp, nylon, or wire rope as applicable) are pulled through raceways for cable pulling.

4. Woven-basket-type grips should be used to pull coaxial, triaxial, and other small cables in single or multiple pulls. Alternatively, the ends of smaller cables may be formed into pulling eyes for attachment directly to the cable.

5. Patent cable grips attached directly to the cable conductor should be used to pull larger cables. A swivel connection should be used between the cable grip and the pulling line to pull 250-MCM size and larger.

6. All sharp edges and points on pulling-line hardware are securely taped to prevent damage to the raceways or the previously pulled cables in the raceways.

7. The correct size and type of cable and wiring are installed and routed as specified by the engineer's drawings.

8. During cable pulling, care is exercised to prevent cable damage by pulling across sharp or abrasive surfaces. Sheaves or other appropriate devices are used to pull cable around bends in cable trays. Flexible tubing or appropriate bushings are used where cables enter conduits.

9. Appropriate lubricants that are not detrimental to cables and insulation are used when required to reduce friction during pulling through conduits.

10. Pulling tensions should be measured with an appropriate and properly calibrated tensiometer or dynamometer when using a powered cable puller. The pulling tension should be monitored during the entire pull and must not exceed the maximum allowable for the cable being pulled. The pulling speed should remain relatively constant with no sudden stops or starting or jerking.

11. Cables should be installed in their trays or raceways in an orderly manner and crossing avoided whenever possible.

12. The percentage-fill factors of cables in conduit, trays, and raceways must not exceed the requirements specified by the engineer's specifications.

13. The conductors of all phases of each power circuit must be grouped together and routed in the same raceways.

14. Conductors of over 600 V should not occupy the same wiring enclosures, boxes, and raceways with conductors of 600 V or less.

15. Conductors of 600 V or less may occupy the same wiring enclosures, boxes, and raceways without regard to alternating current or direct current.

16. In manholes, boxes, or other enclosures having any dimension over 3 ft (0.9 m) through which conductors are routed, all conductors must be racked and/or supported in an orderly manner.

17. Open wiring installations, when required, shall comply with the criteria specified in Art. 320 of the **National Electrical Code**®, NFPA No. 70.

18. Cables and wiring in vertical raceways must be supported with one support at the top of the raceway and additional supports at the spacing intervals defined in Table 2.8-8.

19. Adequate conductor lengths for proper termination must be allowed at all termination points.

20. All cable and wiring runs are identified as specified by the engineer's drawings.

Cable and Wiring Termination and Splicing. The following checklist contains the basic criteria for termination and splicing of electrical conductors consistent with good industrial practices. The field inspector should perform the surveillance, observation, and inspection actions necessary to assure compliance.

TABLE 2.8-8 Spacings for Conductor Supports
(Reference **NEC** NFPA No. 70, Table 300-19a)

Conductors		Aluminum or copper-clad aluminum*	Copper*
No. 18 through No. 8	Not greater than	100 ft	100 ft
No. 6 through No. 0	Not greater than	200 ft	100 ft
No. 00 through No. 0000	Not greater than	180 ft	80 ft
211,601 CM through 350,000 CM	Not greater than	135 ft	60 ft
350,001 CM through 500,000 CM	Not greater than	120 ft	50 ft
500,001 CM through 750,000 CM	Not greater than	95 ft	40 ft
Above 750,000 CM	Not greater than	85 ft	35 ft

*1 ft = 0.3048 m.

1. All cables and wiring are connected to the termination points specified by the engineer's wiring diagrams.

2. Insulated conductors should be neatly routed, trained, and bundled from the raceway exits to the respective termination points. Conductor bundles should be laced with appropriate nonconductive materials such as nylon or plastic Ty-Raps at approximately 6-in (152.4-mm) intervals.

3. All conductors are appropriately supported (as required) so that no mechanical load is applied to the terminations or connectors.

4. The method of splicing conductors and the materials used should be as recommended by the conductor manufacturer for each type of conductor unless otherwise specified by the engineer.

5. Conductors should be spliced only in boxes or equipment enclosures where space is adequate for the purpose.

6. The methods of terminating conductors and the materials used should be as recommended by the conductor manufacturer unless otherwise specified by the equipment manufacturer or engineer.

7. When splice and/or termination kits are used, the splice or termination instructions contained in the kit must be strictly followed.

8. No splices should be made in buried cable in exterior lighting circuits.

9. All noninsulated connector splices must be taped with insulating tape as recommended by the cable manufacturer and then (preferably) sealed with heat-shrink-fit sleeves.

10. All shielded power and control cables should be grounded at both ends and at each splice unless otherwise specified by the engineer. The minimum size of ground conductor for shield connection should be No. 10 AWG copper.

11. The shields of instrument cables should be grounded to the instrumentation ground at one end only as specified by the engineer or the instrument manufacturer.

12. Compression-type connectors should grip the cable or wiring conductor with a diamond-type grip or a ring-tongue-type grip and include insulation-gripping sleeves.

13. All tools used for cable and wiring termination and splicing must be appropriate for the work and as recommended by the cable or connector manufacturer unless otherwise specified by the engineer.

14. Compression connectors and splices for No. 2 AWG and larger cable should be installed with a hydraulic crimping tool. Hand crimping tools may be used for cable and wiring sizes No. 4 AWG and smaller.

15. All crimping tools should be periodically checked for proper operation and, if required, adjusted or repaired in accordance with the tool manufacturer's instructions.

Lighting Systems and Component Installations. The following checklist contains the basic criteria for proper installation of lighting systems and components.

1. Feeder circuits for lighting systems are the size and type specified and are routed and installed in accordance with the engineer's drawings.

2. Overload protection is provided and installed according to the engineer's drawings.

3. The lighting system is properly separated into the number of circuits specified by the engineer's drawings.

4. The lighting fixtures are the type specified by the engineer's drawings and are properly mounted in accordance with the manufacturer's instructions and/or the engineer's drawings.

5. The number and type of switches are provided as specified by the engineer's drawings. Light switches should be mounted on the striker side of doors and approximately 4 to 4½ ft (1.2 to 1.4 m) above the floor unless otherwise specified by the engineer's drawings.

6. The number and type of convenience outlets are provided and located as specified by the engineer's drawings. Convenience outlets should be mounted approximately 12 in (304.8 mm) above the floor unless otherwise specified by the engineer's drawings.

7. Appropriate switch and outlet boxes are provided for each switch, convenience outlet, and lighting fixture. The boxes are of adequate size for splices and taps and for the installation of associated devices.

8. All boxes, panels, and associated lighting-system components are properly connected to ground. Convenience outlets contain a ground terminal connected to the ground conductor.

9. No unnecessary splices or taps have been made within or on a lighting fixture or switch.

10. All switches and outlets are provided with an appropriate cover plate properly secured to the outlet box.

11. All wiring is routed so that it is protected from abrasion or other damage.

12. All exposed conductors, splices, and taps are contained inside appropriate boxes.

13. All wiring connections and terminations are made up tight and secure.

14. Lighting-system wiring shall not be smaller than No. 18 AWG.

ELECTRICAL TESTING

The most common tests performed by an electrical contractor are presented herein. The basic test methods and parameters for each test are presented in checklist form. Properly calibrated test equipment with sufficient range, capacity, and accuracy is of prime importance to assure the integrity of any test.

Insulation-Resistance Testing.　The purpose of insulation-resistance testing is to confirm the insulation integrity of electrical cabling, wiring, and equipment.

　Test Equipment.　Industrial megohm tester, preferably with an integral output of 0 to 500 V dc, 0 to 1000 V dc, or 0 to 2500 V dc, as required; ohmmeter capable of measuring in the 0- to 500- megohm range; and a dc voltmeter capable of measuring in the range of 0 to 500 V dc, 0 to 1000 V dc, or 0 to 2500 V dc, as required.

　Cable Test Procedure

1. Ensure that the conductors on both ends of the cable are disconnected and not grounded.
2. Ensure that cable ends are dry and clean.
3. On shielded cables, connect the shields to the raceway or building ground.
4. Ensure that the megohm tester is in the OFF position.
   a. Connect the *ground* lead to the raceway or building ground.
   b. Connect the *test* lead to the conductor to be tested, ensuring that the conductor is isolated from grounds, shields, and other conductors.
5. Check the megohm-tester output control and ensure that it is set to 0.
6. Turn the ohmmeter range-selector switch to the highest range.
7. Ensure that all personnel are clear of the cable being tested prior to starting the test.
8. Place the megohm-tester output power switch to the ON position. Slowly increase the output voltage at a steady rate to the required test voltage as defined in Table 2.8-9.

9. Maintain the test voltage on the cable for at least 1 minute prior to reading the measured insulation resistance.

10. Adjust the ohmmeter range-selector switch to the position that gives an ohmmeter rating that is nearest to the meter's midscale. Read the ohmmeter, and note the insulation resistance.

11. The minimum acceptable insulation resistance in megohms for the respective cable operating voltages is given in Table 2.8-10.

12. The insulation resistance of multiconductor cables must be checked between all conductors and between each conductor and ground. To simplify this procedure, connect all conductors to ground except the one to be tested. Apply the test voltage to this one conductor, and measure the insulation resistance as defined in Steps 2 through 11. The insulation resistance is thus checked between the one conductor and all other conductors and ground. After the test, isolate the conductor tested. Repeat this procedure for each conductor in the cable.

Electrical-Equipment-Test Procedure

1. Disconnect all cabling, wiring, and power connections from the equipment.

2. Isolate all windings, buses, and/or terminals of the equipment from paths to ground.

3. The test-procedure sequence for testing equipment is the same as defined in the subsection "Cable Test Procedure" Steps 4 through 10. Test voltages to be applied and minimum acceptable values of insula-

TABLE 2.8-9   Cable Test Voltages

Test voltage, V dc	Cable operating voltage, V
500	To 150
1000	151−600
2500	601−1000

TABLE 2.8-10   Minimum Acceptable Insulation Resistance

Cable operating voltage, V	Minimum insulation resistance, MΩ
To 150	5
151−600	10
601−1000	40

tion resistance for motors [less than 150 hp (111.9 kW)], generators, buses, transformers, and similar equipment are given in Table 2.8-11.

4. *Motors.* Measure the insulation resistance between all windings and between each winding and ground.

5. *Generators and DC Motors.* Measure the insulation resistance between the armature and ground.

6. *Bus Installations and Buses of Switch Gear, Motor-Control Centers, and Similar Equipment.* Measure the insulation resistance between all phases and between each phase and ground.

7. *Transformers.* Measure the insulation resistance between primary and secondary windings and between each winding and ground.

High-Potential Testing. The purpose of high-potential testing is to verify the dielectric strength of electrical-conductor insulation. During a high-potential test, proper application and control of the high voltage with reference to leakage-current behavior is of prime importance. As the applied voltage is increased, the leakage current will increase proportionally until the insulation breakdown voltage is reached. As the insulation breakdown point is approached, the leakage current will increase rapidly. *Caution:* At the breakdown point, short-circuit conditions and insulation burn-through will occur, which can result in damage to the item under test.

Test Equipment. Proper high-potential-test equipment must be selected. The high-voltage-output capability must be within the range required (0 to 30 kV, 0 to 50 kV, or 0 to 100 kV). The equipment must include a microammeter to measure leakage currents. Adjustable overload protection that can be reset should be provided in the high-voltage-output circuit.

TABLE 2.8-11 Insulation-Resistance-Test Parameters for Electrical Equipment*

Normal operating voltage, V	Test voltage V dc	Minimum acceptable insulation resistance, $M\Omega$
To 150	500	5
151–600	1000	10
601–5000	2500	40
5001–13,000	2500	100
Above 13,000	2500	300

*Test parameters are applicable unless otherwise specified by specific equipment manufacturers.

High-potential testing should not be attempted in wet or damp areas or when the relative humidity is high. Erroneous leakage currents will flow over the damp surfaces, and the tests will be invalid.

Procedure. The testing of high-voltage cables and buses (5 kV and higher operating voltages) is presented in the following procedure:

1. The ambient temperature and relative humidity should be measured or determined from a local weather station. If the ambient temperature is at or near the dew-point temperature, high-potential testing should not be attempted. Dew-point temperature is the temperature at which the moisture in the surrounding air starts to condense.

2. Select proper test equipment that has the capacity to provide the high-potential-test voltages defined in Table 2.8-12.

3. Test personnel should use rubber gloves to connect and disconnect the high-voltage-test leads.

4. Disconnect the cable or bus to be tested from equipment and power sources.

5. Ensure that the cable or bus is dry and clean. Dirt, water, oil spills, and other debris must be cleaned from and around exposed ends of the item to be tested.

6. Check to ensure that raceways, gutters, and equipment through which the cable or bus is routed are properly grounded.

7. Ensure that the test-equipment power switches are in the OFF positions and the output-voltage control is set to 0.

8. Connect the test-equipment grounding cable to the raceway or equipment ground.

9. Connect the test-equipment high-voltage-output cable to the conductor or bus to be tested.

10. Ensure that all personnel are clear of the cable or bus being tested.

11. Turn the test-equipment power and the high-voltage-output switches to ON.

TABLE 2.8-12   High-Potential-Test Voltages

Operating volts, kV	Test volts, dc kV	
	Shielded cable	Nonshielded cable and bus
5	25	15
7	35	18
15	55	33

NOTE: Determine from Table 2.8-12 the test-voltage level required for the item under test according to its normal operating voltage. The test voltage must be slowly increased in several equal increments or steps (5 kV to 10 kV) until the required level is reached. The leakage current must be monitored at all times during the test.

---

12. Slowly increase the test voltage to the first increment, or step, level. Hold the voltage constant at this level for approximately 2 minutes to allow the leakage current to stabilize. After the leakage current has stabilized, record its level.

13. Successively repeat Step 12 until the required high-voltage-test level is reached.

NOTE: At any voltage step, if the leakage current suddenly increases or begins to rise rapidly, the test should be stopped immediately. This condition indicates that the insulation has broken down and the item has failed the high-potential test.

---

14. After the high-voltage-test level has been reached, hold the voltage constant for at least 5 minutes, and then record the leakage-current level.

15. Slowly decrease the high voltage to 0, and turn the test-equipment power to OFF. Allow several minutes for any charges that may have built up to bleed off before disconnecting the test leads.

16. A linear increase in the leakage-current levels recorded in Steps 12, 13, and 14 indicates that the cable or bus has successfully passed the high-potential test.

Rotation Test for Three-Phase Motors. The purpose of rotation testing of three-phase motors is to verify proper phase connections for correct motor rotation before the motor is energized. Rotation testing should be performed and proper phasing determined before the motor power leads are terminated.

Test Equipment. Industrial-motor-rotation-indicator test set.

Procedure

1. Connect the three-phase color-coded leads (A is black, B is red, and C is blue) of the test set to the power leads of the motor.

2. Determine the proper rotation direction of the motor and the driven machinery.

3. Turn the test-set power switch to ON, and manually rotate the motor shaft slowly in the proper direction until the first test-set meter deflec-

tion is observed. This meter deflection will indicate the phasing of the test connections made in Step 1. Proper phasing should be ABC.

Example: If the first meter deflection indicates phase CBA, switch test leads A and C on the motor leads. Repeat Step 4 to verify phase ABC.

4. After motor phase ABC has been established for proper rotation, identify the motor leads as follows: A, black; B, red; C, blue. The motor is now ready for termination of the power leads.

Balanced-Loading Checks. Balanced-loading checks should be performed on the feeder and all branch circuits after the electrical system has been energized and all normal loads have been applied. The purpose of these checks is to verify that the loads are appropriately distributed among all phases.

1. Determine from the engineer's drawings or available load calculations the expected load currents on each feeder and branch-circuit phase.

2. Select a clip-on ammeter with adequate range to measure the expected load current.

3. Measure the load currents on each phase conductor at the feeder panel and at each branch-circuit panel. Record the load currents measured on an appropriate data record.

4. In general, the measured load currents should be within ±20 percent of the calculated loads unless otherwise specified by the engineer.

5. The maximum load unbalance between phases should not exceed ±10 percent unless otherwise specified by the engineer.

6. Conditions of noncompliance with the requirements defined in Steps 4 and 5 must be reported to the engineer for resolution.

SUMMARY

Because of the extreme risk of personal injury or death and property damage that may be caused by improper or careless workmanship in *electrical* installations, it is essential that the strictest adherence to established procedures and **Code** requirements be observed.

Vertical Transportation: Elevators and Escalators

Edward A. Donoghue
Manager—Codes and Safety
National Elevator Industry, Inc.
New York, New York

Robert L. Seymour
Vertical Transportation Consultant
Lerch, Bates & Associates, Inc.
Elevator Consulting Engineers
Crofton, Maryland

GENERAL CONSIDERATIONS

Vertical transportation is the lifeline for moving people and freight in all multistory buildings. Office buildings, apartments, hospitals, hotels, mercantile buildings, etc., all must be provided with adequate vertical transportation in one or more of the following forms: elevators, escalators, dumbwaiters, material lifts, sidewalk elevators, special-purpose personnel elevators, inclined elevators, and moving walks. During construction, permanent elevator equipment may be installed and used for transporting construction personnel and material.

All multistory buildings, even two- and three-story buildings, will most likely be provided with vertical transportation of some type because of requirements which mandate access to all floors by the handicapped. In all new buildings, access is provided by elevators. (See Figs. 2.9-1 and 2.9-2.)

In this chapter, we will highlight the installation inspection process for the equipment mentioned above. This process is ongoing, starting before the elevator contractor arrives on the jobsite and culminating with acceptance of the equipment.

The inspection process outlined in this chapter is intended as a guide only and should not be considered all-inclusive. No vertical-transportation equipment should be placed in service for general use without first being tested and inspected by a qualified elevator inspector.

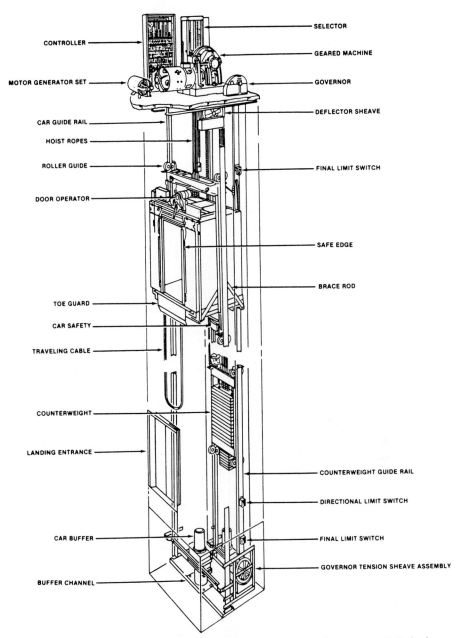

FIG. 2.9-1   The elevator system: typical installation of an overhead one-to-one (1:1) single-wrap geared-traction machine. *(Courtesy of National Elevator Industry, Inc., New York, N.Y.)*

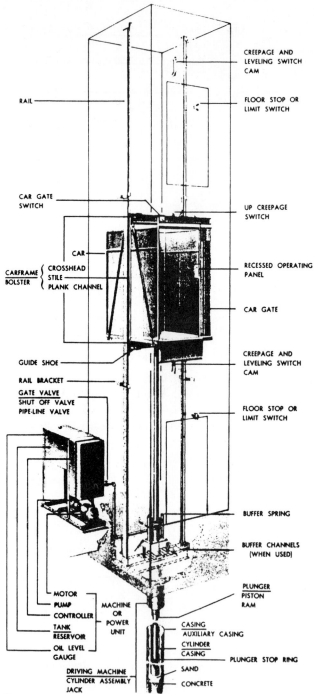

CREEPAGE AND
LEVELING SWITCH
CAM

FLOOR STOP OR
LIMIT SWITCH

RAIL

CAR GATE
SWITCH

UP CREEPAGE
SWITCH

CAR

CARFRAME { CROSSHEAD
BOLSTER { STILE
{ PLANK CHANNEL

RECESSED OPERATING
PANEL

CAR GATE

GUIDE SHOE

CREEPAGE AND
LEVELING SWITCH
CAM

RAIL BRACKET

GATE VALVE
SHUT OFF VALVE
PIPE-LINE VALVE

FLOOR STOP OR
LIMIT SWITCH

BUFFER SPRING

BUFFER CHANNELS
(WHEN USED)

MOTOR
PUMP
CONTROLLER   MACHINE
TANK   OR
RESERVOIR   POWER
                   UNIT
OIL LEVEL
GAUGE

DRIVING MACHINE
CYLINDER ASSEMBLY
JACK

PLUNGER
PISTON
RAM

CASING
AUXILIARY CASING
CYLINDER
CASING
                    PLUNGER STOP RING
SAND

CONCRETE

FIG. 2.9-2 Hydraulic-elevator components. (*Courtesy of National Elevator Industry, Inc., New York, N.Y.*)

2.9.4

This chapter covers procedures for new installations only. While it does not cover alterations of existing equipment, many of the inspection procedures would be similar, and it could be consulted as a reference.

To shorten the time that actual inspection takes, it is recommended that the equipment be pretested and all adjustments made by the elevator contractor prior to the final acceptance inspection and test.

In making inspections, the duties of the inspector are to determine whether or not all parts of the installation conform to the requirements of the applicable code, regulations, and contract documents and whether or not the required safety devices function as stipulated therein. It is not the function or duty of the inspector to make any repairs or adjustments to the equipment. The inspector should be accompanied by a person familiar with the operation of the equipment to assist in the inspection. Qualified elevator personnel should perform all tests, and the inspector should only witness these and record the results.

Safety Precautions

Inspectors are cautioned that many potential hazards are involved in the inspection of elevators, escalators, moving walks, etc. Since any accident not only can be disabling but may be fatal, inspectors are reminded of the hazards involved; statistics reveal a number of accidents involving inspectors.

The inspector should be suitably clothed before starting the inspection. Wearing of loose clothing, particularly neckties, should be avoided. Keep buttons, especially those on cuffs, buttoned. The inspector should at all times be alert for moving objects and, when on top of an elevator car, for moving counterweights, hoistway projections such as beams, adjacent moving cars, cams, and other equipment attached thereto or mounted in the hoistway. The overhead clearance should always be noted, as a number of fatal accidents have resulted from cars running into limited overhead spaces while an inspector was on top of the car. Similarly, when working in the pit, the inspector should always note the position of the car and keep clear of descending counterweights in the hoistway of the elevator being inspected and those in adjoining hoistways. The disconnect switch for the power-supply line should be opened, locked, and tagged when it is desired to prevent movement of the elevator or when electrical parts are being inspected.

Before starting the inspection it should first be determined that the operating device, emergency-stop switch, and all other safety devices or switches are in proper working order and in the proper position for inspection. When dual or attendant operation is provided, the change-over switch should be in the position for operation from the car only.

Before inspecting an elevator in a bank of group-operation elevators, have the elevator to be inspected disconnected from the group operation.

If means of communication is provided in the car, determine that it is operative. The top-of-car operating device is to be used to operate the car when on top of the car instead of depending on an operator in the car.

Inspectors should never enter pits containing water.

Inspectors should familiarize themselves with the *Elevator Industry Field Employees' Safety Handbook,* published by *Elevator World,* Mobile, Alabama, before starting any inspection.

Elevator Contracts

To complete an elevator installation, the following items normally must be performed or furnished by other than the elevator contractor, in accordance with governing codes:

1. The hoistway enclosure and entrance interfacing, including means to prevent accumulation of hot gases or smoke from a fire.

2. Hoisting beam, with location and size as determined by the elevator contractor, for each machine; trolley beam, if required.

3. Location of supports in the overhead for the elevator beams as required by the elevator contractor; beam pockets required for elevator beams and patching of pockets after beams have been set in place.

4. Suitable machine room with legal access and ventilation, with a reinforced-concrete slab. The slab is not to be poured until the elevator machinery has been set in place. Means are to be provided to ensure that the temperature in the machine room is maintained between 55°F (128°C) and 105°F (40.5°C).

5. Adequate rail-bracket supports, with bracket spacing as required by the governing code; separator beams where required.

6. Dry pit reinforced to sustain vertical forces on car and counterweight rails and impact loads from car and counterweight buffers.

7. Where access to a pit over 3 ft (0.914 m) in depth is by means of the lowest hoistway entrance, a vertical iron ladder extending 45 in (1.143 m) above the sill of the access door must be provided.

8. Adequate support for the sill angle across the full width of hoistway at each landing; vertical surfaces of entrance-sill supports to be plumb, one above the other, and square with the hoistway; finished floor and grout, if required, between door frames to the sill line.

9. Front-entrance walls are not to be constructed until after the door frames and sills are in place. If front walls are poured-concrete walls, rough openings are to be provided to accept entrance frames and

filled in after frames have been set. The rough opening size is to suit the elevator contractor.

10. Any cutting, including cutouts to accommodate hall signal fixtures, patching, and painting of walls, floors, or partitions together with finish painting of entrance doors and frames.

11. A fused disconnect switch or circuit breaker located in the machine room for each elevator per **National Electrical Code** ANSI/NFPA No. 70 with feeder or branch wiring to the controller. The size is to suit the elevator contractor.

12. A separate power supply with a fused disconnect switch and feeder wiring to one controller for the elevator signal system, as specified by the elevator contractor.

13. A 120-V ac, 20-A single-phase power supply with a fused single-pole single-throw disconnect switch for each elevator, with feeder wiring for car lights, as specified by the elevator contractor.

14. Suitable light and convenience 110-V, 20-A duplex outlets in the machine room with light switches located within 18 in (457.2 mm) of the lock-jamb side of the machine-room door.

15. Convenience 110-V, 20-A duplex outlet and light fixture in the pit, with switch located adjacent to the access door.

16. Telephone instrument or means within the car for communicating or signaling to an accessible point outside the hoistway or central exchange system or approved emergency service, unless stated elsewhere in the specifications.

17. Sensing devices for heat or smoke or products of combustion, located as required by the local code or contract documents, with wiring from the sensing devices to each elevator controller.

18. Should operation of the elevators be required on emergency power, others are to provide an emergency-power unit and means for starting it and deliver to the elevator disconnect switches in the machine room sufficient power to operate one or more elevators at a time at full rated speed. Provide a transfer switch for each feeder for switching from normal power to emergency power and a contact on each transfer switch closed on normal-power supply with two wires from this contact to one elevator controller. Provide means for absorbing the power regenerated by the elevator system when running with overhauling loads such as a full load down.

19. Guarding and protecting the hoistway during construction. The protection of the hoistway shall include solid panels surrounding each hoistway opening at each floor, a minimum of 48 in (1.219 m) high. Hoistway guards are to be erected, maintained, and removed by others.

20. All electric power for light, tools, hoists, etc., during erection as well as electric current for starting, testing, and adjusting the elevator.

21. Should any elevator be required for use before final completion, others shall provide to the elevator contractor temporary car enclosures, required guards or other protection for elevator hoistway openings, main-line switch with wiring, necessary power, signaling devices, lights in car, and elevator operators together with any other special labor or equipment needed to permit this temporary usage.

The following additional items apply to hydraulic-elevator installations:

1. Provide standard water connections and water, if required, for equipment and an outlet line for discharging excess water while the cylinder is sunk.

2. Removal of the excavation spoils deposited in the pit.

3. Means of access to and egress from the location of the cylinder well is to be provided for truck-mounted drilling equipment.

Similar provisions apply to other types of vertical transportation equipment and should be reviewed before the job is commenced. To ensure timely completion of the work, the items performed or furnished by other than the elevator contractor should be closely coordinated with the elevator contractor's schedule.

Reference Material

The following references should be reviewed before and consulted during an inspection.

1. Contract documents, specification, plans, and work change orders.

2. Edward A. Donoghue, *Safety Code for Elevators and Escalators*, Handbook A17.1. This handbook contains the complete text of the ANSI/ASME A17.1 Safety Code for Elevators and Escalators augmented by commentary, diagrams, and photographs that are intended to clarify the requirements of the code. Publisher: American Society of Mechanical Engineers, 345 East 47th Street, New York, N.Y. 10017.

3. *Inspectors' Manual for Elevators and Escalators*, ANSI/ASME A17.2. Publisher: American Society of Mechanical Engineers, 345 East 47th Street, New York, N.Y. 10017.

4. **National Electrical Code**®. This handbook contains the complete text of the ANSI/ NFPA No. 70 **National Electrical Code** ®. Publisher: National Fire Protection Association, Battery-March Park, Quincy, Mass. 02269.

5. *Checklist for Initial Inspection and Test of Electric or Hydraulic Elevators or Escalators or Moving Walks*. Publisher: American Society of Mechanical Engineers, 345 East 47th Street, New York, N.Y. 10017.

6. Elevator and building codes adopted by the enforcing authority.

Additional reference materials that might be consulted are:

1. *Vertical Transportation Standards.* Publisher: National Elevator Industry, Inc., 600 Third Avenue, New York, N.Y. 10016.

2. *Suggested Minimum Passenger Elevator Requirements for the Handicapped.* Publisher: National Elevator Industry, Inc., 600 Third Avenue, New York, N.Y. 10016.

3. *Standard Making Buildings and Facilities Accessible to and Usable by the Physically Handicapped,* ANSI A117.1. Publisher: American National Standards Institute, 1430 Broadway, New York, N.Y. 10018.

4. George R. Strakosch, *Vertical Transportation: Elevators and Escalators,* John Wiley & Sons, Inc., New York, 1967.

ELECTRIC ELEVATORS

Inspection during Construction

Several items are best inspected during the construction period. After complete installation correction is extremely costly, and a less than perfect product must usually be accepted.

The most critical of these items for operational performance is guiderail alignment and fastening. Rail installation is usually the first thing that the elevator contractor does. Assurance that rails are properly located, aligned, and fastened will go a long way toward providing a top-performing installation.

Following rail alignment closely are the location and alignment of hoistway entrances. This procedure includes not only the alignment of each individual frame but also the vertical alignment of all the frames in each hoistway. Properly installed hoistway entrances will greatly reduce future problems and provide good operation.

Hoistway construction is extremely important from another point of consideration. In most buildings hoistways penetrate fire floors, and fire-resistive hoistway construction is accordingly required. It is essential that this construction be undertaken in accordance with the requirements of the specifications and the local code. Joints and patching seem to be the place of greatest concern and should be investigated to assure that they are properly done.

Hoistways should also be checked for ventilation, windows, flush construction, emergency access, and presence of other than elevator-related equipment. Ventilation of most hoistways to prevent the accumulation of smoke and hot gases is a requirement. Exact specific points should be checked with the proper governing code. Windows are not permitted in hoistways. Determine that substantially flush construction is provided or that projections are beveled at a 75° angle in accordance with code requirements. Emergency hoistway entrances are required in all single blind hoistways at every third floor but not more than 36 ft (10.97 m) from sill to sill. Only elevator-related wiring and pipes or ducts conveying gases, vapors, or liquids are allowed in elevator hoistways, machine rooms, or machinery spaces. Main feeders for supplying power to the elevator shall be installed outside the hoistway. All through the construction period the installation should be checked to assure that the following items are level, straight, and plumb: hoist machine and other sheave alignment, elevator sling and platform, elevator car, hoistway doors and hangers, etc. Checking during construction makes final inspection easier and provides a finished product that will perform properly.

Final Inspection

Inside Car.   The elevator car is the first order of review. It must be checked for safety-code requirements as well as for specification requirements. While the size of the car enclosure, ventilation, and illumination should have been checked at the time of contractor submittals, these must be assured now. Code requirements cover each of these items. In addition, this is what the public sees of an elevator installation and should be closely reviewed for specification requirements and workmanship.

All elevators are provided with an emergency exit in the top, which must be operable only from the top of the car. This exit should be checked for size and proper operation. Some installations include an electric contact which opens when the exit is opened, thus preventing the car from moving.

In addition to top exits, some installations have side exits. In a three-car common-hoistway arrangement, the middle car may have an exit in both sides. These exits must swing in and be opened from the inside only by using a special-shape removable key, be opened from the outside by a nonremovable handle, and be provided with an electric contact which prevents the car from moving when the exit is open. The distance between cars should not exceed 30 in (762 mm), and no fixed obstructions other than separator beams must exist between the cars.

The operation of car doors must be examined thoroughly. Whether the doors move horizontally or vertically, they must be closely reviewed. Closing force, reopening devices, full sequence of door and gate closing in the cases of vertically operated entrance assemblies, open and close limits, and smooth operation are all functions which must be checked. Audible warnings, as in the case of vertically operated doors provided with an automatic closing feature or in the case of horizontally operated doors provided with a feature that cuts out some reopening devices and allows the doors to move closed at a reduced speed, should be checked for proper operation and provision of the intended notification.

Car-operating and signal fixtures should be reviewed for specification compliance, workmanship, appearance, and proper operation. Standards for accessibility by handicapped persons include specific suggestions and requirements concerning these devices. These suggestions and requirements should be considered when inspecting these devices. Included in each car-operating panel is a red emergency-stop switch which, when operated, will promptly stop the elevator and sound the alarm bell. An alarm switch or button should also be included in the panel.

Every elevator must be provided with a means of two-way communication. Additional requirements are imposed for buildings which are not provided with continuous supervision or for buildings which must have specific fire communications. Specific requirements should be reviewed to assure proper compliance.

All passenger elevators must be provided with an on-board emergency-lighting source. The lighting shall illuminate the car operating panel with a minimum of 0.2-fc (2.15-lx) intensity for 4 hours.

The capacity of all elevators must be displayed in a conspicuous position inside the car. A freight elevator must also include a sign that identifies it as a freight elevator, states that passengers are not permitted to ride, and stipulates the type of loading for which the lift was designed. (See Figs. 2.9-3 and 2.9-4.)

Outside Hoistway. An extremely important part of the inspection is the thorough investigation of each hoistway entrance. Assurance that the frame is properly interfaced into the front-wall construction is essential to maintain the fire rating. The interface must be in accordance with the frame manufacturer's instructions; normally this stipulation is carried out by the wall constructor (see Fig. 2.9-5). Each entrance should be closely checked to assure that maximum clearances have been maintained and that the frames and door panels are straight, level, and plumb. Proper installation will assure good operation. The interlock device and overall operation should be checked for compliance with code requirements. If a fire-rated entrance is required, a test label indicating the fire rating must be provided.

The corridor operating and signal fixtures should be reviewed for specification compliance, workmanship, appearance, and proper operation. Standards for accessibility by handicapped persons have specific suggestions and requirements concerning these devices, including the location of call buttons, the design and operation of corridor lanterns, and requiring a floor designation on the hoistway entrance frames. These requirements should be reviewed and applied where applicable.

Architectural considerations should also be included. These include the wall surfaces around the entrances and operating and signaling de-

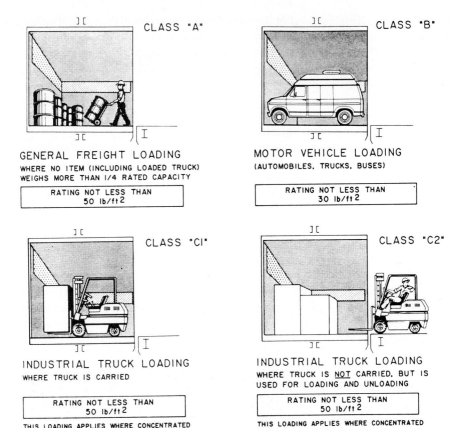

CLASS "A"

GENERAL FREIGHT LOADING
WHERE NO ITEM (INCLUDING LOADED TRUCK)
WEIGHS MORE THAN 1/4 RATED CAPACITY

RATING NOT LESS THAN
50 lb/ft^2

CLASS "B"

MOTOR VEHICLE LOADING
(AUTOMOBILES, TRUCKS, BUSES)

RATING NOT LESS THAN
30 lb/ft^2

CLASS "CI"

INDUSTRIAL TRUCK LOADING
WHERE TRUCK IS CARRIED

RATING NOT LESS THAN
50 lb/ft^2

THIS LOADING APPLIES WHERE CONCENTRATED
LOAD INCLUDING TRUCK IS MORE THAN 1/4
RATED CAPACITY BUT CARRIED LOAD DOES NOT
EXCEED RATED CAPACITY.

CLASS "C2"

INDUSTRIAL TRUCK LOADING
WHERE TRUCK IS NOT CARRIED, BUT IS
USED FOR LOADING AND UNLOADING

RATING NOT LESS THAN
50 lb/ft^2

THIS LOADING APPLIES WHERE CONCENTRATED
LOAD INCLUDING TRUCK IS MORE THAN 1/4
RATED CAPACITY BUT CARRIED LOAD DCES NOT
EXCEED RATED CAPACITY.
THIS LOADING ALSO APPLIES WHERE INCREMENT
LOADING IS USED, BUT MAXIMUM LOAD ON CAR
PLATFORM DURING LOADING OR UNLOADING DOES
NOT EXCEED 150% OF RATED LOAD.

FIG. 2.9-3   Vertical-transportation standards: freight elevators. (*Reprinted by permission from* Vertical Transportation Standards, *1983 edition, copyrighted 1983, National Elevator Industry, Inc., New York, N.Y.*)

vices. Poor workmanship in this area stands out like the proverbial sore thumb. Installation of a good joint sealant between the wall and the sides and top of the hoistway entrance frame is necessary to seal the hoistway. The sealant will prevent hoistway dirt and dust from being deposited on the surface of the corridor wall because of air movement resulting from the elevator moving up and down the hoistway. A proper fit of the floor covering to the entrance sill is important. The covering should meet the sill level or be slightly below it. Tripping hazards and ease of loading must be the first considerations. In addition, heavy wear and tear will result on floor covering installed above the entrance sill.

NOTE

THE PICTORIAL FREIGHT LOADING
SHOWN FOR THE DIFFERENT CLASSES
OF LOADING IS INTENDED FOR BOTH
ELECTRIC AND HYDRAULIC ELEVATORS.
SOME DIFFERENCES OCCUR IN RAIL
FORCES.

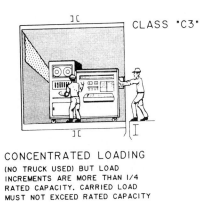

CLASS "C3"

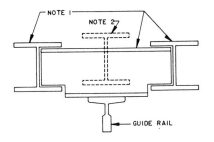

GUIDE RAIL

CONCENTRATED LOADING

(NO TRUCK USED) BUT LOAD
INCREMENTS ARE MORE THAN 1/4
RATED CAPACITY. CARRIED LOAD
MUST NOT EXCEED RATED CAPACITY

RATING NOT LESS THAN
50 lb/ft^2

NOTE 1   VERTICAL RAIL COLUMN SUPPORTS AND CROSS TIE MEMBERS ARE REQUIRED AND PROVIDED BY OTHER
THAN THE ELEVATOR SUPPLIER WHEN RATED LOAD EXCEEDS 8000 lb. THE SIZE OF THE
RAIL COLUMNS ARE DETERMINED BY OTHERS FROM RAIL FORCES FURNISHED BY THE
ELEVATOR SUPPLIER.

NOTE 2   ALTERNATE METHOD OF RAIL COLUMN SUPPORT. WHEN RATED LOAD IS 8000 lb OR LESS
THE SIZE OF THE COLUMNS ARE DETERMINED BY THE OTHERS FROM RAIL FORCES
FURNISHED BY THE ELEVATOR SUPPLIER.

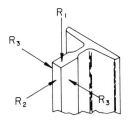

GUIDE RAIL FORCES (FOR A SINGLE RAIL)	ELECTRIC ELEVATOR	HYDRAULIC ELEVATOR
	lb	lb
R_1	FOR THESE FORCES,	
R_2	CONSULT ELEVATOR SUPPLIER	
R_3		

FIG. 2.9-4   Vertical-transportation standards: freight elevators. (*Reprinted by permission from* Vertical Transportation Standards, *1983 edition, copyrighted 1983, National Elevator Industry, Inc., New York, N.Y.*).

Top of Car.   The top of each elevator car must have an operating device which will allow slow-speed movement of the car. Specific requirements for the device are included in the elevator safety code. Assurance that these requirements have been met and that the device operates properly must be secured before the inspection is continued.

Each elevator must be provided with a refuge space on top of the car enclosure. This space shall be an unobstructed area of not less than 650 in^2 (0.419 m^2) and measure not less than 16 in (406.4 mm) on any side.

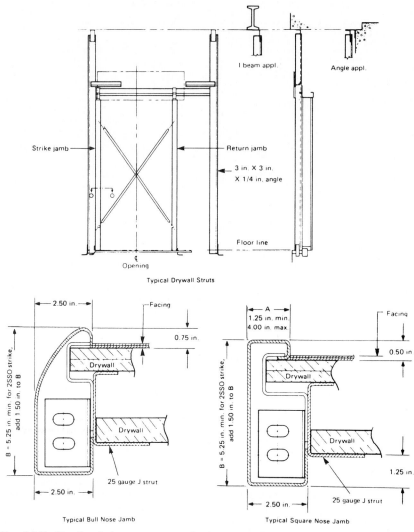

FIG. 2.9-5   Details of elevator entrance-jamb construction. (*Edward A. Donoghue*, Safety Code for Elevators and Escalators, *A17.1 Handbook, American Society of Mechanical Engineers, New York, 1984.*)

The minimum vertical clearance between the car top and the lowest obstruction when the car has reached its maximum upward movement is illustrated in Fig. 2.9-6.

Car frame, sheaves, ropes and fastenings, data tags, top emergency exit, door operator, leveling switches, guiding devices, work light, and convenience outlet can be checked before the car moves. Examination of

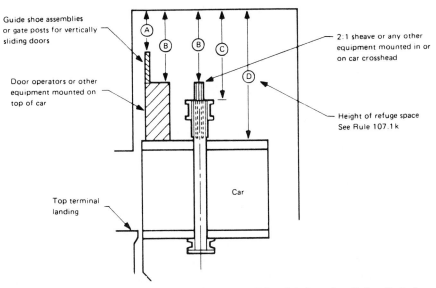

Guide shoe assemblies or gate posts for vertically sliding doors

Door operators or other equipment mounted on top of car

2:1 sheave or any other equipment mounted in or on car crosshead

Height of refuge space See Rule 107.1k

Car

Top terminal landing

FIG. 2.9-6 Diagram of top and bottom clearances. (*Edward A. Donoghue*, Safety Code for Elevators and Escalators, *A17.1 Handbook, American Society of Mechanical Engineers, New York, 1984.*) When the car floor is level with the top terminal landing, all the following conditions must be met:

$$A > t$$
$$B \geq t + 6$$
$$C \geq t + 24$$

where t = maximum possible travel of the car above the top terminal landing, as shown below:

Type of hundredweight buffers	Compensating rope tie-down	Maximum travel above top landing, in (t)
Oil buffers which are compressed with car at top landing	Yes	$S - S_c$
	No	$S - S_c + V_r^2 (3.423 \times 10^{-5})$
Reduced-stroke oil buffers	Yes	$R + S$
	No	$R + 1.5S$
Other oil buffers	Yes	$R + S$
	No	$R + S + V_r^2 \times (3.423 \times 10^{-5})$
Spring buffers	No	$R + S + V_g^2 \times (2.588 \times 10^{-5})$

where
R = bottom counterweight runby, in
S = counterweight buffer stroke, in
S_c = distance counterweight buffer is compressed when the car is at the top terminal landing, in
V_r = rated speed, ft/min
V_g = governor tripping speed, ft/min
NOTE: 1 in = 25.4 mm; 1 ft/min = 0.00508 m/s.

2.9.15

the condition of the wire ropes is especially important if the elevator has been used as a material hoist or workers' elevator during construction of the building. Frequently, such ropes will be covered with lime, sand, and mortar and may be worn or damaged to such an extent that they should be replaced. If ropes show an appreciable amount of gritty building material but are otherwise sound, they should be thoroughly cleaned and relubricated in accordance with the manufacturer's recommendation. Sheaves should be closely examined when the above conditions are evident. Rope tension should also be checked. Each rope should have been adjusted to equal tension to equalize the load on the sheaves; unequal tension can cause premature wear of a sheave. The inspector should not enter the hoistway on top of the elevator car unless accompanied by a person familiar with operation of the equipment.

A thorough inspection of the hoistway must be made to assure proper installation of items noted for inspection during the construction period. Determine that top-of-car and counterweight clearances and running clearances conform with code requirements.

Final limits should be checked for proper operation. Operation of this switch will prevent movement of the elevator by normal means in both directions of movement. Normal limits may be located in the hoistway, on the car, or in the machine room. Operation of this switch will prevent movement of the car in the up direction when the car activates the top switch and in the down direction when the bottom switch is activated. When conditions require emergency terminal speed-limiting devices, their operation also must be checked.

Each entrance must be checked for proper operation. Hangers, door sills, closers, and interlocks should be closely checked for proper adjustment. Doors must be self-closing when the elevator car is away from the floor. The interlock must be positioned so that the doors are closed and locked before the car leaves the floor. The wiring from the interlock device to the hoistway conduit riser must be **National Electrical Code**® Type SF-2 or its equal. Supporting means, hanger covers, fascia plates, and landing-sill guards should be checked.

Traveling cables must be hung in accordance with **National Electrical Code**® requirements. They may be hung anywhere between the midpoint of the rise and the top of the hoistway, depending on the contractor's wiring scheme. Hoistway wiring also must comply with the respective requirements of the same code. Only elevator-related wiring is allowed in the elevator hoistway.

Examine the counterweight to determine that filler weights are securely held in place and that tie rods are properly fastened. Guide devices, rope fastenings or sheaves, buffers (if attached to the frame), and compensating ropes or chains must be inspected. If occupied building space is present under the counterweight, a safety device is required on the counterweight to protect against a runaway. This device must be checked.

Pit. Safe and convenient access must be provided to all elevator pits. Access can be from the lowest hoistway door or from a separate door. If the pit extends more than 3 ft (0.914 m) below the entry, a ladder which meets code requirements must be provided. Access shall be to authorized persons only. The inspector should not enter the pit unless accompanied by a person familiar with operation of the equipment.

Confirm that bottom-of-car and counterweight clearances are in accordance with code requirements. This is done first to assure operating space.

Every elevator is required to have a pit stop switch at the point of entry into the pit. If entry is by ladder, the stop switch shall be located 18 in (457.2 mm) above the access-pit floor level, accessible from the entry, and adjacent to the pit ladder. When pit depth exceeds 6 ft 7 in (2.01 m), a second switch is required. It shall be located 4 ft (1.22 m) above the access-pit floor and adjacent to the ladder.

A permanent lighting fixture is required. It shall operate from a switch located so as to be accessible from the pit access door.

Car and counterweight buffers shall be examined for code requirements. Specific tests are detailed for hydraulic buffers.

Pit floors are required to be approximately level. Exceptions are allowed for existing conditions and for the installation of buffers, sheaves, or vertical operating doors. Sumps are also allowed, but direct connection of sump lines to drain or sewer lines is not allowed. If adjacent pits are at different levels, protection is required. A difference of up to 2 ft (0.61 m) requires a metal railing not less than 42 in (1.07 m) high. A greater difference requires a 6-ft- (1.83-m-) high guard. All open sides of the counterweight runways shall have a guard, which shall extend from not more than 12 in (304.8 mm) above the floor to a point not less than 7 ft (2.13 m) or more than 8 ft (2.44 m) above the floor. Counterweight guards are not required when either chain or rope compensation is included.

The car safety should be closely inspected to assure proper operation. Each safety requires a data tag indicating the type, maximum tripping speed, and maximum load. Confirm that the safety is adequate for the application. The governor tension sheave must be examined to assure proper operation.

Check compensating chains or ropes, if any. Check the fastening of the bottom of the car. If ropes are used, check the tension sheave and contact in accordance with code requirements.

Bottom final and normal limit switches should be checked for proper operation just as the top switches were checked. Emergency terminal speed-limiting switches may also be required. These must be checked as previously described.

Traveling cable mounting shall be inspected along with fixed wiring for compliance with **National Electrical Code**® requirements.

The car platform shall be examined for code compliance. The underside of wood platforms shall be protected against fire by covering it with metal or fire-retardant paint. On the entrance side of each platform there is required a guard which extends not less than the width of the opening. It must have a vertical face not less than the length of the leveling zone plus 3 in (76.2 mm), but in no case less than 21 in (533 mm).

Machine Room and Machinery Spaces.   The elevator safety code and building code detail specific requirements concerning the type of enclosure, access, lighting, ventilation, headroom, floor construction, etc. These should be closely reviewed before inspection.

The hoisting machine should be closely examined for alignment and operation. Check all lubrication points for the proper quantity and type of lubrication in addition to possible leaks. When gear machines are used, visually check the drive gear for the correct worm-engagement pattern. The brake should also be examined for free operation and correct clearance of shoes.

Motors and generator lubrication should be checked. All connections and insulation should be examined. Brushes should also be examined and their operation checked.

Wire, starters, and fused disconnects should be checked for proper sizing. The **National Electrical Code**® should be consulted for requirements. The disconnect is included in these requirements. Each hoist machine and the respective disconnect switch should be identified.

Control equipment should be examined for general workmanship. Proper connections, insulation, and operation should be checked. Fuses should be checked specifically for proper size and mounting. All equipment must be grounded in accordance with **National Electrical Code**® requirements.

The governor must be checked in accordance with **Code** requirements. Proper operation of this device is essential and must be closely checked. Equipment must be located so as to meet required clearances. These clearances must be checked to assure safe operating conditions in this area. Some local codes also require that insulated floor covering be installed around control equipment.

Testing.   Safety testing of elevators is performed by the elevator contractor and witnessed by the inspector. The elevator safety code must be closely followed when conducting these tests. Specific requirements concerning allowable results are detailed, and these must be followed to assure safe operation. Testing of the governor, car safety, counterweight safety (if used), car buffer, and counterweight buffer is critical.

Door operation is also a function that must be closely checked. Check all reopening devices to assure proper operation. Operating forces should also be tested. Requirements for handicapped persons specify operating times. If applicable, these requirements should be consulted and operation adjusted accordingly. If no specific requirements are dictated, timing should be adjusted to suit passenger movement to the respective elevators.

The function of all corridor and car operating and signal devices should be checked to assure proper operation. Special attention should be directed to special operating features. The function of these devices should be included in project specifications.

All elevators having a travel of 25 ft (7.62 m) or more above or below the main floor must be provided with firefighters' operation. The specific requirements projected in the code must be followed. This operation is designed for use under extreme conditions, and its ability to perform correctly is absolutely essential. Close examination of the operation is required.

HYDRAULIC ELEVATORS

Hydraulic-elevator installation is quite similar to electric-elevator installation. Consequently, inspection is conducted in much the same manner. This subsection therefore will cover only items unique to the hydraulic elevator. (See Fig. 2.9-2.)

Inspection during Construction

Proper installation of the jack assembly is as critical as installation of guiderails to ensure a top-performing installation. It is of the utmost importance that the jack assembly be located in accordance with contractor's requirements and that the assembly be positioned plumb. Improper installation directly affects performance and is very expensive to correct later.

In most hydraulic-elevator installations, the jack assembly is located below the ground. In these installations, the assembly is provided with some sort of outer protective covering. An inspection should be made to assure that the covering is properly applied and that care is exercised in placing the jack assembly in the hole so as to prevent damage to the covering. Damage will affect the life of the elevator installation because corrosion and electrolysis will attack the exposed metal.

One advantage of a hydraulic installation is the opportunity it presents to locate the machine room far from the hoistway. However, installing the necessary supply-line piping and wiring must then be considered. Supply piping is our main concern at this time because of potential leak problems. Consideration must be given to assure proper installation, especially when piping is installed underground, as is the case in many remote installations. Piping should not pass through an expansion or a seismic joint.

Final Inspection

Inside Car. As one might expect, the inside of a hydraulic-elevator car is the same as that of an electric elevator. When making this part of the inspection, refer to the comments noted for electric-elevator inspection inside the car.

Top of Car. For the most part, this portion of the inspection follows electric-elevator procedures, but there are a few differences. While the vast majority of hydraulic installations employ direct-plunger operation, there may be an occasional installation in which counterweights are employed. Even though the practices employed in the electric-elevator section will be used, a direct review of actual code requirements is suggested to assure complete inspection.

Final limit switches are not required on hydraulic elevators. This is so because all jacks must have a positive stop to prevent the plunger from leaving the assembly. The test procedure to assure its inclusion will be described later.

Pit. The jack assembly should be closely examined. The packing should be examined for excessive leaking. A very light film of oil on the plunger is desired. All debris should be removed from the top of the jack head to prevent damage to the plunger and packing. Means must be provided to collect oil leakage from the cylinder packing gland.

The plunger should be inspected from top to bottom for corrosion, pitting, scratches, and, in the case of multisection plungers, improper fitting. These conditions can cause excessive wear and damage to the packing gland and result in a poor installation. Also check to see that the plunger is securely fastened to the bottom of the car. Improper fastening can result in separation of the elevator car and plunger, placing the car in potential danger of falling.

Supply piping should be closely observed for leaking. Special attention should be given to valves, strainers, etc., that may be in the supply line. Be sure that the supply line is properly fastened and supported, especially if the line is so located that someone may step or stand on it.

Machine Room. The entire pump unit and supply piping should be checked for leaks. Check the pump and pump motor for vibration or unusual noises. Most pumps are driven by belts; these should be checked for correct and even tension. If a direct drive is employed, check for excessive play in coupling. Be sure that adequate guards are provided to protect the exposed equipment. The tank must have means to indicate clearly the permissible minimum liquid level.

Some installations include flexible hose assemblies or flexible couplings in the supply line between the control valve and the jack assembly. These must be closely checked for evidence of leaking, slippage of hose fittings, and damage to the outer hose covering sufficient to expose reinforcement or distortion or bulging of the hose body. If this occurs, the hose or coupling must be replaced. These flexible fittings are required to meet special requirements, and it is advisable that the code be consulted for specific details.

A manual shutoff valve is required on all hydraulic elevators in which the cylinder is not exposed to inspection. The valve is required in the machine room and shall be located between the control valve and the jack assembly.

Testing. As previously mentioned, every plunger must be provided with a positive stop to prevent it from leaving the assembly. This can be easily checked by raising the car above the top floor in slow speed until the stop is engaged.

Conversely, a check should be made at the bottom of the plunger stroke to assure that the plunger does not bottom in the cylinder. This is done by placing the contract load on the car and moving the car down to its buffers. Observe that the car comes to rest on the buffer springs and not the plunger bottoming.

Because hydraulic elevators can move down from the floor for various reasons, a leveling device is required to maintain the car within 1 in (25.4 mm) of the landing. It is required that this protection be provided even if the emergency-stop switch in the car is activated. This function should be demonstrated.

All hydraulic systems must include a check valve, which is required to hold the car with rated load when the pump stops. A relief valve is also required to limit the system operating pressure. The code should be consulted for detailed testing requirements. A seal must be placed on the adjustment after setting.

ESCALATOR INSPECTIONS

When making escalator inspections (see Figs. 2.9-7 and 2.9-8), the following additional precautions shall be observed:

1.   Before entering the escalator machinery space, at either the upper or the lower landing, disconnect the electric power from the escalator driving machine and brake by opening the safety stop switch or main-line disconnect switch provided within the space. Tag and lock the switch if necessary.

2.   When steps are removed from the escalator to permit inspection of the interior, always ride behind the stepless opening. Stand facing in the direction of travel, and grasp the handrails. Close inspection should not be attempted until the escalator is securely stopped.

3.   If steps are removed or machinery spaces are exposed, safely barricade both ends of the escalator.

Fire Protection.   When an escalator pierces a fire-rated floor assembly, means shall be provided to protect the floor opening against the passage of smoke, gases, or flame in the event of a fire. The required means must be installed in accordance with the requirements of the local building code, or if there is no building code, the NFPA Life Safety Code or the NFPA Standard for Installation of Sprinkler Systems should be consulted.

One of the means used is power-operated automatic rolling shutters which, when activated, close off the wellway. Rolling shutters are permitted for openings above the street floor only and shall be activated by a smoke or heat detector in the vicinity of the escalator. The shutter must be equipped with a sensitive leading edge which, when contacted by a force not in excess of 20 lb (9.07 kg), will cause the shutter to stop, reverse for approximately 6 in (152.4 mm), and then continue to close until fully closed. A rolling shutter must also be provided with a manual means of operation such as a hand crank. If a hand crank is provided, it shall not be removable.

All rolling shutters and fire doors on an escalator wellway must be provided with a device which will remove electric power from the escalator drive motor and brake as soon as the shutter or door starts to close.

Not all escalators penetrate a fire-rated floor assembly. An example of one that does not is an escalator in an atrium.

The sides and undersides of the escalator truss and machinery spaces should be inspected to see that they are enclosed in fire-resistive materials. A truss or machinery space suspended in an approved fire-rated ceiling assembly does not meet this requirement unless the truss and machinery spaces are separately enclosed with the rated ceiling assembly.

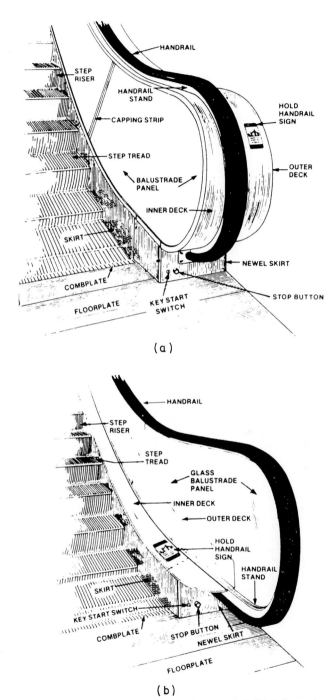

HANDRAIL

STEP RISER

HANDRAIL STAND

CAPPING STRIP

HOLD HANDRAIL SIGN

STEP TREAD

OUTER DECK

BALUSTRADE PANEL

INNER DECK

SKIRT

NEWEL SKIRT

COMBPLATE

STOP BUTTON

FLOORPLATE

KEY START SWITCH

(a)

HANDRAIL

STEP RISER

STEP TREAD

GLASS BALUSTRADE PANEL

INNER DECK

OUTER DECK

HOLD HANDRAIL SIGN

HANDRAIL STAND

SKIRT

KEY START SWITCH

STOP BUTTON

COMBPLATE

NEWEL SKIRT

FLOORPLATE

(b)

FIG. 2.9-7 Nomenclature for escalators. (*a*) Solid balustrade. (*b*) Glass balustrade. (*Courtesy of National Elevator Industry, Inc., New York, N.Y.*)

2.9.23

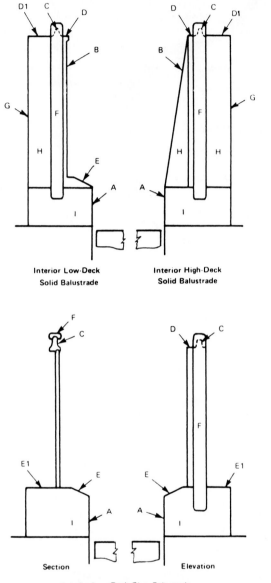

NOTES:
A = Skirt panel
B = Interior panel
C = Handrail stand
D = High-deck interior
D1 = High-deck exterior
E = Low-deck interior
E1 = Low-deck exterior
F = Handrail
G = Exterior panel
H = Newel
I = Newel base

Interior Low-Deck
Solid Balustrade

Interior High-Deck
Solid Balustrade

Section

Elevation

Interior Low-Deck Glass Balustrade

FIG. 2.9-8 Nomenclature for escalators. (*Edward A. Donoghue*, Safety Code for Elevators and Escalators, *A17.1 Handbook, American Society of Mechanical Engineers, New York, 1984.*)

Construction Requirements.   The width of the escalator step tread should be measured at a right angle to the direction of travel. It should not be less than 16 in (406.4 mm) or more than 40 in (1016 mm). The distance between the balustrades and the centerline between handrails should be measured to confirm conformance with code requirements. Also determine that the designed escalator angle of inclination does not exceed 30° from the horizontal. The installation may exceed the designed maximum by 1° owing to field conditions.

Inspect the balustrade for broken or cracked panels. The panels should be solid (unperforated). Gaps in glass or plastic balustrades of ⅛ in (3.175 mm) or less in width are acceptable. If the balustrade is glass or plastic, confirm that it conforms to code requirements.

Check on the step side of the balustrade that no moldings, etc., are raised or depressed more than ¼ in (6.35 mm) from the parent surface and that the edges are beveled unless parallel to the direction of travel. All fasteners used to hold panels or molding in place should have flush or oval heads free from burrs.

Examine all intersections between the tops of balustrades and the penetration of the floor at the ceiling or soffit to determine that a solid, rigid guard conforming to code requirements is provided.

When the top deck of the balustrade is more than 12 in (304.8 mm) from the centerline of the handrail or an adjacent escalator and the distance between handrails is greater than 16 in (406.4 mm), determine that antislide devices are provided. These devices shall consist of raised objects fastened to the decks no closer than 4 in (101.6 mm) to the handrail and spaced no more than 6 ft (1.83 m) apart. Their height shall be not less than ¾ in (19.05 mm). They shall have no sharp corners or edges.

Determine that caution signs conforming to code requirements which are clearly visible to boarding passengers are provided at top and bottom landings.

Next, stop the escalator and examine the skirt panels along the sides of the moving steps. The surface of the panels must be smooth and solid (unperforated). Measure the clearance on either side of the step tread and the adjacent skirt panel on every other step to determine that it does not exceed 3/16 in (4.762 mm).

Each balustrade must be equipped with a moving handrail which travels in the direction of the steps at substantially the same speed. The handrail must extend at least 12 in (304.8 mm) beyond the comb-plate teeth at both landings. Finger guards must be provided where the handrail enters and exits from the balustrades. Carefully examine the condition of the handrail, especially at the joints. It should be smooth without burrs, cuts, scratches, etc.

Examine the steps by having one removed at random for inspection. Check that the steps are horizontal and are made of noncombustible material and that the treads afford a secure foothold. The depth of the treads should not be less than 15¾ in (400 mm), and the rise should not be more than 8½ in (216 mm). The step tread and riser must be slotted or grooved in conformance with code requirements. With the step replaced and the escalator stationary, test every couple of steps for excessive play in the direction of travel and at right angles to the direction of travel. Check that the slotted step rises with slots on the adjacent step tread as the steps make the transition from incline to horizontal.

Determine that a comb plate is provided at each landing and that they are provided with a means for vertical adjustment. Check that no comb-plate teeth are broken, and that they mesh with and set into the slots in the tread surfaces with adequate clearance between the teeth and the step slots. The underside of the comb-plate teeth should always be below the upper surface of the step treads.

Check that access is provided to the driving machine or machines and that ample space is afforded for one person.

Visually inspect the escalator supporting structure, including the trusses, girders, and step-wheel tracks for obvious defects and/or installation inadequacies. See whether or not there is excessive slack in the step chains, and check that they are lubricated. Check that a tightening device which is not presently at its limit of movement is provided to take up slack in the step chains. Chain-tightening devices utilizing tension weights must also be provided with a positive means to retain the weights within the truss if the weights are released.

Have a few escalator steps removed and check that the truss, pit pans, machine room, tracks, chain, etc., have been thoroughly cleaned of construction dust and debris.

Driving Machine, Motor, and Brake.   Determine that an electrically released, mechanically applied brake is provided. When the electrically released, mechanically applied brake is installed on the driving machine, a separate brake must be installed on the main drive shaft. This additional brake need not be of the electrically released type. When the electrically released, mechanically applied brake is installed on the main drive shaft, no separate brake is required on the driving machine.

Operating and Safety Devices.   Every escalator must be provided with key-operated-type starting switches located so that the escalator steps are within sight. Emergency-stop buttons must also be provided at both the upper and the lower landings. Button location and operation must conform to all code requirements.

Determine that there is a stop switch or a main-line disconnect switch in every accessible machinery space. Check that the following devices are provided in accordance with code requirements:

Broken step-chain device   Reversal-stop device
Broken drive-chain device   Step-demarcation lights
Skirt-obstruction device   Step-upthrust device
Rolling-shutter device   Tandem operation

Electrical Work.   Determine that all wiring conforms to the **National Electrical Code**® ANSI/NFPA No. 70. All wiring in the escalator must be encased in rigid metal conduit, electrical metallic tubing, or metal wireways. Electric safety switches and controllers must be enclosed to prevent accidental contact. An enclosed fused disconnect switch or circuit breaker arranged to disconnect electric power to the escalator must be provided in the machine space. Electrical voltages are restricted and must conform to code requirements.

Each machine space must be provided with lighting and a 110-V, 20-A duplex receptacle. The light-control switch must be located so that it can be operated without passing or reaching through or over any moving machinery.

Testing.   Many tests for all new installations are required by the ANSI/ASME A17.1 code. These tests should be performed by the company which installed the escalator and witnessed by an inspector from the authority having jurisdiction.

SIDEWALK ELEVATORS

Sidewalk elevators are basically electric or hydraulic elevators which have been modified to suit a special application. The practices previously described will provide guidelines for the major portion of the inspection. A review of the code rules will describe modifications to the installation needed to suit the special environment.

DUMBWAITERS

Dumbwaiters also follow the requirements for electric and hydraulic elevators. A dumbwaiter is a lift device that has been restricted in size to prevent people from riding in it, thus not needing the highly protective requirements of an elevator. When dumbwaiter installation is observed, the similarity to a conventional elevator is very obvious. A review of the code is again recommended to gain familiarity with the respective requirements.

The code also covers a special application–type dumbwaiter. This is a dumbwaiter which includes an automatic load-transfer device. In addition, it covers material lifts with transfer devices. A material lift is a unit that exceeds the limits of a dumbwaiter but has a transfer device and other required safeguards so that people cannot ride it. Because transfer devices are unique in design and application, special requirements have been written to cover these conditions. Again, review the code for specific details.

INCLINED ELEVATORS

The inclined application of an elevator installation does not change the basic installation to any great degree. The code describes the changes needed to operate on a slant.

OTHER TYPES OF EQUIPMENT

Among other types of equipment are special-purpose personnel elevators, material lifts and dumbwaiters with automatic transfer devices, screw elevators, moving walks, and construction elevators. These are very similar to the equipment previously described, and inspection procedures are similar. The ANSI/ASME A17.1 code contains the detailed requirements for these installations.

Horizontal Transportation: Automated People Movers Substructures and Guideways

J. Thomas Sheakley

Senior Engineer
Transportation Division
Westinghouse Electric Corporation
Pittsburgh, Pennsylvania

The automated-people-mover transit system is a category of mass transit which falls between the capabilities of heavy-steel-wheel–rail subway systems and buses. Such systems have been installed in numerous airports in the United States and in major activity centers such as parks or shopping centers and are presently being constructed in the central-core business districts in several large United States cities.

Through the experience of installing automated rubber-tired transit systems (eight systems in operation plus two on the drawing boards) commonly referred to in the transit industry as automated people movers, the Westinghouse Transportation Division has gained a significant amount of insight into the design and construction of various types of guideways. Figures 2.10-1 and 2.10-2 are photographs of a typical people-mover vehicle and elevated guideway.

The guideway structures, which are used to support, provide guidance, and control the motion of the transit vehicles, come in many different configurations. Below-grade (tunnel), at-grade, minimum-height, and elevated are the four main categories. Oftentimes combinations of these categories occur in the same transit system. Figures 2.10-3 through 2.10-7 show typical configurations of several different categories.

The guideways are designed as simple supported structures or as continuous structures with multiple-span bridges or combinations thereof. The guideway structure is divided into two main elements, a substructure and a superstructure. The substructure is the footings and/or foundation, the columns or piers, and the column or pier caps. The superstructure is everything above the column caps, i.e., beam spans, trackwork, guideway switches, etc. Figure 2.10-5 shows substructure versus superstructure for a typical elevated guideway.

FIG. 2.10-1   Orlando Airport automated people mover. (*Photograph courtesy of Westinghouse Transportation Division.*)

FIG. 2.10-2 Two views of the Orlando Airport automated people mover. *(Photographs courtesy of Westinghouse Transportation Division.)*

For most transit systems installed within the last 15 to 20 years, including Westinghouse's, substructures have been constructed of reinforced cast-in-place concrete. This is also the most common approach uséd today.

For the superstructure of an elevated system, structural-steel beams are the primary load-carrying members. Running surfaces of cast-in-place reinforced concrete are constructed over the steel beams. Other primary load-carrying-beam types used are cast-in-place reinforced concrete, precast concrete, and precast posttensioned concrete. Regardless of the type of primary-support beams used, running surfaces are installed to optimize the ride quality of the vehicles. Figures 2.10-5, 2.10-6, and

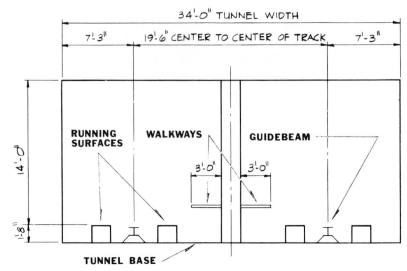

FIG. 2.10-3   At-grade guideway through tunnel. *(Courtesy of Westinghouse Transportation Division.)*

2.10-7 show the main components of a typical elevated steel superstructure, a precast-concrete superstructure, and a precast posttensioned superstructure, respectively.

For superstructures of nonelevated guideways, which are either at grade or below grade, cast-in-place reinforced concrete is the predominant construction material and method used.

As Westinghouse engineers have learned, the as-built suitability of a guideway structure, regardless of its configuration, becomes vividly apparent once vehicles are placed on the guideway and ride-quality measurements taken. Too often this realization occurs after the structure is built, when repair time, costs, and schedule delays are prohibitive.

An emphasis on top-quality construction, clear and precise definitions of required tolerances and interface requirements, and the use of a well-planned and -implemented inspection program will minimize problems identified after the structure has been built, thus ensuring a better overall transit system for the customer.

GENERAL CONSIDERATIONS

Field inspection requirements during construction of an automated-people-mover-system guideway will vary significantly with the type of structure being installed, the local code requirements, and the requirements specified on the design drawings. There are typical inspection

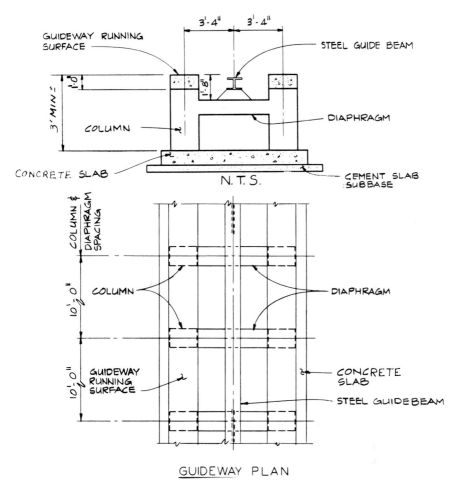

FIG. 2.10-4 Minimum-height guideway. (1 in = 25.4 mm; 1 ft = 0.3048 m.) *(Courtesy of Westinghouse Transportation Division.)*

requirements which are common from project to project, and these will be the ones addressed in this chapter. The special inspection requirements are normally those specified by the engineer because of a special design requirement which needs to be monitored closely during construction. These special requirements will not be covered in this chapter and are better addressed on their own in other publications.

Field inspection during the installation of a guideway requires an understanding of many different aspects of construction. Some of the more important aspects are: (1) being able to read and understand engineering drawings, (2) being familiar with engineering terminology and symbols, (3) understanding the American Concrete Institute (ACI), the

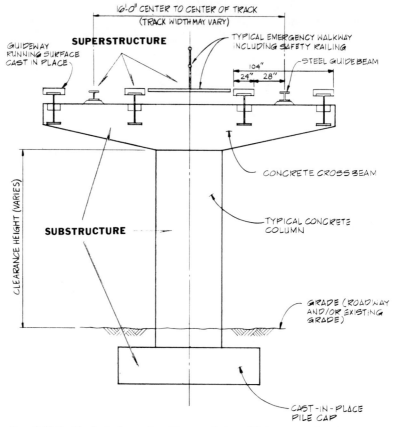

FIG. 2.10-5 Typical elevated guideway. (1 in = 25.4 mm; 1 ft = 0.3048 m.) *(Courtesy of Westinghouse Transportation Division.)*

American Society for Testing and Materials (ASTM), the American Association of State Highway and Transportation Officials (AASHTO), and the Uniform Building Code (UBC) test methods applicable to concrete and steel construction, (4) being able to measure and verify conformance to the tolerances and dimensions specified on the drawings, (5) being able to document inspection results, (6) having a full understanding of construction techniques, and (7) understanding the potential ramifications of poor quality in construction.

Owing to the importance of obtaining a guideway that conforms in all respects to the design drawings, a common practice is to employ testing specialists throughout the construction and installation phases of the project. These specialists provide expertise and specialized testing and measurement capability and instrumentation at various critical phases. Survey crews, geotechnical specialists, concrete and weld testing labora-

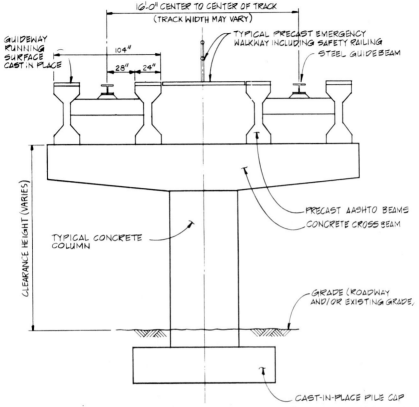

FIG. 2.10-6 Typical elevated concrete guideway. (1 in = 25.4 mm; 1 ft = 0.3048 m.) *(Courtesy of Westinghouse Transportation Division.)*

tories, shop-fabrication inspectors for both steel and concrete components, field inspectors during on-site construction, and field engineers are some of the more important participants in the field inspection program required for construction of an automated-people-mover-system guideway.

There are some basic reasons why field inspection is so important in the installation of guideways for automated people movers. One of the most important is customer satisfaction. The customer contracts to have the transit system engineered and constructed and expects to get a quality product and one that meets its requirements. The guideway is a major element of the system and, if not constructed correctly, can have a detrimental impact on vehicle performance, which in turn affects the passengers who ride the system.

One major interface between the transit vehicles and the guideway is

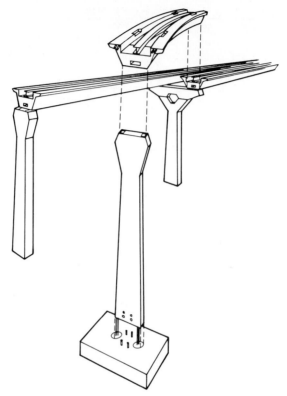

FIG. 2.10-7   Typical elevated concrete guideway. *(Courtesy of Westinghouse Transportation Division.)*

the running surfaces, as shown in Figure 2.10-8. If these are not installed according to tolerance and smoothness requirements, several major consequences result. The ride quality experienced by the passengers is not acceptable, the service life of the vehicles is reduced, and passenger perception of the system is less than desirable.

Ride quality is a direct result of the final as-built condition of the running surfaces. Problems with the running surfaces can be readily identified when the field inspector's criteria have been clearly defined for a project and implemented according to the construction schedules.

Ride quality is one of the major criteria on which passengers judge a transit system. Smooth acceleration and deceleration zones, vibration-free movement of the vehicles on the guideway, smooth transitions in and out of curves and up and down slopes, and smooth running over guideway expansion joints and switches are some of the major characteristics resulting from guideways constructed according to the drawings and verified through good inspection programs.

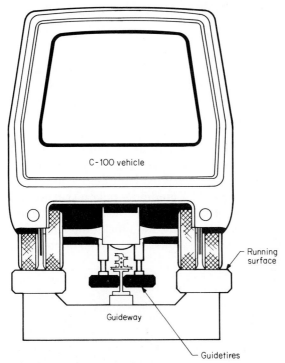

FIG. 2.10-8   Vehicle-guideway interface. *(Courtesy of Westinghouse Transportation Division.)*

Another reason why correct installation of running surfaces is so important is the service life of equipment. Excessive vibrations induced into equipment from rough running surfaces will shorten the service life of the vehicles.

One final reason why inspection programs are important, and possibly the most important one, is the fact that a correctly administered program will catch problems before they become large enough to affect the project cost or schedule. Most large guideway projects take several years for design, fabrication, construction, erection, and final assembly. During this time many inspections and tests are conducted to verify conformance to the drawings and specifications. If problems are identified early during construction as the result of inspections and tests, corrective measures are usually minor. If problems are not identified early, the magnitude of corrective action becomes almost prohibitive. A properly planned and administered inspection program is well worth the time, expense, and effort required. Since most automated-people-mover systems are located in areas of high public visibility, the consequences of not implementing a good inspection program far outweigh any investments needed in this area.

FIELD INSPECTION

Field inspections and tests for the construction of guideways can be categorized in two major areas: (1) those which are standard state-of-the-art procedures typically carried out on all transit-related projects, for example, highways, bridges, heavy-rail mass-transit systems, etc.; and (2) those procedures which are peculiar to people-mover systems.

Inspection requirements for guideways which are common to the transportation industry will only be mentioned here since detailed explanations are given in other publications and references. The inspections and tests peculiar to people-mover guideways will be explained in detail since few references exist that explain their requirements.

The major elements of a guideway field inspection program fall into the following categories: alignment verification, substructure verification, and superstructure verification including running surfaces, guidebeam, switches, expansion joints, and general dimensional and tolerance verification.

ALIGNMENTS

Alignments for people-mover systems often become very complicated owing in part to the fact that most are constructed over, in, around, under, or in conjunction with existing buildings, streets, highways, or downtown high-density areas. The preliminary alignments are usually provided in the technical documents furnished by the owner.

Horizontal and vertical surveys to verify preliminary alignment are conducted at the onset of most projects. These surveys are made to establish control points for guideway design and construction. This initial effort is extremely important since the entire guideway effort is based on this information. These data points become useful for the field inspector once construction begins. From them come locations of piers, elevations of the guideway including running surfaces and guidebeam, distances, interface data with existing structures, etc.

Alignments for people-mover systems are typically more complicated than those for conventional mass transit. This is due to the wider operational capability of the vehicles, which are smaller, lighter, and more maneuverable. As a result, tight-radius horizontal curves with a minimum radius of curvature of 75 ft (22.86 m), tight vertical curves, superelevations to 10 percent, grades to 10 percent, and minimum-length lead-in and lead-out spirals are commonly used. These alignment characteristics increase the effort and knowledge required by field inspectors, who must verify that the guideways have been constructed to the exact geometric data specified from the alignment drawings.

Field inspectors need to be familiar with the alignment characteristics of the system, know how to interpret them, and know how to relate them to the actual physical construction. Problems found at this stage of construction can be corrected with minimal impact on the overall program. If problems are left unnoticed or unreported, their impact becomes significant. The field inspector has a lead role in this area to ensure that the guideway is constructed to the alignment given on the design drawings.

SUBSTRUCTURE

The substructure of the guideways, as mentioned earlier, is composed of the foundations, piers or columns, and pier or column caps. For most Westinghouse projects, this portion of the guideway is steel-reinforced cast-in-place concrete. While this is typical in the transit industry, precast columns and caps are also common.

For cast-in-place substructures as well as other configurations, the field inspector must be concerned with centerline and positioning locations as specified on the drawings. This is done for the foundations, which are normally piles or caissons, and for the columns and column caps. Elevation checks become important as construction progresses. This process is repeated for every column structure.

Material certification and material property verification are other areas requiring significant involvement of the field inspector. For guideway substructures, steel rebar and cast-in-place concrete are the two major materials used. For the rebar, the field inspector should review mill certifications and any test reports available from the steel supplier. The drawings will show the details of rebar installation, schedules, stirrup spacings, rebar assemblies, and fabrications required for the entire guideway substructure. Installation of the rebars should be checked against the drawings and approved prior to pouring of the concrete.

For cast-in-place concrete, owners or contractors normally use the services of an independent testing laboratory to perform the field tests. During construction the concrete is sampled and tested periodically. The major tests include sampling, slump, air content, temperature, compression, and strength. Even though field inspectors do not conduct these tests, they are an important part of the inspection program. These tests are standard in the construction industry and are ASTM-approved and -regulated.

The final area on the substructure which requires inspection consists of dimensional checks, workmanship, and finishes. The formed concrete must meet the drawings and specified tolerances dimensionally. Workmanship must be of high quality, with the particular surface finishes provided as specified by the architects. For people movers, oftentimes the columns are positioned on or near sidewalks, next to buildings, or in high-traffic areas and are highly visible to the public. Because of this, workmanship and exposed surface textures are especially important.

SUPERSTRUCTURE

The superstructure of the guideway is everything from the column or pier caps up. It is the primary-support girders, decking or running surfaces, and all associated trackwork. For Westinghouse projects, it is constructed with running surfaces of structural steel and cast-in-place reinforced concrete. The superstructure, from an inspection viewpoint, requires more attention to detail and more specialized inspection requirements. It is the direct interface with the vehicle. If dimensions don't match and tolerances aren't met, vehicle ride quality is compromised, which affects the public's reaction in riding the system.

There are several important areas on the superstructure that require close inspection and attention to detail. These include the running surfaces, guidebeams, expansion joints, switches, and their alignment and dimensional verification.

RUNNING SURFACES

The most obvious but least-understood area deals with the construction of the running surfaces. Regardless of the guideway design, whether steel or concrete, elevated or at-grade, concrete running surfaces are always constructed over the primary-support structure for Westinghouse systems. Improperly constructed running surfaces create abnormal vehicle motion, such as pitch and yaw or vibrations and wheel spin which may be intolerable to passengers and owners.

Running surfaces typically are composed of cast-in-place, steel-reinforced, 5000-psi (34, 475-kPa) concrete. The same field quality tests conducted on the substructure concrete are carried out on the running-surface concrete. Sampling, slump, air-content, temperature, compression, and strength tests are the major ones conducted. The field inspector needs to be heavily involved in these tests since failures will require that additional, more detailed tests be conducted. If the second level of laboratory tests also results in failures, then the field inspector is required to advise the contractor that the section of running surface tested must be removed and replaced.

During construction of the formwork for the running surfaces, the horizontal and vertical alignments and the dimensions with respect to the centerline of the guidebeam are of critical importance. For the vertical profile of the running surfaces, they should not depart more than ⅛ in (3.175 mm) from the theoretical elevations and ⅛ in from a 10-ft (3.048-m) straightedge placed anywhere on the 24-in- (609.6-mm-) wide running surface. The inspector must ensure that these tolerances are being met by the contractor. One method of doing this is to have survey crews check the formwork prior to pouring the concrete.

Another elevation check which must be measured during construction and conform to the required tolerances is that of one running surface with respect to the other. The maximum variation between specified running-surface elevations at any given cross section is ⅛ in (3.175 mm). The inspector must ensure that this drawing requirement is met. Nonconformance to this tolerance results in a vehicle yawing from side to side as the right and left wheels alternately go over the high and low points. An inspection for this condition will identify the problem when corrections can be made. If it is found after the running surfaces have been poured, the only solution is grinding, which, while expensive and time-consuming, is imperative.

For curves, spirals, and superelevations the same alignment and elevation checks need to be performed. Typically, the inspector need only to refer to the drawings for these data. The complicated geometry for these configurations is calculated by the engineers and the results put on the drawings.

Trueness and flatness are other features of the running surfaces that are closely monitored and measured during construction. The inspection criterion used permits a maximum of ⅛-in (3.175-mm) deviation from the edge of a 10-ft (3.048-m) straightedge placed anywhere on the 24-in- (609.6-mm-) wide running surface. All surface areas are checked for this requirement. Locations along the guideway that are found not to meet this requirement are marked, and concrete grinding equipment is used to correct the bad areas. Most projects, no matter how good the installation is or how careful the contractor is, will require some amount of grinding.

The surface finish typically used for the running surface is a standard broom finish perpendicular to the guideway centerline. Uniform striations approximately 1/16 in (1.588 mm) deep are commonly specified, with test samples being required for approval prior to pouring the concrete.

The final important area requiring inspection is the dimensional verification of the formed-concrete running surfaces. The tolerances permitted are specified on the drawings. The inspector needs to verify these dimensions as part of the normal inspection procedure. Some typical tolerances used on the running surfaces are as follows: running-surface width, 24 in (609.6 mm) plus or minus ¼ in (6.35 mm); centerline of guideway to inside edge of running surface, 28 in (711.2 mm) plus or minus ½ in (12.7 mm); and top of guidebeam to top of running surface, 2 in (50.8 mm) plus ⅛ in (3.175 mm) and minus ¼ in (6.35 mm).

GUIDEBEAMS

As seen in the figures presented earlier, people-mover vehicles are locked onto the guideway via guidetires that run on the web of a steel beam positioned between the running surfaces. This is normally referred to as the guidebeam. Steel safety disks are used above the guidewheels to prevent derailment and overturning and to lock the vehicles positively onto the guideway.

Since the vehicle guidetires roll on both web surfaces of the guidebeam, horizontal alignment and positioning of the beam are critical because it controls the location and orientation of the vehicle on the running surfaces. The inspection criteria for the guidebeam are that once installed it shall be within ⅛ in (3.175 mm) of the theoretical alignment and should not depart more than ⅛ in in any 10-ft (3.084-m) interval from the theoretical alignment.

The centerline of the guidebeam once installed corresponds to the centerline of the guideway track. Once the guidebeam has been installed, it should be checked by a survey crew to verify its elevation and alignment. Once these have been verified, it is permanently attached to the super-structure. The inspector can then use this as a reference point when checking dimensions and interface between the running surfaces and the guidebeam.

Splices in the guidebeam, conduit and power feeds through the guidebeam, and expansion joints are areas where there is a potential for misalignment of the guidebeam-web surfaces. Since the guidetires run on the web, any misalignment will affect the ride quality of the vehicles. Inspectors need to check these areas to assure proper web alignment at discontinuities in the guidebeam.

Vertical alignment of the guidebeam with respect to the running surfaces is also important. If the dimension between the top of the guidebeam to the running surface exceeds the ⅛-in (3.175-mm) toler-ance, there is a potential that the steel safety disk above the guidetires will rub against the upper flange of the guidebeam. If this dimension is smaller, this problem does not exist, and the tolerance given on the minus side is ¼ in (6.35 mm).

The mounting of the guidebeam to the superstructure is designed to be adjustable. High-strength structural bolts and mounting hardware are used with slotted holes and shim-pack designs to permit adjustment during installation. Once the guidebeam has been installed, all alignment and positioning dimensions are verified; then the mounting hardware is welded to ensure a permanent attachment. The inspector plays a key role throughout this process to verify the correct installation of all guide-beams.

EXPANSION JOINTS

Another area on the superstructure that requires close scrutiny is the expansion joints. There are typically two types used on Westinghouse systems. For simply supported guideway structures in which the super-structure spans are independent of each other and are relatively short [50 to 70 ft (15.24 to 21.34 m)], the expansion gaps required do not normally exceed 1 in (25.4 mm). The gaps are perpendicular to the longitudinal direction of the guideway, and as long as they do not exceed 1 in, vehicle ride quality is not affected. Along with checking dimensions of the expansion gaps, the inspector is required to check their elevations. A vertical tolerance of plus or minus $\frac{1}{16}$ in (1.588 mm) and a horizontal tolerance of plus or minus $\frac{1}{8}$ in (3.175 mm) are generally specified.

When larger expansion gaps (greater than 1 in) are required, specially designed 45°-skewed gap assemblies are used. Since dual rubber tires are used on the vehicles, a skewed expansion gap allows the tires to traverse the gap alternately with no impact on ride quality. As with the preceding gap configuration, a vertical tolerance of $\frac{1}{16}$ in (1.588 mm) and a horizontal tolerance of $\frac{1}{8}$ in (3.175 mm) are normally specified.

When checking expansion gaps, the inspector needs to be aware that dimensions will vary with ambient temperatures. Typically on the drawings there will be tabulations of temperature versus expansion-gap distances.

GUIDEWAY SWITCHES

On some people-mover systems, the guideway alignment and track plans create the need for numerous routing alternatives. To handle these, Y-type guideway switches are used as part of the guideway configuration. They allow the vehicles to switch guideways, change directions, or enter or exit from the maintenance or main-line tracks.

The switches used by Westinghouse are the in-guideway type and employ a center guidebeam as the primary moving component during switching. Changing the alignment of the guidebeam in the switch area physically forces the vehicle to follow either the tangent or the turnout direction. Figure 2.10-9 shows a typical switch span as part of the guide-way structure.

The major duties of a field inspector during the installation of a switch

FIG. 2.10-9   Guideway switch span. *(Photograph courtesy of Westinghouse Transportation Division.)*

include (1) verification of the switch-span alignment and position, (2) checking for damage due to transporting or erection, (3) ensuring that the expansion gaps with the concrete running surfaces are correct in both vertical and horizontal directions, (4) ensuring that the guidebeams in the switch move freely prior to installation of the mechanical linkages and hydraulic control system, and (5) checking for the correct alignment of the guidebeams in both tangent and turnout positions.

Numerous other tests and inspections are carried out at the steel fabricator's plant. Typically the switch beams are fabricated, inspected, assembled, inspected, and tested in the shop. Welds are inspected and tested, critical dimensions verified, and all the mechanical subassemblies installed on the spans. Load or deflection tests are run, switch-beam movements are checked under simulated full-load conditions, and running surfaces are checked for conformance to tolerances. Since a significant amount of switch inspection occurs in the shop, on-site field inspection effort has been minimized except for the items previously mentioned.

CONCLUSION

Field inspection for construction of people-mover guideways is essential. A significant amount of effort and assistance from specialists in many areas is required.

Inspection programs that are properly planned, coordinated, and implemented are a vital factor in the success of the installation of a guideway structure. They bridge the void between design and construction.

Vehicle ride quality, service life of vehicles and equipment, customer satisfaction, passenger perception of the system, and system contractor satisfaction are all areas which greatly benefit from a good field inspection program for people-mover guideways.

Index

About the Editors

Dan S. Brock has been involved in nearly every type of construction while serving as an inspector and project engineer for the Pennsylvania Department of Highways in Pittsburgh, as a resident engineer for Madigan-Hyland, consulting engineers, New York, on the West Side Highway and Belt Parkway in New York City, as vice president and assistant foreign manager for Johnson, Drake & Piper, Inc., general contractor of New York and Minneapolis, and as executive vice president of C. W. Blakeslee & Sons, Inc., general contractor of New Haven, Connecticut. As a construction consultant based in Woodbridge, Connecticut, he has served all elements of the construction industry, including consulting engineers, contractors, architects, owners, financial institutions, sureties, and government agencies, for the past 20 years. His engineering, contracting, and consulting activities have included projects throughout the United States and in more than 40 countries overseas.

A graduate of the University of Florida, **Lystre L. Sutcliffe, Jr.,** has devoted his career to construction inspection with Parsons Brinckerhoff of New York. As a resident engineer, he served on a highway project in Albany, New York, a vertical-lift bridge over the Cape Fear River in Wilmington, North Carolina, the port of Toledo, Ohio, and the third Sunshine Skyway in St. Petersburg, Florida. He was a key engineer for the Cove Point liquefied-natural-gas tunnel and dock in Maryland, the center-city commuter rail line in Philadelphia, the extension of the Albany County airport, and the James River lift bridge in Virginia.